GW00643856

MURDERS
AT THE VICARAGE

Vijitha Yapa Publications
Unity Plaza, 2 Galle Road, Colombo 4, Sri Lanka
Tel. (94 11) 2596960 Fax (94 11) 2594717
e-mail: vijiyapa@gmail.com
www.srilankanbooks.com
www.vijithayapa.com

ISBN 978-955-665-259-8

First Edition July 2015

Printed by Saveco Printing and Packaging, Boralesgamuwa

MURDERS AT THE VICARAGE

THE MATHEW PEIRIS CASE

Professor Ravindra Fernando

MBBS, MD, FCCP, FCGP, FRCP (Lond)
FRCP (Glasgow), FRCP (Edin), FRCPath (UK), DMJ (Lond)

Senior Professor of Forensic Medicine and Toxicology
Faculty of Medicine, University of Colombo, Sri Lanka

VIJITHA YAPA
PUBLICATIONS

www.vijithayapa.com

CONTENTS

FOREWORD

In the annals of the legal history of Sri Lanka, very few cases have decided the guilt or innocence of an accused from medical evidence. The murder trial of Mr. Russel Ingram and Mrs. Eunice Peiris by the introduction of anti-diabetic drugs to their meals is the best example of a case where medical evidence played a pivotal role in the outcome of the trial of the accused.

Professor Ravindra Fernando, Senior Professor of Forensic Medicine and Toxicology, has spent over four years to give the readers the details of the investigation and the prolonged trial of the so called 'Mathew Peiris Case', in which I had the privilege of being the prosecuting counsel.

After successfully murdering Mr. Russel Ingram, his lodger at the Vicarage, Rev. Mathew Peiris gathered enough courage to murder another person, this time his own wife, hoping that he would escape justice again. This did not happen. A team of smart and intelligent police officers, renowned medical specialists, family physicians and junior medical officers ably assisted the administration of justice.

Professor Fernando has summarized the evidence led in the case giving the reader an account of what happened in Court. This must have been an arduous and time consuming task for him.

He has documented the detailed and analytical judgement of the Trial-at-Bar, which will mainly benefit the legal professionals. The judgement is not reported. It is interesting how the Court interpreted the complex medical evidence to establish the guilt of Rev. Peiris and Mrs. Ingram.

Professor Fernando has given the background to this tragic double murder, which gives an idea of the motive and circumstances leading to the deaths. He states that this is the first trial in the world where an oral anti-diabetic drug was used to kill two people. He has mentioned that the first murder in the world using insulin, the injectable anti-diabetic drug, was committed by Kenneth Barlow in England.

As the chief prosecuting counsel I spent considerable time studying the complex medical evidence, as the case was based on circumstantial evidence. There was no murder weapon. There were no positive post-mortem findings about the causes of death. Mr. Ingram's murder was not investigated at all for many months.

The senior defence counsel Mr. R.I. Obeysekera and Mr. Cecil Goonewardena made a sterling effort to defend the two accused.

Professor Fernando's book should be an excellent reference to all members of the legal profession. It is a 'must read' like his other book, 'A murder in Ceylon - the Sathasivam case', where he analyzed the medical evidence of the celebrated Sathasivam murder case. Reading the address to the jury by Mr. E.F.N. Gratiaen in that case, as well as the detailed judgement of the Trial-at-Bar of Rev. Mathew Peiris case, is as good as reading many tomes.

Tilak Marapana, President's Counsel
Former Attorney General of Sri Lanka

PREFACE

The two murders committed at a Vicarage, situated very close to the Faculty of Medicine, Colombo, where I have studied and worked for over four decades, are unique for many reasons.

I was involved with the case from the beginning. Therefore it was my intention to document this case for the benefit of all. The book took over four years to complete. It was not an easy task to find documents to provide a truthful account of the murders of Mr. Russel Ingram and Mrs. Eunice Peiris, who left this world without knowing what happened to them. This is the first time in the world, that oral anti-diabetic drugs were used to commit two murders. The accused Rev. Mathew Peiris and Mrs. Dalrene Ingram were convicted purely on circumstantial evidence at the Trial-at-Bar.

A galaxy of eminent consultant physicians, surgeons and pathologists, all of them my teachers, and several other doctors and nurses were important witnesses in the trial and were known to me (except Dr. E.V. Peiris, who had retired before I became a medical student, and Dr. S. Subramaniam and Dr. S.C. Abeysuriya, who were not in the General Hospital, Colombo, then).

I did my internship at the Professorial Surgical Unit of the General Hospital, Colombo, with Professor R.A. Navaratne, Professor Chummy S. Sinnatamby, Dr. A.H. Sheriffdeen and Dr. Gerry Jayasekera, where one victim, Mr. Russel Ingram, died. Mrs. Eunice Peiris died in the ward of Consultant Physician Dr. K.J. Nanayakkara, with whom I did my medical internship. Dr. P.A.P. Joseph was the first surgeon under whom I studied surgery. Dr. N. Nagaratnam, Dr. Dayasiri Fernando and Professor Ganeswari Sri Balasubramaniam were my teachers while Dr. Bandula Wijesiriwardena and Dr. Upali Banagala were my school mates.

The judges have scrutinized the medical evidence with great care in arriving at their judgment. A greater part of the analytical judgement of the Trial-at-Bar has been referred to in the book with unavoidable repetitions in keeping with essence of authenticity.

I have to apologize to members of the families of Rev. and Mrs. Mathew Peiris and Mr. and Mrs. Russel Ingram, if I have inadvertently hurt their feelings. This is inevitable when writing a book of this nature.

I sincerely thank Mrs. R.I. Obeysekera for providing me with well-preserved newspaper cuttings of the case kept by Mr. R.I. Obeysekera, the senior defence counsel.

I thank Professor Sharya Scharanguivel, Mrs. Radhieka Yapa and Mrs. Nirmala Abeysekera for their useful comments on this manuscript, and Dr. Niyomi Jayathilaka, Ms. Sushmitha Thayanandan, Mrs. Dilani Mannan, Mr. Lakshitha Ranatunga for their assistance. I thank Mr. K. P. G. Kumarasiri, former Chief Librarian and Mrs. Rasika Liyanagama, the Deputy Librarian of the Wijewardena Memorial Media Library and Documentation Centre of the Associated Newspapers of Ceylon Limited for their cooperation.

Professor Ravindra Fernando
MBBS, MD, FCCP, FCGP, DMJ (London), FRCP (London) FRCP (Glasgow), FRCP (Edinburgh), FRCPath (UK)

Senior Professor of Forensic Medicine and Toxicology
Faculty of Medicine, University of Colombo

ravindrafernando@hotmail.co.uk

CHAPTER 1

THE BEGINNING OF THE TRAGIC STORY

Mathew George Frederick Peiris was the son of Canon T.C.J. Peiris and Mrs. Peiris of Moratuwa. He was the eldest in a family of six.

Mathew has said that he never had any desire to be a priest. He took up motor engineering and did a correspondence course from London and then acquired the British technical qualification of Associate Member of the Institute of Motor Trade.

He married Felicia Lois Eunice Mendis on 16th September 1944 and had four children. One died at the age of nine months. After the marriage he took up a position as manager of civilian repairs during the war.

In 1950, Mathew suffered from a serious illness, what was thought to be a brain tumour. He was in hospital for six weeks with his limbs paralyzed. Lying ill and anguished, Mathew said he had a series of visions where his godmother appeared to him and said that he would be healed by God, and to seek solace in the Ministry working for God. She asked him to go to London via India, and also to exercise the Ministry of exorcism.

In India, Mathew Peiris lived for awhile in an *ashram*. It was there that he decided he would never shave nor cut his hair.

In 1951, he went to London and met the Bishop of Lincoln who took him to Lincoln. He was well by then and after the Bishop spoke to him, he was a given a place in a College in Lincoln.

In 1954, he was ordained as a priest by the Archbishop of Canterbury (the senior bishop and principal leader of the Church of England and the symbolic head of the worldwide Anglican Communion and the diocesan bishop of the Diocese of Canterbury, residing in Lambeth Palace, London). He worked at St. Francis of Assisi of Welwyn Garden City. *(Saint Francis of Assisi -1181 – 1226, was an Italian Catholic friar and preacher. He founded the men's Order of Friars Minor, the women's Order of St. Clare, and the Third Order of Saint Francis)*. Rev. Peiris was a Deacon later and then the priest in charge of St. Mary Magdalene Hatfield Hide. (*St. Mary Magdalene is a Church of England Parish Church serving the parish of Hatfield Hyde on the eastern side of Welwyn Garden City*).

Rev. Peiris had the unique opportunity of attending a Buckingham Palace summer party, given by His Majesty King George the Sixth.

Rev. Peiris returned to Ceylon in 1956 and in 1957, Rev. Basil Jayewardene invited him to Sri Lanka to be his assistant at St. Paul's, Kynsey Road, Colombo, and later he succeeded him when Rev. Jayewardene died on 13th July 1958 after a long but undiagnosed illness.

Rev. Peiris was known to manifest the stigmata, marks resembling the wounds of the crucified Christ, which bled on Tuesdays and Thursdays. He became an internationally known exorcist. He also claimed to be a good interpreter of psychic dreams and used to contribute to the daily press some time ago on this subject. Rev. Peiris would hold the cross to the forehead and pray. Those who sought favours from Rev. Peiris were not only people who were ill but also men and women who had family problems, violence at home and even those embroiled in land disputes! Whenever redress was not forthcoming after such services, Rev. Peiris would gently tell each of them to write their history and their past as far back as they could remember. He suggested this as a means of helping them, assuring them fervently that no one would get to know and their most intimate secrets would die with him.

Rev. Peiris used life stories of the people given in absolute confidence to get his own way. If the life stories included powerful or influential people such as police officers, he would leave the person alone, but would target only the meek and the humble. He would drive home the message of miraculous healing and get them to help the church. Rev. Peiris requested some to meet him alone and at strange times not in the church but in a wooden shed at the back, which the he had christened the 'Good Samaritan's Inn'.

Rev. Peiris instilled fear in his innocent followers, by implying that they would fall victim to serious illnesses such as cancer. He would drive home the message of miraculous healing and get them to help the church. Several youngsters assisted Rev. Peiris at these services and looked on in wonderment as people would just fall during these services.

An unusually gifted person, Rev. Peiris was an expert in the art of embroidery and once displayed his work at a 'Needlework and Embroidery Exhibition!'

A young couple, Russel Ingram and Dalrene Millicent Ingram with their children came to live in the Vicarage with Rev. Mathew Peiris and his wife in 1977. That was the beginning of the end.

CHAPTER 2

DEATH OF RUSSEL INGRAM

On 3rd July 1978, Russel Ingram, a 32-year-old man, was admitted to General Hospital, Colombo, under the care of Consultant Physician, Dr. N. Nagaratnam. There was a letter attached to the Bed Head Ticket (BHT) from retired Consultant Physician, Dr. Ernie (E.V.) Peiris, which mentioned the possibility of an "insulinoma" or an insulin-producing tumour of the pancreas. It is a very rare condition, which affects 1 in 100,000 and the majority of such tumours are benign.

Dr. D.U.R. Goonawardana, who was the acting physician in the absence of Dr. Nagaratnam, referred Russel to Dr. A.H. Sheriffdeen, Consultant Surgeon, for a second opinion. He also referred Russel to Professor S.A.W. Dissanayake, Professor of Psychiatry, Faculty of Medicine, University of Colombo for his opinion. Professor Dissanayake who examined Russel later said that he did not appear to be having a psychiatric condition.

Russel was wheeled in on a stretcher to ward 18 to be examined by Dr. Sheriffdeen. There was a priest, Rev. Mathew Peiris and a fairly timid looking woman, Dalrene Ingram, the patient's wife and priest's private secretary, accompanying the unconscious patient.

Rev. Peiris gave the history of Russel's case to Dr. Sheriffdeen confidently. He had a good command of the English language. Rev. Peiris referred to an episode sometime back when Russel had come to the Vicarage after a cricket match. He said Russel was in a daze with his eyes rolled up, sweating profusely, that his hand was cold and clammy and the pulse was bounding. He had tried to wake him, but he could not. Then he had quickly got a cup of tea and fed him. A little later Russel woke up and asked what had happened to him. It was clear to Dr. Sheriffdeen that Rev. Peiris was describing in detail the 'classic symptoms' of hypoglycaemia.

During the course of his hospitalization, Russel suddenly left his ward without permission of the doctors on the morning of 13th July. He was brought back to hospital later in the evening by his father.

Russel was discharged on 14th July and was asked to report back for a Glucose Tolerance Test (GTT). Russel was re-admitted to ward 18 in an unconscious state on 18th July. He had remained so till his death at 3.30 a.m. on 10th August. Dr. K.U.R.A. Banagala, a House Officer in the ward certified the death, and after discussing with Dr. Karunakaran, the Surgical Registrar of the ward, he referred the death to the Coroner for an Inquest. Two hours later the body was sent to the mortuary. A post-mortem examination was arranged to be performed at 8.00 a.m. the following day by Dr. S. Subramaniam, the JMO, Colombo.

Rev. Mathew Peiris and Mrs. Dalrene Ingram visited the ward at about 7.30 a.m. and they gave consent for a pathological post-mortem. As Rev. Mathew Peiris was urging to release the body soon, a pathological post-mortem was performed at 2 p.m. by Dr. A.H. Sheriffdeen, the surgeon, in the hospital mortuary. He was not aware that the death was referred to the Coroner for an Inquest.

Mr. Walter D. Perera, the City Coroner commenced the inquest at 11.30 a.m. on 11th August at the Coroner's Court, situated in the General Hospital. The evidence at the inquest was led by Constable Abdeen of the Maradana police. Dr. Sheriffdeen reported that the direct cause of Russel's death was respiratory failure following pneumonia and coma from an unknown cause.

Mrs. Cora Ingram, mother of Russel, giving evidence stated that she suspected that her son was poisoned by the food brought by Mathew from the Vicarage.

The Coroner returned an open verdict on Russel's death and directed the police to make further investigations and make their report to the Magistrate. The body of Russel was brought to the Vicarage at 4.30 p.m. on the 11th.

It is a tragic fact that when a Coroner gives an "Open Verdict" in Sri Lanka, police does not conduct further investigations and the Coroner never calls the case again. The case is forgotten forever!

When Russel's body was at the Vicarage, voices were raised outside and there was considerable confusion. Russel's father Alex commenced shouting, "They have killed my son. They have slowly poisoned him". He had to be controlled by others and was led away. Rev. Peiris telephoned the Maradana police and some officers arrived at the Vicarage. They were on duty to prevent a breach of the peace. The funeral of Russel was held at the General Cemetery, Kanatte.

CHAPTER 3

PRIEST BRINGS ANOTHER PATIENT

One afternoon in early February 1979, my batch mate Dr. Rudra came to my room at the Department of Forensic Medicine, Faculty of Medicine, Colombo. Dr. Rudra joined the Department of Pathology as a demonstrator at the same time I joined the Department of Forensic Medicine as a lecturer. He sat on the chair in front of my desk. Usually calm and quiet Dr. Rudra appeared somewhat excited.

"Ravi, there is a worrying issue in the hospital, I had lunch at the doctor's quarters and they were discussing a patient brought by a priest. She was unconscious and admitted to ward 47B."

"So what is the issue?" I asked.

"She came with hypoglycaemia, but the issue is that a few months ago the same priest brought a man with severe hypoglycaemia, who died in the hospital. Doctors are talking about both these patients being poisoned by anti-diabetic drugs."

"Have the doctors informed police?"

"I don't know," Dr. Rudra said.

I told him I would go to the ward and find out what the situation is.

I hurriedly went to ward 47B and met a house officer Dr. (Miss) Kanthi Pinto. She was a few years junior to me in the medical faculty but I knew her well. She explained to me the circumstance of the admission of the patient, 59-year-old Mrs. Eunice Felicia Lois Peiris, by Rev. Mathew Peiris to the ward on 31st January. I saw Mrs. Peiris with Dr. Pinto. She was deeply unconscious. I told her to take a blood sample and keep in the refrigerator and to inform the police immediately about their suspicion of poisoning.

I then informed Dr. S. Subramaniam, the Judicial Medical Officer (JMO), Colombo, about this incident and he said he would wait for the Police to inform him to start investigations.

CHAPTER 4

DEATH OF EUNICE LOIS PEIRIS

Dr. Terrence Rajah de Silva, having passed out from the Medical Faculty, Colombo, was serving his year's internship at the General Hospital. He had completed six months in the surgical ward under Senior Surgeon Dr. M.H.G. Siriwardena and was on the final six months in the medical ward under Senior Physician Dr. K.J. Nanayakkara. The Senior House Officer (SHO) of the ward was Dr. Sarath Wickramasinghe and the other Intern House Officer was Dr. (Miss) Kanthi Pinto.

During the lunch break on 31st January 1979, Dr. de Silva was informed by a nurse that a 'bad' patient was admitted. When a critical patient was brought in, the Outpatients Department (OPD) put a seal in the admission sheet that the House Officer should see the patient immediately (the so called 'Stamped Case').

The patient was unconscious. She was brought in by two priests. One was bespectacled and bearded and the other priest, who was a close relative, was crying.

Dr. de Silva took the history of the patient from her husband, Rev. Mathew Peiris, who spoke on her behalf as she was unconscious. Dr. de Silva was shown a letter from Dr. Lakshman Weerasena, a General Practitioner, advising hospitalization the previous day, but the patient was brought in only at noon the next day.

Rev. Peiris said that the patient had returned from England in December 1978 and began complaining of body pains, excessive thirst and loss of appetite. She was also depressed and had been treated by a Psychiatrist. She had felt giddy two to three hours after meals and was under the care of a General Practitioner. She had developed slurring of speech and been in and out of consciousness since 6 p.m. the previous day.

Dr. de Silva then went through the medical routine of asking whether the patient had a headache, chest pain, high blood pressure, asthma or diabetes. Rev. Mathew Peiris answered 'No' to all queries. When asked whether she had been taking anti-diabetic drugs, the answer had been negative.

Rev. Peiris denied that she was on any medication. He showed a photocopy of a letter from another doctor and some laboratory reports including a glucose tolerance test (GTT) done two days before. Dr. de Silva realized that there were certain abnormalities in fasting blood sugar in the reports.

Rev. Peiris told Dr. de Silva that 'Glucose was bad' for his wife!

Dr. de Silva then examined her. She was in a deep coma and was not even responding to pain. There were no external injuries. There was a needle puncture on her right hand as a result of a blood test carried out earlier. Mrs. Peiris's blood pressure was a very low 60/40 mm mercury, the normal being 120/80. Her pulse could only be "just felt" and the rate could not be recorded. Dr. de Silva realized that she was in a state of collapse.

After meticulously noting the case history and his findings of the clinical examination on the BHT, Dr. de Silva wrote his tentative diagnosis –'Hypoglycaemic coma due to low blood sugar levels', followed by small question marks, 'Pancreatic tumour', 'Overdose of hypoglycaemic agents' and 'Poisoning'. As his second diagnosis, Dr. de Silva wrote 'Cerebro-vascular accident' (CVA), which means a stroke.

Considering her age that was a possibility as the patient was a 59-year-old lady he administered 50 millilitres of 50% dextrose, along with hydrocortisone and a dextrose drip to revive the patient. In a usual case of hypoglycaemia, the patient gets up and walks after a dextrose injection. But Mrs. Peiris did not regain consciousness. Dr. de Silva thought either his diagnosis was wrong or that the patient had permanent brain damage. Later that day, his tentative diagnosis of hypoglycaemic coma was confirmed by the laboratory reports.

With no apparent signs of recovery, Dr. de Silva informed Rev. Peiris that the patient's condition was poor. The reaction was "neither happy nor sad", with the only question being, "Will she die?" When he queried why Rev. Peiris was asking him that, he told Dr. de Silva that he wished to inform their children.

After the initial treatment, as the telephone in the ward was not working, he rushed to the telephone exchange to make a call to his Consultant or Senior House Officer (SHO) about the 'bad' patient. There were no mobile phones at that time. There was a huge rush around the telephone exchange as many interns were attempting to contact their senior doctors.

He, however, knew that his Consultant Dr. K.J. Nanayakkara would be in the ward at 2.50 p.m. sharp and decided to have some food and get back soon. Dr. Nanayakkara, with whom I did my medical internship, was one of the few Consultants who visited the ward even in the afternoons of Sundays or public holidays to see new admissions and bad patients.

While having lunch with the other intern medical officers in the doctors' quarters, Dr. de Silva mentioned about the new patient. It was then that a casual reference was made about a similar case several months before, where another patient too had been brought by a priest. Dr. de Silva was told that the patient (later to be identified as Russel Ingram), had died, and suspecting that it may have been due to an insulin-secreting tumour, a post-mortem had been performed but no tumour had been found.

Immediately seeing the danger signals, Dr. de Silva went back to the ward and told not only Dr. (Miss) Kanthi Pinto but also the SHO, with events occurring quickly thereafter. It was high drama at the General Hospital - an entry on the BHT, referral to the Police

Post and a warning that no one, other than medical and nursing staff, be allowed at the bedside of the patient. Mrs. Peiris was in the ward for 47 days before her death on 19th March 1979.

The ward doctors referred the death to the City Coroner and a post-mortem examination of Mrs. Peiris was conducted the following day by the Consultant Judicial Medical Officer, (JMO) Colombo, Dr. S. Subramaniam. Professor H.V.J. Fernando, Professor of Forensic Medicine, University of Colombo, Dr. Sarath Abeysuriya, Consultant Neurosurgeon, General Hospital Colombo, Dr. (Mrs.) M.T.B. Kariyawasam, the Assistant Judicial Medical Officer, Colombo, and at the request of Professor Fernando, I also attended the post-mortem. In his detailed post-mortem report Dr. Subramaniam had mentioned that he did the post-mortem with Professor H.V.J. Fernando.

Mrs. Peiris was five foot two inches in height. She had infected bedsores on the back of the head. The upper arms, forearms, wrists and legs were swollen. Her left breast had been removed at surgery and she had a scar of a Caesarian section in the lower abdomen. There was no evidence of an insulinoma of the pancreas and any other tumour in the body. Her lungs were swollen (oedematous) with pneumonia being marked in the right basal lobe. Dr. Subramaniam did not find any cause for the hypoglycaemia. He took the entire brain and samples of body tissues for histology.

The death of Mrs. Peiris not only led to the police investigation of her death, but also the death of Russel Ingram a few months previously.

CHAPTER 5

THE INQUEST

According to the Criminal Procedure Code of Sri Lanka, an inquest must be held when the cause of death is not known or violent or suspicious. The General Hospital doctors referred the death of Mrs. Eunice Peiris to the City Coroner for an inquest.

The inquest proceedings commenced on 24th March 1979, before the City Coroner, Mr. Walter D. Perera.

I attended the emotionally charged Coroner's Court, where Rev. Mathew Peiris and the daughter of Rev. and Mrs. Peiris, 30-year-old Mrs. Mihiri Wickramasinghe of Cardiff, United Kingdom, gave evidence, led by Assistant Superintendent of Police (ASP) Mr. Hema Weerasinghe of the Homicide Squad. He was assisted by Inspectors of Police (IP) Mr. Lambert Perera of the Homicide Squad and Mr. T.M. de Crusz of the Maradana police.

Mr. A.C. (Bunty) de Zoysa, President's Counsel and a renowned criminal lawyer appeared for Rev. Peiris and he questioned Rev. Mathew Peiris as well as Mrs. Wickramasinghe.

Mr. M.L.M. Ameen and Mr. Dudley Fernando watched the interests of Mrs. Mihiri Wickramasinghe.

The JMO Colombo, Dr. S. Subramaniam who conducted the autopsy gave the cause of death as "Pneumonia and pulmonary oedema following prolonged unconsciousness". The pathological reports on some of Mrs. Peiris's internal organs sent to the Government Analyst had not been received.

Giving evidence Mrs. Mihiri Wickramasinghe said she resided in Cardiff since she got married in 1973. Her mother and father visited her in March 1978. Her mother appeared quite fit and had not aged, she said. She was aware that a Mr. and Mrs. Ingram were staying with her parents as Mrs. Dalrene Ingram had sent her the flight particulars of the visit of the parents.

On the way to Cardiff from the airport, they visited the two churches her father had served when he became a priest. At Welwyn Garden City where two Anglican Churches were located, two funerals had been in progress.

That night, her mother had said that her father in a trance had said that seeing the two funerals was not a good sign.

That same night, she said, her mother called her to come and see something. She saw her father who appeared to be in a trance and was speaking in his sleep. The next morning her father gave an explanation, which none of them understood!

After spending three weeks, Rev. Peiris left for Sri Lanka alone in April.

"My mother insisted on accompanying him back, but he told her to stay back and enjoy her holiday. My mother was worried about his meals, but he insisted he could manage somehow. My father telephoned one day in November last year and spoke of a bad dream he had. He wanted to know how mother was and whether there was anything physically wrong with her. He mentioned about her heart. My mother phoned me immediately and appeared to be upset. I wanted to send a doctor home, but my mother said it was not necessary. However, I had her examined by Dr. Parsons, the family doctor, and he did not find anything wrong with her. Thereafter, my father made several calls from Sri Lanka inquiring after her state of health. Since Dr. Parsons had already examined her and said nothing was wrong, my mother was puzzled as to why my father should have such a vision," said Mrs. Wickramasinghe.

"My mother was very devoted to my father and wrote regularly to him. He had mentioned that the Ingrams would continue to live at the Vicarage without paying rent and he would pay them for the meals. My mother did not agree to that arrangement, but my father had asked her not to get worried," Mrs. Wickramasinghe said.

Mr. de Zoysa asked, "Why did your mother object?"

"My mother said she thought it was not nice for a young woman like Dalrene to stay in the house in her absence," said Mrs. Wickramasinghe.

When asked by Mr. de Zoysa whether she believed her father had some divine guidance, she replied, "It is hard to say. At one time, I felt that as a man of God he had it. But later I thought God would not divulge to anyone his intention of taking or bringing to an end a life through his divine powers. In the end, I got disenchanted with the idea that it was divine guidance that he had."

Mrs. Wickramasinghe said that she had been in England since 1973 and her parents visited her in 1978 and at that time she had remarked at the fact that her mother had looked very well. She said that she was aware that the Vicarage was being looked after by Mr. Russel Ingram and his wife during her parents absence abroad.

About May 1978, his father had written to her mother telling her that she had over stayed her leave and requested that the principal of the school be written to under express cover indicating that she was retiring because they may otherwise consider her to have vacated her post. Since she intended on retiring, he had also said that there was no need for her to return home soon.

On 3rd December 1978, her mother and her sister Malrani returned to Sri Lanka, said Mrs. Wickramasinghe. She herself returned on 19th December as her mother invited her to come for the Christmas. She was met by the parents at the airport. While in Sri Lanka she was living with her husband's parents at Bambalapitiya.

"In July last year my father wrote to my mother saying that Russel Ingram was in a coma and doctors were unable to diagnose what was wrong with him. On 7th August mother received a cable from Sri Lanka saying something like 'Husband in big scandal. Return immediately'. It had been signed by 'Bert'. Mother was worried and wondered whether this was something connected with his church work concerning exorcism. Mother posted the cable to father asking him to check on the contents and the sender. She had also rung father about this around 9th or 10th August, but he had said that this was not the time to act about this because Russel was very ill and his relations were at the Vicarage," said Mrs. Wickramasinghe.

"Do you know whether your father checked?" asked Mr. de Zoysa.

"Yes he did. He informed mother that he checked with the Post Master-General and he found that the sender lived at Wellawatte, but he did not want to take any action. My mother also telephoned him and wanted the Ingrams to leave the house and my father said that Russel was dying and his relations were at the Vicarage. He could not ask them to leave at that time. A few days later my mother telephoned again and my father was annoyed and stated that Russel was either sinking or dead."

Mr. de Zoysa asked, "Why did your mother want the Ingrams to go?"

"She wanted to eliminate any form of scandal. My mother felt that because Russel was in hospital, it was not nice for Mrs. Ingram to stay in the house with my father. Later my father informed mother that Russel was dead and wanted Mrs. Ingram's parents in London informed."

When she visited the Vicarage in December, she saw an unknown woman having meals. She made inquiries from her sister, Malrani and she said it was Mrs. Dalrene Ingram, "the person who is supposed to be looking after house." Since she recalled that her father had written to them saying that Russel Ingram had died, she went up to Mrs. Ingram and sympathized with her.

She said that her mother invited her family for Christmas lunch at the Vicarage.

"This was her first Christmas lunch there since marriage and she had expected it to be a strict family affair. But I noticed an outsider, Mrs. Ingram, and her children being there. I asked my mother why, and she said that father had insisted on their presence, threatening not to sit at table himself if Mrs. Ingram was not asked. No further issue had been made of this," she said.

Mr. de Zoysa asked, "Did you question your father?"

"It was not possible because my father always insisted that none of us should question him on anything. Mrs. Ingram was also present at the New Year lunch. I was really annoyed as I had to sit down with a widow and an outsider on such an auspicious day in the year."

She recalled that her sister Malrani had a party on 29th December. As the party was over at about 1 a.m., Mrs. Ingram stayed the night in the visitors' bedroom. She too stayed at the Vicarage that night.

"The next day," she said, "I heard my mother screaming out and crying. I rushed to the bedroom where my father was lying by her side. I asked mother why she was crying and the reason she gave was that my father had told her that this would be the last party my mother would attend in this house. I asked my father why he had said that and he did not answer. My mother complained that ever since her arrival in Sri Lanka, my father had said he was receiving 'Heavenly messages' and that 'I have to face an irreplaceable loss'."

"My mother felt it was clear to her that the end of her life was near. My father had predicted a calamity and told her that. My father had also told my mother that there would be three calamities. One was Russel Ingram and two others to follow. My mother also said that father had guidance from a heavenly messenger asking him to take her mother to Dr. Lakshman Weerasena, a general practitioner."

She said that she had told her father that her mother was not ill and there was no point in taking her to a general practitioner. Instead she suggested that her mother be taken to Dr. Ernie Peiris, a specialist, who was a family friend. "Father asked me not to interfere with his guidance. He took my mother to a general practitioner," she said.

"At this stage was your mother in a state of depression?" asked Mr. de Zoysa.

"To me she did not appear to be depressed. The night Malrani left for England, my father told Mrs. Ingram to give my mother her tablets and a cup of milk. I saw Mrs. Ingram taking the tablets and milk. Mummy complained that after taking the drugs, she had long sleeping spells."

"At this stage, I thought there was more to my mother's depressions than my father's predictions. After what my sister told me about the gossip, I felt that there was no divinity about my father's predictions but it was only a method to get my mother out of the way."

"You mean to get rid of her?" Mr. de Zoysa queried.

"No. No I never said so. I mean to have her out of the way," Mrs. Wickramasinghe said.

"When I telephoned my mother on 14th January 1979, the call was answered by Mrs. Ingram. She said my mother was admitted to Durdans. My father came on and said that there was a slight drop in her blood sugar, and she was admitted for a checkup but that she would be back home in two days. He did not mention that my mother was unconscious. I asked father what Mrs. Ingram was doing in the house and he replied it was his house and he could have anyone he wanted in his house. He asked me to mind my own business. I received a letter from mother dated January 14 in which she stated her father had trust in Dr. Weerasena because he was a Catholic and would believe anything father said and would do as he told. Dr. Weerasena was an admirer of my father and believed in his visions," she said.

Mrs. Wickramasinghe said that on 2nd January 1978 her sister Malrani went to England and her father saw her off. He had asked her mother not to accompany them to the airport because she was not well and asked Mrs. Wickramasinghe too to stay back at home to look after her mother.

"To me mother didn't appear to be depressed. The only complaint was that her tongue was dry. My mother was never a diabetic," Mrs. Wickramasinghe said.

Mrs. Wickramasinghe said that she was due to leave for England on 11th January and on 6th January there was to be a party at her mother-in-law's to which her mother looked forward to, but was unable to attend because she had been sleeping after taking the drugs. Soon after she returned to England, her sister Malrani said that she had heard gossip linking her father's name to Dalrene.

"My husband mentioned that my father's association with Dalrene was out of the ordinary and was not one born of sympathy. I knew that father had found Dalrene employment as a telephone operator at Colonial Motors. After the discussion with my sister I felt there was more to my mother's depression," she said.

"When my mother returned home from Cardiff, my brother, sister and I spoke to her on the phone. She appeared quite rational and asked them not to worry. We had spoken to father too and suggested that he get rid of Dalrene. All he said was 'Mummy is all right, Mummy is all right', which gave me the impression that either her mother or Mrs. Ingram was beside him and he did not want us to hear what was being said," Mrs. Wickramasinghe continued.

On 2nd February Malrani returned to Sri Lanka on receipt of a cable from Rev. Peiris informing them of her mother's hospitalization. Mrs. Wickramasinghe said she also returned to Sri Lanka on 16th February. She found her mother in a coma and she remained in that state until her death.

She said her mother did not bring any drugs from Britain and that she sent her father 50 Euglucon tablets by post. He had bought 100 tablets on a prescription obtained by her at the time her parents were in Cardiff.

"I made a statement to the police and requested that the death of my mother be fully investigated," she concluded.

Rev. Mathew Peiris, who was 60 years old, giving evidence at the inquest, said that his wife was 59 years old. He said that he was not a priest at the time of marriage. He became a priest in 1954 and had initially worked in two churches in the UK. His wife joined him in Britain in 1953 and was followed by the two children, Mihiri and Munilal, whom they had at that time. The third child (who died) was born in England as was the fourth, Malrani.

The family had returned to Sri Lanka in 1957. That year he began working at St. Paul's Church where he became Vicar the following year. In April 1958 the family had moved into the main house from the curate's section they had earlier occupied.

Rev. Peiris said he went on a world tour with his wife in 1978. They visited the US and came to England where they stayed with their daughter Mihiri at Cardiff. He had returned home in April 1978 while his wife had stayed back with Mihiri. His wife returned home on 6th December 1978 with their younger daughter Malrani. He said that they returned in connection with a marriage proposal for Malrani. Since the marriage did not take place his wife was very much depressed because she had made elaborate arrangements. She had brought cakes, the bridal clothes, confetti etc. Rev. Peiris said that a second proposal too did not work out and that this had added to his wife's depression.

Malrani went back to England on second February. Her wife did not accompany her to the airport because of depression.

Continuing his evidence he said that his wife was admitted to Durdans in an unconscious state. She was taken there by ambulance as she was unconscious. When she regained her consciousness, she was referred to Dr. D.J. Attygalle, Consultant Physician and Dr. Sathanandan, a Consultant Psychiatrist. Dr. Sathanandan who had spoken to him after the examination had asked him whether she had contemplated suicide. The doctor had also asked whether there were any family problems.

Dr. Sathanandan had told her that she would worry about the children if she remained here and about her husband if she went to England. It was suggested that she stays here and that the doctor would help her out of the condition she suffered. Rev. Peiris had said that in fact she had been in England while he was here. Dr. Sathanandan later told him that his wife suffered from depression apparently due to family problems and he should attempt to solve them.

Rev. Peiris said, "When my wife returned to Sri Lanka after a holiday she was in a state of depression and I took her to Dr. Lakshman Weerasena. She also complained of puffed stomach, pain in knee joints, abnormal thirst and had difficulty passing urine and lack of sleep. She arrived from England with these symptoms. She also complained of drowsiness after taking drugs. Dr. Weerasena after examination noticed that her tongue was milky white, and suspected she would go in for cerebral ischaemia and suggested she be hospitalized for investigations."

ASP Weerasinghe asked, "Did Dr. Sathanandan suggest your wife to get back to England?"

"Yes. As my wife had told him that the house was too old and too big and she had no transport, no friends, no neighbours etc. my wife appeared to be anxious to go. There was no problem in her going back as she had retired from her job. The doctor had also jokingly asked her what would happen to her husband if she went away. She did not answer that question," said Rev. Peiris.

He also said that there was no displeasure between himself and his wife at any time. She did not worry about him as he was looked after by a family staying in his house. They had been there before the world tour he did with his wife. When they were away the house had been in their charge.

"Who was this family?"

"Mr. and Mrs. Ingram."

"Were they still in your house when your wife returned from England?"

"No. Mr. Ingram died in August 1978 but Mrs. Ingram left my house on 25th January 1979."

"After my return in April 1978, they had provided me meals. When my wife returned with the children the Ingrams had left. Mrs. Ingram left the house on 25th January 1979. Mr. Ingram died in August 1978 and Mrs. Ingram and their children were at the Vicarage at the time of his death. Mr. Ingram died at the General Hospital and I did not know the cause of death. He had been taken to hospital and treated by several doctors. Mr. Ingram had been unconscious when taken to hospital. He had been discharged once but had been re-admitted in an unconscious state and had remained so till his death on 10th August, four months later. Mrs. Ingram had continued to stay at the Vicarage with her sister and brother-in-law. The brother-in-law's child was also there," said Rev. Peiris.

He said that his wife was discharged on 2nd January from Durdans and did not go back to England. She was not completely well after her return from hospital and the reports of certain test done at Glass House were given to the General Hospital when she was admitted on 31st January. She was taken to hospital because she was found unconscious that morning. He said that before she was admitted to the General Hospital she had been at home for about two weeks during which time she was seen by a specialist and a general practitioner. The general practitioner had advised hospitalization on the night of 30th January and had said to keep her off the drug she was on. She was conscious but drowsy that night. She also spoke to the doctor.

Rev. Peiris gave evidence relating to his wife's admission to hospital and her condition there. He said he had informed his children of their mother's condition by cable on 31st January. He said that his wife had no history of diabetes to his knowledge. He himself was a diabetic and received treatment.

ASP Weerasinghe asked, "Was your wife a diabetic?"

"I don't know. To the best of my knowledge she had not been treated for diabetes," said Rev. Peiris.

"Has there been any displeasure between your wife and you?" asked Mr. de Zoysa.

"No, never."

After the conclusion of evidence of Rev. Peiris, Mr. de Zoysa said, "If ever there is a tragic case, this is it. The reputation of an honourable priest held in high esteem by the church and society has been brought into the arena. Justice must be done and every law abiding citizen will give the police all co-operation in bringing the culprits, if there are any, to book if what has been alleged is true. The police must go all out to clear the good name of the priest whose name has been dragged in due to unfortunate circumstances."

On 24th March, the City Coroner, Mr. Walter D. Perera returned an open verdict into the death of Mrs. Peiris and instructed the Police to continue their investigations.

The younger daughter of Rev. and Mrs. Peiris, Miss Malrani Peiris, who was working as a secretary in England, made a statement to the Police before she left Sri Lanka.

CHAPTER 6

THE INVESTIGATION

After the City Coroner returned an open verdict into the death of Mrs. Peiris, the police began a comprehensive investigation into the deaths of Russel Ingram and Mrs. Peiris. The City Homicide Squad contacted Scotland Yard to obtain certain information which they believed would help them in their probe. Three vital documents relating to the case had been sent to the police by the two daughters of Mrs. Peiris, who lived in the United Kingdom.

The police team investigated the deaths of Mrs. Eunice Peiris, Mr. Russel Ingram and also Rev. Basil Jayewardene who was the priest in the Vicarage before Mathew Peiris. Among the people they interviewed were Rev. Mathew Peiris and a number of people who had attended exorcist ceremonies.

The Police collected and studied all available medical records connected with the prolonged illness of Mrs. Eunice Peiris and Mr. Russel Ingram, which were maintained by the General Hospital, Colombo. They also collected the prescriptions issued by certain private medical practitioners. Some of them were collected from the Vicarage of St. Paul's Church, Kynsey Road. Rev. Mathew Peiris was also present when the detectives of the City Homicide Bureau visited the Vicarage. The medical records obtained were studied by a team of investigators.

Investigations were handled by a special team, headed by the ASP Mr. Hema Weerasinghe and comprising ASP Gamini Weerasinghe, and Inspectors Lambert Perera, Terrence Perera, Cyril Selvaratnam,

Malcolm Crusz and Hillary Oorloff, and Sub-Inspectors Anton Fernando and J.S. Jayatilaka. The team was led by Detective Superintendent Tyrrell Goonatilleke and was directed by the City Police Commissioner, Mr. S. Vamadevan.

On 29th March 1979, in a very unusual move, the Police forwarded a preliminary report on their investigation into the death of Mrs. Eunice Peiris to President J.R. Jayewardene, His Excellency the President of Sri Lanka.

The police also decided to exhume the body of Russel Ingram for a full post-mortem. An order to this effect was signed on 29th April afternoon by the City Coroner Mr. Walter D. Perera. The order empowering the police to exhume the body came on a request made by the ASP, Mr. Hema Weerasinghe. The exhumation and post-mortem on the body of Russel Ingram were requested owing to the similarities between his death and that of Mrs. Peiris.

The police Homicide Squad applied to Colombo's Chief Magistrate, Mr. Leslie Abeysekera for permission to take into custody copies of all cables, which Rev. Peiris had received from abroad over the past few years. These copies were expected to clarify many statements made to the police in connection with the Vicarage deaths.

On 30th April the body of Russel Ingram was exhumed at the General Cemetery, Colombo. The day before the exhumation a strong Police guard was posted at the cemetery. Certain body tissues were taken for analysis by a team of pathologists led by the Colombo Judicial Medical Officer (JMO) Dr. S. Subramaniam.

Mr. Alexander Parker Ingram, father of Russel, was at the grave side as the body of his son Russel was exhumed.

When interviewed by the press the following day, he said, "I am very depressed. I can't talk much to you." The long sessions with the police and agonizing grave side vigil as the body of his son was exhumed were mirrored on the tired face of Russel's father as he talked. In the crowded living room of his Ethul Kotte residence, seated bare bodied on a blue settee, Alexander Parker Ingram had to consult other members of his family while answering some questions about his son.

"Russel was an all round athlete," he said speaking about his son's college days at Wesley.

"He was the second boy in the family. He was very entertaining and active and was well liked by his friends. He had done several jobs before his death and it was during one of these that he met Dalrene," Mr. Ingram said.

"Both of them were working at the same advertising company and had a romance, which ended in marriage when Russel was 22 years. Russel, who stayed with us right along except for a brief spell in Kandy, moved into the Vicarage somewhere in March 1977, when Rev. Peiris asked them to come and look after it. He stayed there till he was taken ill and died in August last year," Mr. Ingram mourned.

Leon, Russel's younger brother, said, "My brother was a boxer and a cricketer. He boxed for the Stubbs Shield and played Daily News Trophy cricket. He was a very social and lively person."

Mrs. Cora Ingram, 60-year-old mother of Russel, a homely looking lady, who sat next to her husband appeared to be reminiscing about the days her late son had spent with them. Except for agreeing with her husband on some things he said about their son, she did not make any comment.

During the investigation, the Police had recovered about 20 letters from the Vicarage premises and a close study of them had revealed some information which had been very helpful in their investigations. Some of the recovered letters dated back one year. Investigators of the Homicide Squad also had interviews with some specialists and other doctors who had earlier treated the late Russel Ingram and Mrs. Peiris.

The detectives took into custody a number of letters written to Mrs. Peiris by her two daughters in England along with her passport. According to the passport, Mrs. Peiris was found to have travelled extensively, and visited a number of countries, including the UK, USA, and Australia. Several units of the Homicide Squad searched a number of houses in the outstations for evidence that could prove vital to the investigation.

On 3rd April, Police searched four premises in and around Colombo. The warrants for the search were obtained from the Colombo Magistrate. The search party was led by the special investigators assigned to the case and consisted of members of the Police Narcotics Bureau. The 'search' that took the better part of the day, yielded a number of medical prescriptions, and other documents connected with the late Mrs. Peiris.

The Police also recorded the statement of a lady who reportedly had been boarded at the residence of the late Mrs. Peiris, which is the Vicarage of St. Paul's, Punchi Borella.

Several pills recovered from the Vicarage were handed over to the Government Analyst and the Police began recording medical evidence.

Deputy Inspector General of Police (DIG) R. Sundaralingam (Crimes and Operations) entered the scene of investigations with a top level conference with the investigating team, on April 18th.

Shortly after, it was found that an attempt had been made to direct Mrs. Peiris's commuted pension of Rs. 15,000 to a joint account, by allegedly getting Mrs. Peiris's finger print onto a document related to the transfer. Mrs. Peiris is said to have been unconscious at the time the finger print was said to have been taken.

It was revealed that Mrs. Dalrene Ingram had named Rev. Mathew Peiris executor of her 'Last Will' drawn up on December second, just four days before Mrs. Eunice Peiris returned to the Vicarage from England. He was also appointed guardian of her children by the same document, in the event of her death. It was found that Mrs. Ingram had also registered her family by that time, in the Vicarage householders list.

Meanwhile, the police had taken all vital medical documents connected with Mrs. Peiris including the bed tickets issued to her during her stay in the hospital into custody. The Police, who have recorded statements from a number of persons, questioned Mrs. Dalrene Ingram.

Detectives traced the person who had cabled Mrs. Peiris while she was in London. The investigators who had the copy of the cable stating "Husband in big scandal. Return immediately. Bert" recorded the statement of the sender. The cable had been sent on 7th August 1978 while Mrs. Peiris was staying with her daughter Mihiri Wickramasinghe in England.

Police also interviewed two senior medical officers attached to ward 44 of the Colombo General Hospital. The City Homicide squad contacted Scotland Yard to obtain certain information, which they believed would help in their probe.

In late April, the investigating police officers requested the doctors involved in the medico-legal examination of the two deaths to be present at a case conference.

Professor H.V. J. Fernando, Professor of Forensic Medicine, Faculty of Medicine, University of Colombo, Dr. S. Subramaniam, the JMO Colombo, Professor N.D.W. Lionel, Professor of Pharmacology, Faculty of Medicine, University of Colombo and Dr. H.R. Wickramasinghe, Consultant Neuropathologist, General Hospital, Colombo, participated in the conference. Professor Fernando asked the author to be present as well. DIG Mr. Tyrrell Goonatilleke and Mr. Hema Weerasinghe represented the police. The conference was held in Professor Fernando's office in the Department of Forensic Medicine of the Faculty.

The discussion began with Mr. Goonatilleke presenting the results of the investigation of the deaths, which covered the visits of police officers to the UK to interview the son and two daughters of Rev. Peiris and the police surveillance of movements of Rev. Peiris and Dalrene Ingram. After an exhaustive analysis of the findings, Mr. Goonatilleke said, "Doctors, this is the evidence we have. How can you help us?"

Then Dr. Subramaniam gave an analysis of the post-mortem findings of the two deaths. He explained that the findings were consistent with hypoglycaemia in Mrs. Peiris's death but he could not comment on Russel Ingram's cause of death. He said that he could not find an insulinoma, a tumour secreting insulin in Mrs. Peiris's pancreas and a tiny insulinoma could be easily missed.

"Could you cut the pancreas into tiniest possible pieces and exclude an insulinoma?" asked Mr. Goonatilleke. Dr. Subramaniam said that he did it as much as he could.

When the introduction of Euglucon, an anti-diabetic drug to food and drinks to Russel Ingram while in hospital was discussed, Mr. Goonatilleke wanted to know whether this drug can be easily dissolved. Professor Lionel said he will try to show the solubility of the drug and went to his office in the next building and brought a tablet of Euglucon. He put it into a glass of water and showed everyone how it is very slowly dissolved in water.

After nearly an hour of discussion Mr. Goonatilleke thanked the doctors and concluded the meeting.

Detectives of the City Homicide Squad recorded statements from a number of doctors and hospital staff who had attended on them during their period of hospitalization at the Colombo General Hospital. Police investigators were endeavouring to discover what compelled Russel to suddenly leave his hospital ward on the morning of 13th July 1978 without permission.

According to ASP Hema Weerasinghe, OIC, Homicide and Narcotics, the questions asked by the investigators were centered on the treatment of Mrs. Peiris and Mr. Ingram. Investigators have also made inquiries at a certain chemists shop regarding purchases of drugs by members of Rev. Mathew Pieris's family.

The detectives of the City Homicide Squad investigated the Last Will made by Mrs. Ingram prior to her departure from the Vicarage. The Will, drawn up on 2nd December, just four days before the return from England of Mrs. Eunice Peiris was recovered by the police following the search of a house of a relative of Mrs. Ingram in the outstations. The statements of these relatives too were recorded by the police. According to the terms of the Will, all property had been equally left to the children while Rev. Peiris had been named as the guardian and sole executor of the estate. Police checked the finances of Mrs. Ingram and tried to establish as to the conditions referred to in the Last Will and as to why the drawing up of this will coincided with her own departure from the Vicarage. The police also had in their possession a letter and a cheque connected with the finding of alternate accommodation of Mrs. Ingram.

On 18th April, the Homicide squad officers had a top level conference with the DIG Mr. R. Sundaralingam. They discussed all aspects of the investigations into the deaths of Russel Ingram and Mrs. Eunice Peiris and mapped out the course of further investigations.

On 27th April the Crime Detective Bureau (CDB) interviewed several persons who attended exorcist services conducted by the Rev. Mathew Peiris at St. Paul's Church. The CDB also interviewed a number of clergymen and had also contacted some of the doctors in connection with medical reports relating to the deaths of Mrs. Eunice Peiris, Mr. Russel Ingram and Rev. Basil Jayewardene, former incumbent of St. Paul's Church, Kynsey Road, Colombo. All three died under similar circumstances after being in a prolonged coma.

On 5th May, Police recovered a number of documents believed to be vital for their investigations in to the deaths of Mrs. Peiris and Mr. Ingram. The search was carried out in the early hours of 5th morning at the Vicarage and two homes in Dehiwala and Wattala, on a warrant issued by the Chief Magistrate Mr. Leslie Abeysekera following an application by the ASP Mr. Gamini Weerasinghe.

The detectives questioned Rev. Peiris on certain aspects of the case and also attempted to collect comprehensive details of Rev. Peiris's activities while in Australia and America. Police sources stated that the progress of the investigations was being closely followed by sections of the Australian press particularly in Melbourne.

There was tension when threatening telephone calls were made to Rev. Peiris according to some newspaper reports. A private security organization was brought in to guard the Vicarage premises.

CHAPTER 7

FATHER MATHEW PEIRIS AND DALRENE INGRAM ARRESTED

On 25th May, Rev. Mathew Peiris was arrested. Looking calm, cool and collected, Rev. Peiris walked across from the Gregory's Road Headquarters of the CDB to the residence of the Colombo Chief Magistrate next door at 5.48 a.m. on 26th.

He was escorted by ASP Mr. Hema Weerasinghe and IPs Messrs. Selvaratnam, Oorloff and Crusz.

The Magistrate, Mr. Leslie Abeysekera, allowed a police application for remand and ordered that Rev. Mathew Peiris be held till 9th June. He was in the Magistrate's bungalow only for less than five minutes.

Outside the Magistrate's gate, Rev. Peiris warmly shook hands with the team of police investigators. Accompanied by some of them he got into a police car, which sped away towards the Colombo Remand Jail. Flash bulbs popped as Rev. Peiris got into the car and was driven away.

On 28th May morning, three days after the arrest of Rev. Peiris, Mrs. Dalrene Ingram was also taken into custody. This followed several days of close surveillance by the police on all her movements. She was questioned for little over ten hours. Detectives continued to question Mrs. Ingram at length in connection with the deaths of her husband Russel and Mrs. Eunice Peiris. She was remanded by the same magistrate, till 8th June.

DIG Mr. R. Sundaralingam and the City Police Commissioner Mr. S. Vamadevan reviewed additional evidence the detectives of the Homicide Squad had recorded since the arrest and remand of Rev. Peiris. Detectives prepared extracts from the medical evidence they had collected and reviewed the report of the pathological post-mortem and on the samples of hair, finger nails and tissues removed from the exhumed body of Russel. The report did not throw very much light on the death as the samples had shown no traces of poison or any other foreign substances due to the body having been in an advanced state of decomposition at the time of exhumation.

On 8th June, Rev. Peiris was brought to Chief Magistrate's Court at Hulftsdorp in a prison van and escorted to the well of Court. On application by the ASP Mr. Hema Weerasinghe, the Chief Magistrate of Colombo, Mr. Leslie Abeysekera, remanded him till 2nd July.

Mr. Sarath Muttettuwegama, Senior Counsel, with Mr. Suresh Chandra appeared for Rev. Peiris.

Mr. Muttettuwegama requested Court to release the manuscripts of the book written by Rev Peiris titled "To hell with the devil" and also two cheque books. Mr. Weerasinghe agreed to release photostat copies of the manuscript, but not the original, which Mr. Weerasinghe claimed was vital to their investigations.

The Chief Magistrate also made an order that the specimen handwriting of the Rev. Peiris be taken in Court.

On 30th September 1979, two detectives from the CDB Headquarters, ASP Mr. Hema Weerasinghe and IP Mr. Cyril Selvaratnam left for England to record statements of a number of persons in connection with the two deaths. The officers, who were the first to go abroad from Sri Lanka on a homicide investigation, recorded the statements of the three children of Rev. and Mrs. Peiris: Mihiri, Munilal, and Malrani, and the statements of their son-in-law Mr. Alistair Wickramasinghe, and Dr. (Mrs.) G. Balasubramaniam, Consultant Pathologist.

They also sought the assistance of Scotland Yard to trace two Englishmen who could provide details vital to the investigations. The

Sri Lanka High Commission in Britain was requested by the Foreign Ministry to provide all assistance to the two Police officers.

On first February 1980, Rev. Peiris and Mrs. Dalrene Ingram applied to the Chief Justice to grant them a Trial-at-Bar before three judges of the High Court without a jury. Mr. Sarath Muttettuwegama on behalf of Rev. Mathew Peiris and Mr. Cecil Goonewardena on behalf of Mrs. Dalrene Ingram interviewed the Chief Justice, Mr. Neville Samarakoon in his chambers and made this application for a Trial-at-Bar, which was allowed.

On 19th March 1980, exactly one year after Mrs. Peiris died in hospital following a prolonged state of unconsciousness, the Attorney General Honourable Shiva Pasupati filed indictments in the High Court of Colombo charging Rev. Mathew Peiris and Mrs. Dalrene Millicent Ingram.

The two accused were charged on five counts of conspiracy and murder.

On count one, both Rev. Peiris and Mrs. Ingram have been charged collectively with having between 7th July 1977 and 10th August 1978 conspired to murder Russel Ingram.

On count two, both Rev. Peiris and Mrs. Ingram have been charged collectively on or about 10th August 1978 for murder of Russel Ingram.

On count three, both Rev. Peiris and Mrs. Ingram have been charged collectively with having conspired to murder Mrs. Eunice Lois Peiris, wife of Rev. Peiris, between 7th July 1977 and 20th March 1979.

On count four, Rev. Peiris had been charged for committing the murder of Mrs. Peiris on or about 19th March 1979.

On count five, Dalrene Ingram had been charged, with aiding and abetting Rev. Peiris to commit the murder of Mrs. Peiris.

The indictments were forwarded to the High Court by the Attorney General.

CHAPTER 8

PRE-TRIAL EVENTS

After the indictments were served on Rev. Mathew Peiris and Mrs. Ingram by the High Court on May 1980, the case was called before the Court comprising of High Court Judges O.S.M. Seneviratne, Tudor de Alwis and A. W. Gooneratne on 28th July to fix a date of trial.

On 2nd and 3rd July 1980, a three Judge Bench of the Court of Appeal, comprising of Mr. Justice B.S.C. Ratwatte, Mr. Justice Victor Perera and Mr. Justice H.D. Tambiah heard the applications for bail by Rev. Mathew Peiris and Mrs. Dalrene Ingram.

Mr. Sarath Muttettuwegama, appearing for Rev. Peiris said, "State was opposing the applications on the ground that his client would interfere with the witnesses and abscond. But the state could adopt the necessary safeguards like police supervision allowed in such instances in order to prevent any interference by my client."

Referring to the fear expressed in the affidavit filed by the Attorney General, Mr. Muttettuwegama said that, if there was any fear on the part of the State that Rev. Peiris would go abroad, the simple way to prevent it was by impounding his passport.

Mr. Muttettuwegama said that their main purpose seeking a release of his client on bail was to facilitate adequate consultations, which could not be properly done in the remand prison within the limited time allowed by the prison authorities.

Mr. Cecil Goonewardena, Senior Counsel for Mrs. Ingram said nothing categorical had been said by the State about his client. They had not stated that she was influential like Rev. Peiris. She was the mother of three children and had been deprived of the comfort of her children for one year.

Deputy Solicitor General Mr. Tilak Marapana, representing the Attorney General, opposed the applications on the grounds that the accused might interfere with the witnesses for the prosecution and that Rev. Peiris might abscond. He said that the only ground urged for granting bail was that it would be extremely difficult for the defence to prepare its case without it having adequate consultations with the accused.

"If their complaint was that they could not have adequate consultations in the Remand Prison, more facilities could be provided for consultations," said Mr. Marapana.

On 3rd July, the Court of Appeal ordered that Rev. Mathew Peiris and Mrs. Dalrene Ingram be released on cash bail of Rs. 25,000 each with two sureties subject to certain conditions.

In the course of his order, Mr. Justice Ratwatte (with the other two judges agreeing) said he was of the view that the grounds urged on behalf of both accused constituted special circumstances and that even though the two accused were charged with capital offences, they should be released on bail in order to enable them to prepare for their trial.

The conditions imposed by the three judge bench were:

1. The two accused shall report to the Officer-in-charge of the Crime Detection Bureau, Colombo, between 10 a.m. and 12 noon every other day commencing from the day after they are released on bail.

2. The accused are not to communicate with any witnesses for the prosecution.

3. The accused should not leave the limits of the Colombo Municipal Council without informing the Officer-in-charge of the Crime Detection Bureau, Colombo.

4. If any of the above conditions are contravened the bond shall be subject to cancellation.

5. The Court also directed the police to have the passport of Rev. Mathew Peiris impounded, if that had not been done already.

Mr. Sarath Muttettuwegama, with Messrs. Sidath Sri Nandalochana, Mr. W.G. Deen and Mr. Suren Peiris appeared for Rev. Mathew Peiris.

Messrs. Cecil Goonewardena, C.P. Illangakoon (Junior) and G.G. Ponnambalam (Junior) appeared for Mrs. Dalrene Ingram.

The Trial-at-Bar commenced on 7th November 1980 before a High Court bench comprising three High Court Judges B.E. de Silva, Tudor de Alwis and A. Wickrema Gunaratne.

There was a large crowd both in and outside the Court premises who had come to watch the trial.

Before the indictments were read, Mr. Sarath Muttettuwegama, who appeared for Rev. Peiris, raised a preliminary objection that the indictments against the accused had not been properly framed.

He told the judges that he wished to make certain legal submissions in respect of the charges in the indictments that had already been served on both Rev. Peiris and Mrs. Dalrene Ingram. He told Court that before his client pleaded to the charges in the indictment he would bring to the notice of Court that the two offences were put together in the indictment. He referred to the Criminal Procedure Code and said that the section contained in the Penal Code was very clear that there should be separate charges for separate offences. In this case there was one charge for the death of two persons. That he considered was against the Rule, and as such the State could not maintain the indictment.

Arguing further, Mr. Muttettuwegama said that the accused should not in any way be embarrassed by the two charges being brought together. Criminal Law, Mr. Muttettuwegama said, was based on the assumption that the accused should not be harassed by bringing several charges together. For example, he said that a charge arising out of the second death should not be joined with the charge arising from the first death. There should be two distinct and different charges. Referring to the charge numbers one and two in the indictment, he said that in his opinion it should be one charge. He said both accused were brought before Court jointly.

Mr. Muttettuwegama cited the cases of Cooray vs. Dias, and Manuviyah vs. Empress in England, and an Indian case and said that in all those cases the judges had held that there should be a separate and distinct charge for each offence committed. If it were not so, the accused would not have a fair trial.

"In my opinion", Mr. Muttettuwegama said, "There could not be two charges of conspiracies for the same reason according to the prosecution, the motive of both Rev. Peiris and Mrs. Dalrene Ingram was first to murder Russel Ingram and later Mrs. Peiris. If that was the position of the prosecution, then there could be two charges of conspiracies. On reading the indictment I am of the opinion that there were two distinct conspiracies. In that event there should be two different charges. We are dealing with anticipated evidence. If this trial could have been heard before a jury I would have strongly pressed this case and the presiding judge would have definitely held with him."

Mr. Muttettuwegama said the prosecution had listed over 140 witnesses and a large number of them would give evidence only in respect of the charge of conspiracy and not murder. His client would be highly prejudiced for the reason that he would not know on what charge - whether on conspiracy or murder - the prosecution would lead evidence. The defence would also not know on whose death the witnesses would give evidence.

Mr. Cecil Goonewardena, who appeared for Mrs. Dalrene Ingram said he fully agreed with the submissions of Mr. Muttettuwegama.

In the wider interest of justice the Court should use its discretion in ordering the separation of charges to give separate trial for each charge.

Mr. Tilak Marapana, the Deputy Solicitor General, replying to the objections said, "The State's position was that there had been an agreement to murder Mrs. Peiris between specific times. The evidence would indicate that there had been conspiracy to murder both Mrs. Peiris and Mr. Ingram, the main reason being that Rev. Peiris was in love with Mrs. Ingram. That was the main reason that the two accused wanted to eliminate their spouses. The defence position was that there were two outer terminals with regard to conspiracy. Although there were two outer terminals there was enough evidence to connect both accused together on the two charges of conspiracy. They had a common motive to murder the two people and in the circumstances it had to be considered as one transaction. Mrs. Peiris was aware as to what was happening in the house. At the time the husband of Dalrene was murdered the accused had the intention of also murdering Mrs. Peiris. Mrs. Peiris was in England at the time when Ingram was murdered. In point of fact Mrs. Peiris had on a number of occasions shown her displeasure in Dalrene continuing to stay at the Vicarage. Both accused had taken a grave decision to do away with Russel first at the same time they had decided also to do away with Mrs. Peiris."

The Colombo High Court over-ruled preliminary objections raised by Rev. Mathew Peiris and Mrs. Dalrene Ingram and fixed the trial for 23rd February 1981.

Mr. Sarath Muttettuwegama with Messrs. Sidath Sri Nandalochana, W.G. Deen and Suren Peiris appeared for Rev. Mathew Peiris. Messrs. Cecil Goonewardena with C.P. Illangakoon (Junior) and G.G. Ponnambalam (Junior) appeared for Mrs. Ingram.

Mr. Tilak Marapana, Deputy Solicitor General, with Messrs Ananda Amaranath, Senior State Counsel, Mr. C. R. de Silva and N. Amaratunga, State Counsel appeared for the prosecution.

The accused appealed against this decision of the High Court to the Court of Appeal.

On 10th December, Dr. Colvin R. de Silva supported an application-in revision against an order of the Trial-at-Bar refusing the separation of trial before a bench of three judges comprising Mr. Percy Colin Thome (President), Mr. Justice L.H. de Alwis and Mr. Justice H.A.G. de Silva.

"There could be one conspiracy to kill many but a single conspiracy cannot be split to have many charges for Rev. Mathew Peiris. The finding that all the offences charged in the five respective counts were connected in the same transaction was wrong as the indictment, expressly and on its very face, alleged two separate 'conspiracies' - one to murder Ingram and the other to murder Mrs. Peiris - as opposed to a single conspiracy to commit the murder of both," Dr. Colvin R. de Silva submitted. He contended that the case failed in the first test itself.

He said, "The prosecution itself would seem to have accepted that the case to murder Mrs. Peiris existed side by side with the conspiracy to kill Russel Ingram. The alleged act did not constitute one series, but more than one - that was to say different series which could not be constituted into one series. He said the two indictments had been combined into one indictment illegally in the guise of a joinder under Section 175 of the Criminal Procedure Code."

Dr. de Silva, told the Court of Appeal, the prosecution could not come to the Court with the indictment served on the two accused in that case because there was a misjoinder, which had rendered the whole indictment illegal. "The Court should order separate trials," he said.

Mr. Colin Thome asked, "Was that your position in the High Court Trial-at-Bar?

"Exactly", answered Dr. de Silva.

He further said that there should be separate charges for every single act or series of acts according to the provisions of the law. The indictment did not bear that position. It appeared as if the prosecution had no case against Dalrene Ingram if it did not link her with the first suspect.

"I would call him a suspect and not Rev. Mathew Peiris as he is a Christian father who is still in robes," Dr. de Silva said.

Mr. Percy Colin Thome said, "That would make the position clear as there are many fathers in this case!"

Dr. de Silva said that according to the version of the prosecution, Russel Ingram felt seriously ill in a bus while returning after a church service. That was on 7th July 1978.

"If the position was so, the conspiracy should have begun earlier. Dr. de Silva said the concept of a master plan as a result of which the alleged murders were committed was itself an allegation of a conspiracy to commit the said murders. On that basis, the prosecution was disentitled from breaking up such conspiracy into two conspiracies and joining them in one indictment. The refusal to separate the trials on two separate series of charges in the indictment was wrong and would necessarily result in the grave and irreparable injustice to the defence," Dr. de Silva contended.

He said the prejudice caused to the defence by such a joinder was incalculably grave and irreparable. The indictment was directly contradictory to the position taken up by the Deputy Solicitor General and apparently adopted by the Trial-at-Bar as the basis of its order. The resulting position was that the indictment could not be the basis of fair trial in that it was confusing. It would also be a heavier sentence than if a single conspiracy was charged. A separation of trials would obviate those fundamental irregularities, he said.

Mr. Tilak Marapana making his submissions said, "The first and second accused considered to get rid of their spouses. It is necessary to outline the case for the prosecution to show that it was a series of connected events that culminated in the execution of the conspiracy. Both the deceased had developed similar symptoms before their death. On three occasions Russel Ingram had developed symptoms, which were consistent with the lowering of the blood sugar. After Russel was taken to hospital, Rev. Peiris had insisted that no dextrose should be given to the patient although that was the quicker remedy for the condition. He had also pleaded with the doctors to allow him to die saying that God wanted him. Although Russel was lying unconscious in the Vicarage, Rev. Peiris had not informed Dr. Joseph when he went there to examine him."

On 18th December, the Court dismissed the revision application. The order was unanimous.

Delivering his order Mr. Percy Colin Thome said, "This was an application by the accused petitioners for revision of the order of the High Court at Bar and to quash the indictment or in the alternative to direct the separation of the trials on Counts 1 and 2 of the indictment and Counts 3, 4 and 5 of the indictment. The accused petitioners were indicted before the High Court in Colombo."

"In considering the question of separation of trials it would be wrong to look at the matter exclusively from the point of view of the accused. The interest of justice demands that the Crown should not be unduly hampered in its presentation of the case. In the instant case we hold that a separation of trials will unduly hamper the state in its presentation of the case. For these reasons we refuse the application for revision of the order of the High Court at Bar and the application to quash the indictment or to direct a separation of trials on Counts 1 and 2 of the indictment and Counts 3, 4 and 5 of the indictment."

Dr. Colvin R. de Silva with Mr. R.I. Obeysekera, Mr. Anil Obeysekera and Mr. W.C. Deen appeared for Rev. Mathew Peiris.

Mr. Cecil Goonewardena with Mr. Ananda Malalgoda and C. P. Illangakoon (Junior) appeared for Mrs. Russel Ingram.

Mr. Tilak Marapana, DSG with Mr. C. R. de Silva, Senior State Counsel appeared for the State.

The High Court Trial-at-Bar bench comprising Mr. B.E. de Silva (Chairman), Mr. Wickrema Gunaratne and Mr. Tudor de Alwis put off the case for 11th May 1981 to fix a date for trial.

This Bench heard the case only for a day in the chambers! Thereafter, Mr. Gunaratne retired and Mr. de Silva and Mr. de Alwis were made judges of the Court of Appeal.

The Chief Justice then nominated Mr. Tissa Dias Bandaranayake, High Court Judge of Colombo, to head the High Court Trial-at-Bar to hear the Case. The other two judges of the Trial-at-Bar were Mr. P. Ramanathan and Mr. D.C.W. Wickramasekera.

The commencement of the trial was delayed due to negotiations between the state and Rev. and Mrs. Peiris's children, all three of whom were residing in Britain. These three witnesses, whose evidence was considered to be most vital to the prosecution, had wanted certain concessions from the state if they were to make themselves available for the trial. The Defence Ministry had agreed to pay 50 dollars a day subsistence allowance each and to bear the cost of their air passage to Sri Lanka and back.

An official spokesman said the arrangement would cost the Government about Rs. 200,000. All three of them were expected to arrive early in January, at least a week before the trial commenced.

The eldest daughter Mrs. Mihiri Wickramasinghe was a town planner in Cardiff and son Munilal was working in a hospital in Brentwood, Essex. Malrani was the youngest daughter. They were joined by another prosecution witness, Dr. J.G.C. Peiris, who was practising in Britain.

CHAPTER 9

THE TRIAL BEGINS

The trial finally commenced on 14th March 1983. The Prosecution was led by the DSG Mr. Tilak Marapana with State Counsel Messrs. Ananda Amaranath, C.R. de Silva and Gamini Amaratunga.

Mr. R.I. Obeysekera with Messrs. Anil Obeysekera, D.M.S. Gunasekera, Upali Senaratne, Jayantha Weerasinghe, K.Y. Perera and Mrs. Manel Gunatilleke appeared for the first accused Rev. Peiris while Mr. Cecil Goonewardena with Messrs. Ananda Malalgoda, Vijitha de Alwis and C.P. Illangakoon (junior) appeared for the second accused Dalrene.

One hundred and forty nine witnesses, including twenty five doctors, were listed by the prosecution to testify at the trial.

I have summarized the important aspects of the detailed and extensive evidence of most of the witnesses for the prosecution and the defence. Some of the evidence given was mentioned again in the Judgement.

On the day of the trial, Rev. Mathew Peiris came to the Court and took a back seat, pulling out his handkerchief and wiping his glasses. Mrs. Dalrene Ingram was dressed in a white sari with a white lace blouse to match. She wore a gold chain and a wedding ring, entered Court a little behind Rev. Peiris. She greeted him with a "Good morning" and sat on a chair near him. They were in frequent consultation and even during the 15-minute tea break they were talking to their lawyers.

Rev. Peiris took notes during the opening address of Mr. Tilak Marapana and leaned over the dock to whisper instructions to his lawyer. At the end of the day's proceedings the two accused were remanded to fiscal custody.

Mrs. Malrani Dodangoda, twenty-six-year-old London based younger daughter of Rev. Peiris, who came from England to give evidence, was the first witness summoned by Mr. Marapana.

Rev. Peiris first cast a sharp look from the dock at his diminutive daughter as she walked into the packed Court house to give evidence for the prosecution. Providing Malrani a seat close to the area where the pressmen covering the case were seated, Mr. Bandaranayake asked in a lighter vein whether she felt she was too close to the press. She said she had no complaint to make.

There was however a complaint made immediately later by one of the defence counsels that his view of the witness was obstructed by DSG Mr. Tilak Marapana. Counsel sought the help of the Court in the matter. Mr. Bandaranayake said, "I can't ask the Deputy Solicitor General to move one inch this way or that way. If you want you can move!"

Mr. R.I. Obeysekera, Counsel for the first accused Rev. Peiris said the charges of conspiracy were bad in law, in that they were vague and misleading. He was objecting to the first count where four 'limbs' were rolled up into one count of conspiracy, thereby creating confusion as to which limb the prosecution was relying on he said. He asked that the wording of the first count be changed.

The three-judge bench over-ruled this objection.

Opening the case for the prosecution, Mr. Marapana told the Trial-at-Bar that both victims in this case, Mr. Russel Ingram and Mrs. Eunice Peiris died in a coma and that the state of unconscious in Russel as well as Mrs. Peiris had been brought about by some drug being given them in some form or another.

"Rev. Mathew Peiris the pastor who claimed he had the ability to communicate with angels who spoke of impending disaster had not only predicted the deaths of Russel Ingram and Eunice Peiris, but had also made sure that the predictions came true," Mr. Marapana said.

"According to a clinical diagnosis, the state of unconsciousness, which preceded both deaths, had been attributed to a state of hypoglycaemia that is low sugar level in the blood. If a person's blood sugar level went below a certain point, he would lose consciousness and that would lead to drowsiness. The brain needed sugar for proper functioning. If a person was allowed to remain in such a state of unconsciousness for a protracted length of time, medical treatment could not make him recover. In other words, such a person would not respond to treatment. Medical evidence would be led to show that the lowering of the sugar level in the blood was due to the excess of insulin in the systems of the two deceased persons. There was no evidence whatsoever in that case to show that either Russel or Mrs. Peiris had any internal defect to cause the lowering of sugar levels in their blood systems. Without insulin the conversion of food into energy was not possible. Their deaths were due to a drug being administered in some form or other. Insulin was produced by the pancreas, the organ that controlled the supply of insulin and the correct sugar level was maintained," Mr. Marapana said.

"In the case of diabetes, drugs are introduced to activate the pancreas to secrete insulin. The question which arose in this case was as to how the two deceased persons had an excess of insulin in their systems. Another question that would arise was whether they had taken the drug voluntarily in a bid to commit suicide or whether it had been given to cause their murder."

Mr. Bandaranayake commented, "Or accidently taken?"

"Yes, it could be taken accidently also," Mr. Marapana agreed.

"When one looked at the picture as a whole, the drug had been given intentionally, after much premeditation following from a conspiracy in which both accused had a great deal to do," said Mr. Marapana.

Referring to the first accused, Rev. Mathew Peiris, Mr. Marapana said that he was a well-read person. He was a father of three children.

Before he became Vicar of St. Paul's Church, he had served as a priest in the UK. He had returned to Sri Lanka in 1967 with his three children. Rev. Peiris's family was in England at the time material to the case. Mrs. Peiris was a Vice-Principal of a school at the time of her death.

"The first accused practised exorcism indulging in special services in the church on Thursdays. Certain people were attracted by the divine powers he claimed he possessed. He was supposed to be a person having communication even with the angels through that medium of communication. Rev. Peiris claimed ability to converse with angels. Through them, he predicted some sort of danger or disaster for Mrs. Peiris and Russel Ingram. Not only did he predict such danger or disaster but he made sure they came true!" said Mr. Marapana.

He said that Dalrene was born to a family of seven girls and two boys. Her father was a clerk. She had been a telephonist, typist and did other jobs as well. She and Russel had been working together in an advertising agency before their marriage in 1965.

"Russel had been in very good physical condition at the time he fell ill. According to his father, he had suffered from no ailments till he developed the last sickness. Russel and his wife Dalrene were some of those who attended the special Thursday services conducted by Rev. Peiris from about September 1977. Rev. Peiris had employed Dalrene as his typist-cum-secretary. On 6th February 1978, Dalrene, her husband and children had shifted to the Vicarage, lock, stock and barrel. They were asked to move in by Rev. Peiris because on first January 1978, he had gone on what was called a world tour."

Continuing his opening address, Mr. Marapana said Russel Ingram had died in a state of unconsciousness after about one and a half months. Mrs. Eunice Peiris, he said, had also been admitted to the General Hospital in a similar state and died while being unconscious.

"On a clinical diagnosis it would appear that their condition was brought about by the lowering of the blood sugar. When the blood sugar went down, the person would drift into unconsciousness. In such a state the brain cells were not serviced by the sugar in one's bloodstream. I will also show evidence that if left in this state for a long period without medication, not only will the brain cells be damaged, but it was also irreversible. So it is the case of the prosecution that when the two victims were taken to the General Hospital, in view of the long period they were unconscious, no amount of medication would revive the patients and it was almost certain that death would follow."

"I will also show that this state is caused by excess insulin in the blood. How did this excess insulin come? I am in a position to positively exclude the possibility that both the deceased had internal defects to cause the lowering of the blood sugar. The case for the prosecution is therefore that when the two victims were admitted to hospital in their unconscious state, this condition had been brought about by the intentional introduction of a drug by these two accused."

"Rev. Peiris also indulged in exorcism and getting rid of evil spirits from houses. In this regard he had a special service in his church where he exorcised spirits from his congregation. He also claimed he had the ability to converse with angels, and these angels somehow predicted disaster for someone. So he not only predicted the death of these two people, but also made sure they came true."

"The first and second accused had met for the first time at one of the Thursday afternoon church services in August 1976. By early September Rev. Peiris had invited the Mrs. Ingram to become his secretary saying that he was preparing the manuscript of a book he was going to publish. Soon afterwards, Dalrene was playing a leading role in the Thursday church service. By that time Dalrene's relations with Rev. Peiris were so much so that others who were near and dear to the priest became jealous of her. Russel was without employment at that time by May 1977. The Ingrams were part and parcel of the Vicarage," said Mr. Marapana.

"When Rev. Peiris went with his wife on a world tour, the Ingrams acted as caretakers. However, he returned to Sri Lanka having left his wife in UK. He returned to Sri Lanka on 25th April 1978 leaving his wife in England. From June, the same year Russel became a sick man and on 4th August he died in a coma. We have positive evidence to show that Rev. Peiris was treating him with drugs. There was also evidence to show that Rev. Peiris had an illicit relationship with Dalrene," Mr. Marapana said.

"Russel had been in perfect health up to the time of the return of Rev. Peiris. But we find that in June 1978 just two months after the return of the first accused, the health of Russel deteriorated. He was later hospitalized while unconscious, and continued to remain so until he died. I have positive evidence that Rev. Peiris has been in the habit of giving Russel drugs. It was a case of the angel having told him that Russel was going to die. I will also show that the first and second accused had a relationship, during which the first accused had been having these angelic visits in which he was told that Russel was going to die. He also informed the church and all Russel's friends that Russel had a pancreatic disorder."

"When the police searched the house of the priest they found among other things a book entitled, 'Body, Mind and Sugar'. This book says everything about pancreas, blood sugar and hypoglycaemia, how it occurs, treatment etc. One of the first things he did after returning from his world tour was to go looking for this book which he had in a cupboard. He did not find it. One of the boarders said she had taken it and given it to a friend. Rev. Peiris got very angry over this, and had gone round Colombo looking for this book. The girl had ultimately got a copy down from London.

"During this time no doctor had ever sighted the Vicarage. Even when Russel fell unconscious, no doctor had been brought, and it was only on the insistence of Russel's father that he was hospitalized. It is my contention that Russel had been unconscious for at least two days before he was hospitalized. At the time of admission when the doctor had tried to give Russel dextrose injection, the first accused had objected and said, 'I have followed this case very carefully, do not give him sugar'."

"But of course the doctor had brushed him aside. The same thing had occurred when Mrs. Eunice Peiris was admitted to hospital. The first accused has also been described by a doctor as a person with great knowledge of blood sugar, if this is so, why did he prevent the doctors from giving them sugar?" Mr. Marapana asked.

"The first accused created a situation where all Russel's friends thought that he was suffering from a serious ailment. Dr. Sheriffdeen wanted certain tests done on Russel and at the time of his discharge no drugs had been prescribed by the doctor. However, when Russel went back to the Vicarage he was again given drugs. When he was again admitted to the hospital his blood sugar, according to the doctors, was nil," Mr. Marapana said.

"Russel while in hospital was being fed nasally, and some of the food was brought from the Vicarage. He used to give the nurses the food to put into the food container, or sometimes he put it in himself. I will show that no sooner did Russel take these meals he went in to a hypoglycaemic state. Many a time after the visits of the first accused, the drip sending the saline and glucose to Russel was found to be removed or clamped tight."

Mr. Marapana continuing his submissions said that arrangements for the funeral of Russel were discussed by Rev. Peiris and Mrs. Ingram shortly after they had served him a hearty meal for lunch while he was fully conscious and conversing. He said Mrs. Ingram had been overheard saying that Russel would not survive and that he was doomed. Rev. Peiris and she were discussing where he was to be buried.

"Russel, who went back to the Vicarage from the hospital hale and hearty, was brought back after a few days with the same ailment. I will show that on 16th July, Russel Ingram was fully conscious and able to converse and was given good lunch and even dessert. Soon after this the first and second accused discussed the arrangements for the funeral of Russel. This man who was hale and hearty at lunch time was given a cup of tea with some tablets. There was also a conversation between the first and second accused, where the first accused had said 'The time has come for medicines.' The second accused replied, 'They are with you, father'. However no sooner had Russel taken the tablets, he went into a state of unconsciousness."

"While all these things were happening to Russel, the wife of the first accused, Mrs. Eunice Peiris, who was to return to Sri Lanka in May was made by the first accused to send in her retirement papers to the school in Sri Lanka where she was a Vice Principal. She then returned to Sri Lanka on 6th December 1978 with her daughter Malrani and even at this time we find that the second accused continued to live at the Vicarage. It is significant that an angel again appeared on the same day that Mrs. Eunice Peiris returned. Apparently this angel spoke only Latin. The first accused translated what the angel had said and told Mrs. Peiris that she was not at all well and should be seen by Dr. Weerasena. Mrs. Peiris is then taken to Dr. Weerasena and the first accused does all the talking. It is evident that she faithfully believed what the angel had told him."

"This lady came to Sri Lanka in perfect health but no sooner her health deteriorated and by the end of the year there was nothing left of her. All the time she was being given these drugs; her children had protested and asked her to stop taking them. I will also produce a letter by Mrs. Peiris saying that she had to take the tablets as the angel had said so. It was a slow death. He could have killed her at once with an overdose if he wanted to, but he was conditioning the people around him to believe that she was a very sick person."

"On 29th December their daughter who had also come down to Sri Lanka held a party for her friends. At this time the first accused went into a trance and Mrs. Peiris was heard crying loudly in her room. When her daughter ran into the room her mother informed her that the first accused had predicted that this was the last party she (Mrs. Eunice Peiris) would attend in that house."

"One evening, Dr. Weerasena was informed that Mrs. Peiris was in an unconscious state and rushing to the Vicarage he called an ambulance and sent her to the Durdans Hospital. She was revived, was given dextrose injections and was released about four days later. At this time the first accused had informed the children in UK that their mother had been taken to hospital but he did not mention the comatose state which she had been in. When her brother had visited her in hospital, Mrs. Peiris had told him that the first accused had given her 'a handful of tablets'. This was said in the presence of the first accused."

"At one time the first accused had pretended to make a telephone call to Dr. Weerasena and he kept saying 'You do not want me to give her sugar? No glucose and only high protein diet?' By reading the book 'Body Mind and Sugar' he would have known that sugar was essential. Dr. Weerasena denies that there ever was such a conversation between him and the first accused."

"When Mrs. Peiris was admitted to General Hospital, the first accused had admitted to the doctor that the patient had been in a coma for over eighteen hours before being admitted. Very strangely he never told this to Dr. Weerasena or Dr. E.V. Peiris. At the hospital when the doctor had attempted to give Mrs. Peiris a dextrose injection, the first accused had protested against this and created such a fuss that the doctor got the impression that he was trying to prevent the drip being given to the patient. It has been revealed that shortly after the admission of Mrs. Peiris to hospital, the doctors had become suspicious and informed the police and investigations were started by the Crime Detection Bureau."

"At this time the first accused had gone to see Dr. J.G.C. Peiris who was his good friend and family doctor who was visiting Sri Lanka. He had discussed Mrs. Peiris's case with the doctor and asked him to sign a certificate which he would get a lawyer to draft saying that Mrs. Peiris was a hypochondriac."

"The obituary notice had been given to the press long before Russel Ingram died and even a black suit had been prepared for him. While Mrs. Peiris was in hospital the first accused had gone to the school where she taught and asked the principal if they would like to have the body lie in state at the school. This was even before the lady had died."

"The Police made an application and the body of Russel Ingram was exhumed. When this was carried by the press, the undertakers – Raymonds - say that there was a call from the first accused asking whether they had been informed in respect of the exhumation. Raymonds had said that since it was a police exhumation they had nothing to do with it. He had then asked how the body had been embalmed and what the condition of the body would be after eight or nine months."

Mr. Marapana said he would show that the relationship between the two accused were not of a priest and a parishioner, but that they behaved like 'love birds' while Russel Ingram was unconscious. He would also show that Russel had been very suspicious of the activities of his wife.

"This association between the two accused was such that the second accused had made a 'Will', making the first accused sole executor and guardian of her children. The first accused also inserted an advertisement in the press for an annex for the second accused and even paid the three month advance by cheque. On the same day he inserted another advertisement. This was to purchase a three bed room house. For whom? The second accused had at this time also opened a joint account with the first accused in a bank."

"It is important to note that when Dr. Joseph was called to the Vicarage, Russel had already been unconscious for a whole day. The doctor was not even informed that Russel was unconscious but was told that Russel was resting after a restless night. The only reason why Dr. Joseph came to the Vicarage was to give Rev. Peiris a letter so that Russel could be admitted to the General Hospital. There is evidence that Rev. Peiris administered the tablets. As soon as Russel took them he went into a semi-conscious state. When he was ultimately taken to hospital, Alex Ingram - father of Russel, said Rev. Peiris was adamant that no dextrose be given to the patient, but the doctor had brushed him aside," Mr. Marapana said.

Continuing he said, "Rev. Peiris had given Russel's obituary notice to the newspapers long before his death. The advertisements clerk of one newspaper had been instructed to fill in the date when informed, the entire notice having been written out and handed over in advance. Even Russel's black suit had been prepared for his funeral. They were all in a state of readiness. All they were waiting for was for Russel to draw his last breath! Rev. Peiris, Mrs. Ingram and her sister once discussed funeral arrangements at the Vicarage when Russel was lying critically ill after a heavy meal of rice, meat curry, *wattakka* (pumpkin) and *mellun* (green leaves curry) with a dessert of ice cream, all given to him by Rev. Peiris. All the time Rev. Peiris knew that Russel was doomed, he was destined to die according to what Rev. Peiris claimed he gathered from angelic visions."

"Mrs. Eunice Peiris too was in perfect health when she returned to Sri Lanka in December, 1978 after having extended her stay in the UK at her husband's request. She too was made to believe that the angels had predicted she would die. She had howled and cried when Rev. Peiris had told her of 'a last party that she would be celebrating at the Vicarage'. Like in the case of Russel, when Mrs. Peiris became critically ill and lapsed into a state of unconsciousness, he had continued to drug her and when dextrose was to be administered in hospital to revive her, he tried to prevent it. About three weeks before Mrs. Peiris died, Rev. Peiris had gone to her school, St. Michael's, Polwatte, and asked the Vice Principal whether the school would like to have her lie in state in the premises," Mr. Marapana said.

"The two accused had the opportunity to commit the crimes as they were the only persons at the Vicarage at this time. There were two boarders but they left because they could not get on with Mrs. Dalrene Ingram."

Mr. Wickramasekera asked, "Was one a female?"

Mr. Marapana said, "Both were."

At this stage, Mr. Marapana informed Court that Mrs. Dodangoda had fainted and has also complained of abdominal pain. Mrs. Dodangoda fainted while Court was determining on certain issues raised by the defence prior to calling the witness.

At the conclusion of the first day's hearing, Mr. Marapana made an application that the two accused be remanded. Defence Counsel Mr. Obeysekera submitted that a remand order could only be made in a trial by Jury. As this was a Trial-at-Bar he asked that the two accused be released on bail as they had thus far fulfilled their conditions of bail.

The judges however, ruled that the accused be remanded and the first accused be sent to the remand hospital as he was a diabetic patient needing medication.

Next day, twenty-six-year-old Mrs. Malrani Preethi Dodangoda gave evidence. Examined by Mr. Marapana she said that she was born in England, but from 1957 to 1976 she was in Sri Lanka, and had gone back to England in July 1976 with an uncle. When she left Sri Lanka her mother was in good health and not a diabetic. She next saw her mother when her parents came to England somewhere in 1978. She was not sure where they had been coming from, but it could have been from America. Her mother who stayed behind spent about a year in England. During their period of stay in England, her parents had lived with her sister Mihiri in Cardiff. She also moved in with Mihiri. After about two weeks her father had left Cardiff for London. Her mother, who had stayed behind, had spent about a year in England.

She said that her mother was in perfect health when she visited England. Her mother has said during the period her parents were away that some parishioners were going to look after the Vicarage. She had said that these people were Mr. and Mrs. Ingram.

"The first time I saw Mrs. Ingram was when I returned to Sri Lanka with my mother in December 1978. I never saw Russel Ingram as he died while I was in England," she said.

Mrs. Dodangoda said that his father had claimed that an angel had appeared to him and told him that his wife was suffering from a stomach ailment, and that she should be taken to see Dr. Lakshman Weerasena.

She said that she had heard that her father had been a vicar in a church in London and she had visited the place with her parents during their trip to England. They had visited two churches. In one church a funeral service had just been concluded, and in the other church a funeral was about to commence. After the visit to the churches they had gone back to her sister's home and here her father seemed to be sleeping and talking to an unseen person. This was the first time the witness had seen her father in such a manner. She said he was speaking in what appeared to be Latin and could only remember three words he had said, which were "Pope", "Stigmata" and possibly "Rome". Her mother had been beside her father during this time.

She could also remember that when he was the vicar at St. Paul's Church, Kynsey Road, Colombo, he used to perform exorcism ceremonies on Thursdays at the church vestry. In December when her mother returned to Sri Lanka, she too had returned with her. She said that while in England her mother had been in perfect health, and she had never seen her taking medicines.

After her father had returned to Sri Lanka it had been the intention of her mother to return to Sri Lanka in May as she had got overseas leave from the school at Polwatte where she was working, and had to return to work at that time. Her retirement papers were sent to her at this time, Mrs. Dodangoda said.

Mr. Marapana asked, "Can you remember your mother receiving a cable regarding a scandal involving your father?"

"Yes. It said, 'Husband in great scandal, come immediately'."

"When did your mother get this cable?"

"I think it was 7th August as my mother showed the cable to me."

"Did you talk with your father regarding this cable?"

"I did not. I think my brother and sister did."

"What did your mother do on receiving this cable?"

"She phoned my father in Sri Lanka."

She said that she had been present when her mother had made this telephone call.

She said that she and her mother came to Sri Lanka on 6th December and had lived at the Vicarage with Rev. Peiris. During this visit to Sri Lanka she had noted that close friends of Rev. Peiris, who used to visit him very frequently, did not come there anymore.

On the day they arrived in Colombo her father had again apparently spoken with an unseen person. "In this conversation the angel had mentioned that my mother had a stomach ailment. I think my father also said that would be her last Christmas or the last Christmas," Mrs. Dodangoda said.

Mr. Bandaranayake asked, "Did your father appear to be in a trance as this time?"

"His eyes were closed and he was lying down."

"When he speaks, do you hear any other voice replying?"

"No."

"When it is all over he explains?"

"Yes."

She said that her father had later explained that he had been conversing with an unseen angel and he had said that angel wanted Mrs. Peiris to be shown to Dr. Weerasena. She said that her mother had been very puzzled about the prediction of her illness and she kept asking her about this and also kept asking her father what he had seen.

Mr. Bandaranayake asked, "Did you believe your father in regard to these visions?"

"I did not believe nor disbelieve," she replied.

She said, "My mother had been a very religious person and believed in these visions. She also regularly attended the Thursday church meetings and even accompanied my father when he visited homes to drive out devils. My mother had been very devoted to her husband and she would believe anything he told her."

She said, while on her holiday in Sri Lanka she had not seen any doctor coming to the Vicarage to treat her mother. Her sister Mihiri had also come down to Sri Lanka on 19th December 1978.

She had seen Mrs. Ingram for the first time at a Thursday afternoon service, and after the service Mrs. Ingram had come to the Vicarage with her children. On 24th December, after midnight mass she believed that Mrs. Ingram and her children had stayed over at the Vicarage.

On Christmas day, Mrs. Ingram had been present for the Christmas lunch, which she said had previously been only for the family members. She however did not make inquiries as to why outsiders were present at this family meal. Mrs. Ingram may also have stayed on 25th December, but she was not sure. She however said that Mrs. Ingram had spent a lot of time at the Vicarage.

On the night of 29th December she had held a party for her friends. Although Mrs. Ingram had not been a friend of hers, she had however been present at the party, and she said that her father may have invited her.

"My mother did not like Mrs. Ingram staying at the Vicarage, and she had even told my father that she did not like the Ingrams coming to the Vicarage so often. In reply to this my father had said that the angel had asked him to look after this family."

She said, "Shortly after the Peiris Family had retired for the night after the party on 29th December, Mihiri and I heard mother crying in the next room. Mihiri had then gone into the room and asked her mother why she was crying. Her father at this time was lying on the bed. Her mother had then replied that it was predicted that this would be her last party. I was however not sure whether she had heard her father say 'her' last party or 'the' last party. The next day I asked her father why he had said such a thing and he had replied that this was the 'angel's guidance'. Her father did not have the attachment to her mother that he had previously. At first he used to be very thoughtful, but now he got irritated."

Answering a question from Mr. Marapana, she said that during the month of December her mother had always been drowsy and sleepy but did not know why. When she was returning to England her mother did not go the airport as she was feeling ill. She had said she had been feeling drowsy, and she used to take some tablets.

Mr. Wickramasekera asked, "Did she take these tablets on her own, or were they given to her by someone?"

"My father gave them to her, but I do not know how many she used to take."

"During your stay here, about how many times did your father give these tablets to your mother?"

"Maybe about twice or thrice."

Answering Mr. Bandaranayake's question, "What did she do after taking these tablets?" she said that her mother used to go to sleep most of the time. She said even during the day she used to sleep. She also said her mother had told her that she was taking the tablets as her father wanted her to take them.

She admitted that her brother had wanted to take their mother away from the Vicarage after seeing her condition. She herself suspected that something was happening and her brother had asked their father to take their mother to another doctor. Before she left for England she was aware that her mother was being treated by Dr. Lakshman Weerasena. At that time she did not ask her father to take her mother to any other Doctor. Even after she returned to England she had corresponded with her father and asked about her mother's illness.

Mrs. Dodangoda said that from the time she returned again to Sri Lanka on 3rd March 1979, after her mother's admission to General

Hospital, Colombo, she did not want to speak to her father as she knew there was something serious about her mother's illness. She had not lived at the Vicarage, but at Moratuwa with her uncle and aunt.

She said that she did not know of any arrangements for the Ingram family to stay at the Vicarage.

Mr. Marapana asked, "Was there any talk between you and your father regarding the Ingram family staying at the Vicarage?

"I cannot remember."

"Your mother was not well from December 30th to January 2nd 1979?"

"She was drowsy and in a daze."

"When you left for England on second January, Mihiri, your sister was in Sri Lanka?"

"Yes."

"When was it that you first came to know about your mother being warded at Durdans?"

"Between 15th and 20th January."

"How did you come to know about this?"

"My sister had phoned the Vicarage to find out how my mother was."

"When you heard your mother had been warded, did you try to find out what was wrong?"

"Yes, around 20th January my uncle phoned us and said that my mother was in Durdans and was unconscious."

"Was this the first time you came to know your mother was in an unconscious state?"

"Yes, and that very night my brother came to Cardiff from Essex to discuss what we would do."

"What did you discuss?"

"We felt that, as she was in an unconscious state, one of us would have to go to Sri Lanka."

"Did any of you think of phoning your father for more details?"

"Many calls were being made by my brother and sister."

"Was it discussed who should come to Sri Lanka?"

"Yes. It was decided that I should come and I left Britain on second March."

"Did you take more steps to find out the condition of your mother?"

"There were many calls being made to my uncle and aunt, but as they had no authority, one of us had to come."

"What do you mean by authority?"

"As children, anyone would expect us to look after our mother."

"Was it that one of you could do what your father could not do for your mother?"

"Well, my uncle and aunt were suspicious as to how she got ill, as she was in the best of health and my brother wanted my uncle, Father Edison, to take my mother away from the Vicarage."

"Why was that?"

"Because by this time we thought there was something suspicious and we wanted her taken away from there."

"What made you suspicious?"

"Her sudden illness and tablets."

She said that after she had returned to England in January she had kept writing to her mother and father but could not remember writing and asking her mother to go and see a different doctor.

Mr. Marapana then showed Mrs. Dodangoda a letter which she had written to her mother dated 17th January 1979 and asked her to read it and refresh her memory. She read the letter and said she could now recall having asked her mother to see a different doctor. She said that this was after she had returned to England, but before her mother had been taken to the Durdans Hospital. She said that she was not satisfied with Dr. Weerasena as she had known Dr. E.V. Peiris better.

She said that she may have asked her father to take her mother to see Dr. E.V. Peiris but was not certain as to whether she had said it. She however thought that her brother and sister may have asked someone to take her mother to see Dr. Peiris. She said that until her return to England her mother had not been shown to Dr. Peiris.

"You said that Dr. Weerasena had been chosen by the angel?" asked Mr. Marapana.

"Yes."

"Do you know if your father had shown her to Dr. Peiris?"

"Not to my knowledge."

"You eventually saw your mother on 3rd March in an unconscious state at the General Hospital?"

"Yes. I went there straight from the airport."

She said she knew her mother was in the General Hospital as her father had called her. But she had however not informed her father that she was coming down. At the airport she had been met by Father Mendis's wife and Mr. Somaratne, who was the church warden. They had known she was coming to Sri Lanka without informing her father.

Prior to leaving England for Sri Lanka she received a cable from her father saying that her mother was warded at General Hospital. She had subsequently handed it over to the police.

Shown the cable, she read it out to Court. It said, *"Mom admitted General Hospital, tests reveal organic disorder which caused depression. Condition causing anxiety. Daddy"*

She said that when she came down to see her mother at the General Hospital, she had known she was in an unconscious state as their uncle had telephoned them. She said she had gone straight to the hospital from the airport and her father had come to the hospital that evening. She did not want to speak with her father nor did she stay at the Vicarage. She stayed at Moratuwa with her uncle and aunt.

"That was because of the mysterious circumstances surrounding her mother's sudden sickness and other stories they had come to hear," she said.

Her sister Mihiri had also come down to Sri Lanka about two weeks after her arrival.

"When your father was in Sri Lanka with your mother, what necessity was there for one of you to come all the way from the UK?" asked Mr. Marapana.

"Because of her sudden sickness."

"What is that your father could not have done that you could do?"

"My uncles and sister had become suspicious. Something funny was going on and my brother wanted uncle Edison, a brother of my mother, to remove my mother to his place."

"Why?"

"By that time we thought something suspicious was happening and we did not like our mother being at the Vicarage"

"What made you all to be suspicious?"

"We felt suspicious about various tablets being given to our mother. Earlier she was in good health. There were also various rumours. All these made us to be suspicious."

Mr. Marapana asked, "Why wasn't your father informed?"

"That was because of the suspicious circumstances existing at that time."

Answering further questions by Mr. Marapana, Malrani said, "My mother was in extremely good health condition when she returned together from the UK on 6th December 1978. Barely a month passed and she became such a sick person that she could not come to Katunayake Airport on 3rd January 1979, the day I took my flight back to the UK. She was in a sort of a daze."

She said that she had to go back because she worked in the Department of Employment in Cardiff. Her mother did not request her to stay back. Her elder sister was the Town Planner in Cardiff, her husband was also doing a good job and her brother Munilal was also employed in Essex.

"Mother was really proud of our achievements," Malrani claimed, glancing at her accused father taking down notes of her evidence from the dock, a few yards away from her.

Mr. Bandaranayake asked, "Can you tell us about your father's educational background?"

"I do not know much about it, but I know he obtained a PhD when he was in America, I do not know which university it was from," she replied. She also could not say whether her father had a degree before he got his doctorate.

She said when her mother remarked that it was not nice when Dalrene kept on coming to the Vicarage so often, her father once told her mother that the angels with whom he had communication had requested him to look after Dalrene and her family.

Malrani further said that at the time she left Sri Lanka last, Dr. Lakshman Weerasena was treating her mother. According to her father, Dr. Weerasena had been preferred at the insistence of the angels. In her letters to her mother she had requested her not to take these pills explaining that her drowsiness was due to them. She could not remember whether she requested her mother to consult another doctor because these letters were written quite a long time ago.

At this stage Mr. Marapana moved Court to permit a letter Malrani had written to her mother be shown to her in order to refresh her memory on the matter. The defence counsel objected contending that the letter had not been listed as a document. Mr. Marapana said that the purpose of showing that letter was only to refresh her mind on that particular matter. They were not going to use the contents of that letter as substantive evidence and that they were relying only on her testimony.

The Court overruled the defence objection.

Then Mr. Marapana showed her a letter dated 17th January 1979, and she identified it as a letter she had written to her mother from England. After reading the letter she said she could now remember she had wanted her mother to be taken to Dr. E.V. Peiris. She preferred Dr. Peiris to Dr. Weerasena because he was very well known to the family.

Mr. Marapana then showed a letter, which Rev. Peiris had written to her. She said she recognized the signature as that of her father's, and the address had been written in his hand writing.

She then read the letter.

"To My Darling Children,

A short note and that in triplicate, short because I must catch the Tuesday post. Mom was taken to Dr. E.V. Peiris and Edison accompanied. I am glad that he did for he would have been a witness to the fact that Ernie did endorse the treatment that was done at Durdans and that prescribed. He went through all the reports and told her that the present drugs are non-habit forming and that they must be taken. If this is not done he said, that later she would have complications and more drugs may have to be taken. He assured her that drugs given right along have been correct. He asked her how her sleep was and remarked that if she did not get deep sleep he would have to prescribe something stronger. That should settle your mind that what has been given and is now given is in fact milder than what Ernie thinks as best.

He was anxious for a further series of tests, as her blood sugar level at Durdans had been high and had then dropped a wee bit lower than normal. The range is 80 to 120. She shot to 190 and then fell at 74. The ESR which reveals whether there is a cause for infection, judging the segmentation of blood revealed that was high. Normal about 4 to 10 she had it at 45. On the advice of Lakshman and endorsed by Ernie we had a glucose tolerance yesterday. It was a four hour test. Normally it is 2 ½. She had to give blood every half hour and empty bladder. Something puzzling took place. The sugar level went up after glucose was given, but not to a height as expected, and then fell suddenly. She was at the start 73 where as at Durdans it was 74, a wee bit lower than normal.

At Glass House when the test was under control it fell to a low figure as 54. The ESR too was high, though a wee bit lower than at Durdans and the test at Durdans was done by Dr. Alwis and Glass House, technicians. The ESR shows that there is a blood infection and could have been there long un-noticed. The sugar imbalance is causing Drs. to think, so we have ordered a special X-ray of the stomach, and another blood test called Serum Tests. I have fixed up for tomorrow.

Today she was asked to take a high protein diet and immediately I gave her a plateful of liver, she appeared more refreshed and less drowsy. Drs. warn that we should not repeat or suggested to her the word depression. That itself could aggravate the blood disease. Please refrain from telling her not to take drugs, Mom there was nothing wrong when you were here, Mom what is the matter, etc. That is not going to help her. We have to discover the root cause, whether it is a virus, whether it is bacteriological, or organic disease.

What is being done must reveal and I will see that she has the best whatever the cost. That word does not enter into my mind. She has *to take tablets soon after dinner and she has to sleep. This is all for the present. I trust you will place your trust in God as much as I have done. I was guided to have her under medical care and this I did immediately after she arrived. My guidance is slowly revealing itself to be true and proving that can be done. I do not plan to disturb the plans in hand.*

Love and prayer.
Your ever affectionate,
Daddy"

After Malrani read the letter, in reply to a question from Mr. Marapana, she said there was a reference in that letter asking her to refrain from asking her mother to stop taking the drugs.

Malrani said that she stayed for about one and a half months when she came in February and her mother's funeral also took place during that time. She did not speak a word with her father during that time. Her sister, Mihiri also came to Sri Lanka about three weeks after her arrival. Mihiri brought with her a letter sent to Malrani by her father which had been received in Cardiff after her departure.

Mr. R.I. Obeysekera, counsel for Rev. Mathew Peiris then cross examined Malrani.

"While you were living in Sri Lanka and being the daughter of the vicar of St. Paul's Church, you were also interested in affairs of the Church?"

"Yes."

"Your mother and father were religious persons?"

"Yes."

"Would you say that you are also a religious person?"

"Yes."

"You found that the people who attended the Thursday meetings at the church came there with all seriousness and faith?"

"Yes."

"You submit that some of the people used to feel well after these services?"

"Yes."

She said the services were rather elaborate, and that her father also used to do healing at these services. She said that when a person fainted at one of these services, it was a sign that they were possessed.

When asked by Mr. Obeysekera if on one occasion her father had levitated during prayer, she said this was not to her knowledge.

She said that her father's world trips were not as a preacher, but sponsored by other people because they had heard of the Thursday services. She said she was not aware that her mother used to take down messages which the angel used to tell her father. She was however aware that her father had been a cripple at birth and had one day seen a vision of an aunt and then recovered the use of his legs. She said she was told that it was due to this that her father had joined the priesthood.

Mr. Obeysekera asked, "Your sister Mihiri lived in Cardiff?"

"Yes."

"When you first went to England did your sister come to the airport to meet you?"

"No."

"Was Father Edison who accompanied you, expected to go to Cardiff with you?"

"No."

"Did anyone come to meet Father Edison at the airport?"

"Yes, some friends of his."

"Do you know them?"

"I only know they were his friends."

"The next time you met your parents was in April 1978?"

"Yes."

"That is when they came to London after one of their world trips?"

"Yes."

"From the London Airport you all went to Essex to Frankie's house?"

"Yes."

"You knew that Mrs. Frankie's sister was Dalrene Ingram and that they were looking after the Vicarage until the return of your parents?"

"Yes."

"You used to visit your mother daily while she was in England?"

"Yes."

"She was quite happy and continued to be so until she returned to Sri Lanka?"

"Yes."

"While your father was in Sri Lanka did he write to your mother?"

"Yes. Two to three times a week."

She said that her father had deposited 1000 British Pounds in her sister Mihiri's bank account in England for her mother's use. She said that her sister had not seen her mother since 1973 and that she had not seen her mother for two years, so their parents visit to London was more or less a family reunion.

She said that Rev. Edison Mendis, an Anglican priest, was her mother's brother. He was in charge of a church in Moratuwa.

Mr. Obeysekera asked, "There was rivalry between Rev. Edison and your father?"

"Not to my knowledge."

"What were your feelings towards your uncle Rev. Edison?"

"Like towards any uncle."

"Did you have any occasion to change your opinion of your uncle in London in 1976?"

At this stage, Mrs. Malrani Dodangoda addressing the Judges asked, "Your honours, are all these questions relevant?"

Mr. Bandaranayake said, "Just say what you are aware of."

The question was repeated by Mr. Obeysekera and she answered in the negative.

Mr. Obeysekera asked, "Were you aware that there was a suggestion to unify the Church?"

"Not to my knowledge."

"Were you aware that your father and uncle were on opposing sides?"

"Not to my knowledge."

"Was there any cause for unpleasantness in Mihiri's house when your mother came there?"

"As far as I know she was happy."

"Was there any unhappiness between Mihiri and her husband?"

"The usual arguments as in any family."

"Did your mother get upset about this?"

"Like any mother would."

"Did your sister and her husband have fights?"

"I would say just arguments."

"On account of this displeasure would your mother have liked to return to Sri Lanka?"

"Not wanting to see any displeasure, she might have."

"In the letter to your father you have said 'Mom does not know when to come back, staying at Ali's is awful' and '*Akki* and Ali are fighting the whole time.' Did you write this?" (*'Akki' is the Sinhala word for elder sister and 'Ali' referred to here is Alistair, husband of Mihiri.)*

"If I have written it, it is true."

"Did you write it?"

"Yes, I did."

She said that there was a marriage proposed for her in Sri Lanka, and her mother had been very keen about it as she was the only child unmarried. She said she could not say what the attitude of her sister and brother-in- law had been to this. She did not remember whether they were indifferent or not. When she came to Sri Lanka on 6th December 1978, she meant to get back to England whether the marriage proposal was a success or not.

To a question from Mr. Obeysekera, she said that her sister and bother-in-law would have been very happy if the partner she chose was suitable for her.

Mr. Obeysekera asked, "Were they jealous?"

"I do not think so."

"On 10th October 1978 you wrote to your father saying, 'Please find out as soon as possible if 'X' (Proposed bride-groom) requires any shirts, suiting's etc.'?"

"Yes, that is correct. But only if it took place."

She said that in making these arrangements she had talked it over with her sister Mihiri. She said she did not require any financial assistance from her sister, as she herself was working and had her own money.

In one of the letters to her father, she had said, "This morning *akki* told mom that they will not be coming for the wedding as they cannot make it financially". She had also received a letter from the proposed groom which had been opened by her sister who had read the letter and then giving it to their mother to read.

In a letter to her father she had said "I was also very upset that *akki* had opened the letter and read it and then given it to mom." She said that anyone would get upset if their letters were opened.

"In mid October 1978 did your sister ill-treat your mother?" asked Mr. Obeysekera.

"I cannot remember."

"Did you ever see your mother in tears?"

"Yes, I did."

"Brought on by what your sister had done?"

"I cannot remember if it was because my sister had done anything."

"How often had you seen her in tears?"

"Once when she had received the telegram about the scandal."

"I am asking you about mid October. You have made a statement to the Police about what you know regarding the case as far back as 4th January 1979. This statement was a lengthy one and you have said that your mother's reaction in breaking into tears on receiving the cable was significant."

"Yes."

"How many times in October have you seen your mother in tears?"

"I have not seen her many times in tears as I was not living there. Maybe a few times."

"Did your proposed groom telephone you at Mihiri's House?"

"Yes."

"What was your sister's reaction? Were they jealous?"

"I do not know."

"Did your sister and her husband during this period shout at your mother at every turn?"

"They may have had arguments."

"Would you describe this treatment to your mother as 'pouncing'?"

"I cannot remember."

She was then shown a letter, which she had written on 15th October 1978 to her father. She admitted having said "Mom is being ill-treated by *akki* and she is VJ after 'X' (Proposed groom) phoned me, and what is more, has even stopped talking to me." She however said that by 'stopped talking to me' she meant that her sister had not spoken to her once or twice.

Mr. Obeysekera asked, "You said 'Mom is in tears all the time'?"

"She used to get upset all the time.'

"Your mother was being harassed and ill-treated?"

"I would not say harassed."

"You also wrote 'I am just bearing all this, but cannot stand it much longer'?"

"I used to get upset."

"You said 'the two of them have started to ignore me and *akki* is pouncing on mom at each turn'?"

"I may have exaggerated slightly."

"Your mother was living alone in that house with your sister and her husband?"

"If she wanted to come to Sri Lanka she could have. My father had said that the angel had wanted her to stay with her children."

"Can you remember if things improved at your sister's place later?"

"I cannot remember."

"Did you use your sister's telephone?"

"Yes."

"Did you phone your father in Colombo?"

"I may have."

"How did she react to your using her phone?"

"I cannot say exactly what the reaction was."

Mrs. Dodangoda was then shown a letter dated 8th November 1978, which she admitted was in her handwriting. The letter said "… *with the greatest difficulty I got the call to you even though I had to pay for it. They made such a fuss and cry over it and Ali kept his eye on the watch. I don't think even on a death I can get a call. I was in such pain of mind and so was mom, but the rest of the house was so happy; I could see it in their eyes.*"

"Have you said these things?" Mr. Obeysekera asked.

"Yes."

Mrs. Dodangoda was then shown a letter which she identified as having been written by her mother from England to her father, who was in Sri Lanka. This letter was dated 15th October 1978 and said *"I am rather disturbed now and all the joy I had has been shattered. You know when Mihiri talks she just fights, stamps her feet and blows up. I hardly tell them much of the news you give. I do not know what to say and what not. She just goes on... Then Mihiri got up from the chair and stamping her foot shouted the roof down. It was hell for me. I really do not know what to talk. I thought she will hit me. Mihiri's just impossible she is going on the deep end. This is what I am going through."*

Mr. Obeysekera asked, "You said you were not living with her, but you visited her frequently. Did your mother discuss this ill-treatment with you?"

"It was not ill-treatment."

"Did you then observe anything in your mother, which justified her having written this letter?"

"No, I am not aware."

Prior to the letter being read to Court, Mr. Bandaranayake said he wanted it on record that this letter had not been introduced in Court.

"Did you observe anything which justified your mother's remarks?"

"Not as serious as in the letters."

"Did your mother speak the truth?" asked Mr. Bandaranayake.

"I will not tell that my mother lies."

"And certainly she would not utter an untruth when writing to your father about Mihiri?"

"No."

"Did you give her cause for complaint?"

"No."

She was then shown another letter, which she admitted was in her writing and addressed to her father. She said she was a frequent letter writer when she was calm and collected and in her free time.

The letter stated, *"She simply hates mom, now does not even see to her food."*

Mr. Obeysekera asked, "Is this true?"

"Maybe on one or two occasions, as she does not have the time to always look after my mother. My mother was quite free in the house."

"How did you expect your father on reading that to react?"

"He is an intelligent person, he should understand."

"You meant to convey something to your father. What did you intend conveying by these words?"

"That on one or two occasions this happened."

Mr. Bandaranayake asked, "Would you say your mother was ill-treated?"

"I would not say ill-treated. They argued and the next moment everything was ok. Otherwise she would not have stayed there. She always said she wanted to come back for another holiday," she replied.

"The same letter dated 15th October 1978 read *'Mom is in tears all the time. Today she did not sleep and had tears in her eyes. Then akki shouted at her and said, if you cannot sleep go to the Doctor'.* Did you write this?" asked Mr. Obeysekera.

"Yes, but I did not mean that she was in tears throughout her eight-month stay."

She said that her mother had not been suffering from insomnia but was a very light sleeper. She was however not sure whether her sister had said it rudely, or whether her mother had ultimately gone to see the doctor.

Mr. Obeysekera continued to read the letter. "*I have no joy at all. I have put an advertisement in the papers asking for a flat in November.* Did you say this?"

"I wanted to be independent."

"You do not believe in angels and such?"

"I have said I do not believe or disbelieve."

Mr. Obeysekera continuing to read the letter asked whether she wrote this: "*Please dad pray for us and ask the holy angels to guide us.*"

"Do you seek the assistance of angels?"

She said, "Yes."

Mr. Bandaranayake asked, "According to your religion an angel is not God or Christ?"

"No, I believe they are like saints, and carry good messages."

Regarding her mother's ability to come back to Sri Lanka unaccompanied, she said her mother was not helpless but would have liked to have someone with her.

She said that a person calling himself 'Bert' had sent a cable to her mother in England, addressed to her sister's former address. From here it had been directed to the present address. She said she knew nobody by the name of Bert, and that her mother and sister had thought that the name had been used by a person wanting to remain anonymous, and had suspected that it had come from someone who had known Mihiri's previous address.

Mr. Obeysekera asked, "Were you anxious that your father and nobody else came to meet you at the airport?"

"I cannot remember."

"Had you reached the stage where you did not want your uncle Father Edison Mendis or his wife coming to the airport?"

"I cannot remember."

She was then shown a letter, which she said was written by her to her father, dated 27th November 1978. She had decided to keep her intended marriage away from everyone. She said that at this stage she did not want her uncle Edison to know about this. She went on to say that as her father had said that the proposed bridegroom might also come to the airport, she did not want an audience.

Mr. Obeysekera again read a part of a letter written by her and asked whether she wrote that: "…*I feel they all know about this matter. This topic must be hot in Dehiwala (where father Mendis stays). I do not know why, but I hate all these people and I am D-wild with nana for the shocking way she behaved.*"

"I cannot remember what I mean there."

"Why do you say this?"

"I do not know. My father used to write and poison our minds about them."

"Have you ever said disparaging things about Rev. Edison to your father?"

"I may have."

"Do you remember ever having said anything to your father about the moral conduct of your uncle Rev. Mendis?"

At this point Mr. Marapana objected to all these questions as he did not know where they were leading. In reply, Mr. Obeysekera said he would show that Father Edison was not in good terms with the first accused.

She was then shown a letter which she said she had written on 15th November 1978 to her father. On a question from Mr. Obeysekera, she said that in that letter she referred to Father Edison as 'E'.

Addressing Court she said she would like to say that all the suggestions in the letter were made by her sister. She said that an incident concerning Rev. Edison was brought to her notice.

Mr. Wickramasekera commented, "Mr. Obeysekera, the witness has said that she has written that letter at the suggestion of her sister."

Mr. Bandaranayake said, "I think you have done all you can with that letter!"

Continuing Mr. Obeysekera asked, "Do you know what your father did with this information you conveyed to him?"

"No."

"Your father's relationship with Rev. Edison deteriorated after you wrote this letter?"

"I do not think so."

Mr. Wickramasekera asked, "Did your sister Mihiri write to your father?"

"She may have."

"Did you not ask her to write these things herself?"

"I think she also may have written."

Mr. Obeysekera asked, "You wrote to your mother on 17th January 1979? When you wrote, you were not aware that she had entered Durdans Hospital on 15th January?"

"I did not know."

"Thereafter, you said that your uncle phoned you at Mihiri's home and told you about your mother being unconscious?"

"I have said they phoned my brother."

"Thereafter you received a number of calls regarding the condition of your mother?"

"Yes."

"Whatever you heard, you came to Sri Lanka without informing your father and stayed in Sri Lanka with your aunt and uncle?"

"Yes."

She said that she discussed her mother's condition with her uncle and aunt when she came down and that she may have spoken to some of the doctors at the General Hospital while her mother was there. When asked if she had spoken to Dr. (Miss) Pinto she said she may have spoken to her. She however said she could not remember whether she had discussed charms with this doctor.

She said that after her mother had died, there was an inquest at which her sister gave evidence. She and her sister had also discussed what transpired at the inquest. She admitted that she made her statement to the police on 7th April 1979, seven days after her sister made her statement. However, before they had done this they had discussed the details of their mother's death.

Mr. Obeysekera said, "I put it to you that in this case you have been put up and prejudiced by Father Edison and that accounts for the evidence. I suggest to you that your evidence is false on many matters. I am suggesting to you that your uncle Edison has influenced you?"

"He did not, I deny that."

"When you came to Sri Lanka in February you did not even stay with your father?"

"The reason I did not was as we had heard so many rumors regarding the Ingrams staying at the Vicarage and my mother falling ill, so I did not want to stay there."

"These rumours are what you heard from Father Edison?"

"No they are not."

"Did your brother tell you that Father Edison or his wife had said about rumours or suspicions?"

"Yes, about suspicions etc."

Mr. Obeysekera then concluded his cross examination and Mr. Cecil Goonewardena, counsel for the second accused, Mrs. Dalrene Ingram, commenced cross examining Mrs. Dodangoda.

He showed her a photostat copy of a letter dated 14th January 1979, which her mother had written to her sister Mihiri. It read, "*Fortunately Dalrene sees to marketing and giving things to the servants.*" She was also shown a 'Get well' card dated 14th August 1978, which had also been written by Mrs. Peiris to Russel. It read "*To Russel, May our Lord grant the strength to endure your suffering. Be of good cheer, it is I said the Lord. To Dalrene and children may our Lord the comforter grant you the comfort that you need. From Mathew, Mrs. Peiris, Mihiri, Munilal and Malrani.*"

When shown another card, which was supposed to have been written by Mrs. Peiris, she said she was not sure whether the handwriting was her mother's. She said it could have been her sister's hand writing.

Shown another card she said that this was written by her mother, which read, "*We are deeply grieved at your sad loss. He has only gone on before; we shall meet him on that beautiful shore. Please accept our deepest sympathies, to dear Dalrene (and children) from Mathew, Mrs. Peiris, Mihiri, Munilal and Malrani.*"

Continuing the cross examination next day, Mr. Goonewardena asked, "Yesterday when I asked if Dalrene helped in the preparations of the Christmas Lunch, you said 'She acted as the lady of the house' but in your first statement to the Police you never said this. You gave a sinister twist in your evidence yesterday."

"I standby what I said."

"You made another statement to Hema Weerasinghe when he flew all the way to London to record your statement. Even in that statement you made no reference to having said the second accused acted as mistress of the house."

"No."

Mr. Goonewardena asked, "You said your father said that the angel wanted him to look after the Ingram family?"

"Yes. My father helped the other people with prayers as well as by deed. When people were in distress, poverty stricken or lacked employment he used to befriend them."

"You said that the second accused came to the Vicarage for Christmas lunch. Can you think back and say whether she helped in the preparation of the lunch?"

"Yes she did. She acted like the lady of the house. Sometimes she came to the Vicarage with her children and sometimes without them. And although she was not living at the Vicarage she used to come there most of the time, although she was not working for my father at that time."

Mr. Wickramasekera asked, "At what time did she come?"

"After work at around 5.00 p.m."

"At what time did she leave?"

"I am not sure. I did not keep my eyes on the clock."

Mrs. Dodangoda said that she could remember the second accused had stayed overnight at the Vicarage on three occasions with her children but she did not think the children stayed overnight on the day of her party.

She said that her mother may have sent Mrs. Dalrene Ingram a condolence card when the news of Russel Ingram's death reached them in England. This was in August 1978.

Cross examined further, Malrani said that her father's Thursday services attracted large crowds of all religious groups. Her mother also regularly attended that special service. They attended with all seriousness and had implicit faith in that service. A large number of persons obtained relief through that service. Persons mainly afflicted with varying misfortunes attended that service. Her father had also claimed that he communicated with angels. At the time she was living in Sri Lanka he had not communicated with the angels.

She said that her father's foreign trips were sponsored by various individuals and organizations interested in his Thursday Services. She did not know whether her mother assisted her father in taking down notes or messages he was receiving from angles. She had heard from her mother that her father was a cripple before he became a priest. He was supposed to have had a vision of a dead aunt of his, which helped him to recover and due to this that he had entered priesthood.

Mrs. Dodangoda said she might have heard that her father was a diabetic but as far as she was aware, he had not seen him taking any anti-diabetic drug. He controlled it by regulating his diet.

She said that she was a British citizen and she of course took great pride in the fact that her father had been a vicar of churches in Britain.

Re-examined by Mr. Marapana, Mrs. Dodangoda said that her mother was in perfect health when she visited England. She admitted that her brother had wanted to take their mother away from the Vicarage after seeing her condition. She herself suspected that something was happening and her brother had asked their father to take their mother to another doctor. Before she left for England she was aware that her mother was being treated by Dr. Lakshman Weerasena. At that time she did not ask her father to take her mother to any other Doctor. Even after she returned to England she had corresponded with her father and asked about her mother's illness.

She told Court that after her arrival in Sri Lanka on 3rd February 1979 on hearing that her mother was in an unconscious state in hospital, she did not want to speak with her father nor did she stay at the Kynsey Road Vicarage.

"That was because of the mysterious circumstances surrounding her mother's sudden sickness and other stories they had come to hear," she said.

Under further examination by Mr. Marapana, Mrs. Dodangoda said, "My mother was in extremely good health condition when they returned together from the UK on 6th December 1978. Barely a month passed and her mother became such a sick person that she could not come to Katunayake airport on 3rd January 1979, the day I took my flight back to the UK. She was in a sort of daze."

Answering further questions from Mr. Marapana, she said that on no occasion had she seen her mother take any medicine while she was in England. Neither had she seen her mother take any tablets while travelling during the two days they took to come to Sri Lanka from London. She also said she had never heard her mother complain of a dryness of the throat, or pain in the joints nor was she rushed to hospital in an unconscious state in London.

Referring to the evidence she had given regarding the cable sent by one 'Bert' about a scandal, she said her mother had received the cable in August 1978. On receiving this cable, her sister Mihiri had phoned her father in Sri Lanka and so had her mother. She had heard her mother say to her father to try and find out who had sent it.

She said she remembered having spoken to a lady doctor at the General Hospital discussing the condition of her mother when she came to Sri Lanka.

"You were asked whether your father helped people, prayed for them and went out of his way to assist them," Mr. Marapana asked.

"Yes."

"Are you aware of your father having given shelter to a young widow and three children in other instances?"

"No."

"Are you aware that your father had got apartments for other young widows?"

"No."

"Do you know of an instance where your father had a bank account with any young widow?"

"No."

Mrs. Dodangoda was then re-examined by Mr. Obeysekera, and was shown a letter she had previously said she may have wrongly dated. She was asked to read it and say whether there was any mention that anything was enclosed in the letter, witness said she had not mentioned any such thing. She was then shown the envelope on which was written the words "*photographs - please do not bend.*" She agreed that this notation as well as the address on the envelope was written with the same ink, but on the letter however it had been different.

Mrs. Dodangoda then concluded her testimony, but was informed by Court that she would not be discharged, as she maybe required again.

The next witness called by the prosecution was Mr. Munilal Peiris, son of Rev. Mathew Peiris and Mrs. Eunice Peiris.

Examined by Mr. Tilak Marapana, he said that he had left Sri Lanka on 29th March 1978 and since then had lived continuously in England, except for one occasion when he had come to Sri Lanka on a holiday in 1980. He said that he had married on 29th January 1974. Although he married and left the Vicarage he used to make frequent visits and also made phone calls.

He said he had first met the second accused Mrs. Dalrene Ingram in September 1976 at a Thursday afternoon service at his father's church. He had first seen her at the church and then met her when she had come to the Vicarage after the services. After this he used to see her at the church and also at the Vicarage. He said that he was aware that the second accused had started working for his father shortly after their meeting for the first time.

Mr. Wickramasekera asked, "How long after your first meeting did you become aware that the second accused was working for the first accused?"

"About two months."

He said that he had been aware that the second accused had been residing on and off at the Vicarage. He said she stayed overnight when there were late exorcism ceremonies at the church on Thursdays. She had also stayed overnight when the first accused was making preparations for the consecration of the Bishop. He said that during the services, the second accused used to rush around and assist Rev. Peiris with the holy water etc. He said that there was a church feast during the month of September every year, and during that time in 1976 he remembered seeing the second accused. This was a one day feast.

Munilal also said that towards the end of 1976, there had been a vacancy for the post of secretary at an establishment in Colombo, and he had asked the second accused if she would like to have this post. She had however said no, and that she would work for Rev. Peiris.

He said he was aware that Russel had been admitted to the Durdans Hospital, as he had gone to the Vicarage one day and had found Mrs. Ingram there. She said that Russel Ingram had just been taken to the hospital.

Mr. Marapana asked, "What did you ask the second accused?"

"I asked her what hospital he had been in and she said Durdans."

"Did you inquire as to what was wrong with him?"

"No."

Mr. Bandaranayake asked, "Did you ask Russel Ingram?"

"No."

"Did you ask the first accused?"

"Yes, and he said he had a blackout and was taken to Durdans."

"When you saw Russel Ingram did he appear to be his natural self?" asked Mr. Wickramasekera.

"Yes, he was walking about."

Mr. Marapana asked, "At the time of the incident, you were still attending the Thursday services?"

"Yes."

"And after these services you used to drop into the Vicarage?"

"Yes. Most times."

"On how many such occasions have you seen the Ingram family coming to the Vicarage after the services?"

"On quite a number of times."

"Even at this time the second accused continued to be his secretary?"

"Yes. Not only secretary but also helping in the church."

"Do you know if Russel Ingram was employed during this period?'

"Yes."

"Your mother at this time was Vice Principal at St. Michael's School, Polwatta?"

"Yes."

"After the second accused was employed none of the children of Rev. Peiris were staying at the Vicarage?"

"That is correct, but there were two boarders and a servant."

"The consecration of the Bishop Right Rev. Cyril Fernando was in January 1978?"

"That is right."

He said that the Ingram family had moved into the Vicarage during the time of the consecration, and on Rev. and Mrs. Peiris's departure for the world trip.

Mr. Bandaranayake asked, "Has your father been on a similar world tour before?"

"Yes."

"When was that?"

"Maybe 1976."

"Did your mother accompany him on that trip?"

"No."

Mr. Marapana asked, "Your father was a person who used to travel abroad very frequently and on some of these visits he was accompanied by your mother."

"Yes."

"Prior to 1978, what would you say the state of your mother's health was?"

"I would say it was all right."

"Was she a diabetic?"

"Not to my knowledge."

"You left for England on 20th March 1978?"

"Yes."

"When you left who was residing at the Vicarage?"

"The Ingram family. The day before I left, I had a dinner at Dehiwala at my uncle Rev. Edison Mendis's home and Dalrene and Russel also came."

He said he was aware that the Ingram family had been placed in charge of the Vicarage, but on two or three occasions there had been some domestic problems and Dalrene had phoned him (witness) and he used to go and see that everything was all right. At this time he said that Dalrene had told him that the servant who had been with them for a long period of time wanted to leave as she was having problems with Dalrene. A boarder had also had problems with her and wanted to leave. When the servant left, Dalrene got her own sister to come and reside at the Vicarage.

He said that shortly prior to his departure to England on 29th March 1978, Russel Ingram looked well. Leaving Sri Lanka on the 29th, he went to live with friends in London and his two sisters came and saw him. The following day he went back to Heathrow to meet his parents who were arriving from the United States.

He said he was introduced to one Monty Frankie, who had come to the airport also to see his parents. He did not know Frankie before this.

Mr. Bandaranayake asked, "Before you left for London on the 29th did you know that the second accused had a sister living at the Vicarage?"

"Yes."

He said that after meeting his parents they drove down to Essex to Frankie's house, and later all of them ended up at his sister Mihiri's house. The parents stayed there for about two weeks. He said that following this, his father came back to Sri Lanka but his mother stayed on until December 1978. He too stayed at his sister Mihiri's house for two weeks. During this period his mother was well. He said that prior to his father's departure from Cardiff to London he had spoken about the condition of his mother's health.

"Just before he left for London we went on a picnic with the entire family. At this picnic, my father said, 'I am worried about Mummy's health; she does not look too well.' I then said I could not see anything wrong with her to which my father had replied 'I feel there is something wrong with her' and I then said if she says so I will see that she gets examined by a doctor here," Munilal said.

"Did you take your father seriously?" Mr. Marapana asked.

"As a matter of fact I could not see anything wrong with her. She had even put on weight."

"Your father was not expressing a medical opinion?"

"No."

"Did your father claim to have had supernatural powers?"

"I knew lots of people came to church, and they claimed they had got better."

"Did you ever see your father get into a trance?"

"Yes, somewhere in late 1977. This was the first time I had seen this."

Answering a question from Mr. Wickramasekera he said that at the time he witnessed it, there were people around him.

Mr. Marapana asked, "On such occasions did he give the appearance of talking to somebody unseen?"

"Yes, he claimed to be receiving messages from what he called an angel."

"Can you tell us some of his predictions?"

"On one occasion, which still stands out in my mind, while at the Vicarage he predicted three calamities. At this time my mother, my wife, and I were there and also the Ingram family."

"What exactly did he predict?"

"I asked him and he said 'I have to face three calamities'.."

"He also used to make announcements in church based on these trances?"

"Yes."

"Can you remember any of these announcements?"

"He used to talk of those experiences of his. On one such occasion he said that he was guided by the angel to go to the house of Russel Ingram. The angel had asked him to go there before Russel left for work. He did get up early morning and went there. That was in mid 1977. My father had been guided to ask Russel not to go to work that day, or something would happen to him. Russel had followed his advice. At this time Russel Ingram was staying somewhere in the Battaramulla area."

"Had your father been to this house before?" asked Mr. Bandaranayake.

"He has mentioned that he had."

"My mother believed in visions and trances. Initially I wanted to believe in them, but later could not accept them. I used to see him in the trances number of times. I had my first suspicions when he went into a trance and spoke in a foreign language I could not understand. Secondly, whenever the angel predicted something, it was always something bad, the way I took it, I always thought angels brought good things. The language had to be interpreted and it was he who did the interpretation."

Mr. Marapana asked, "When your father told you your mother was not feeling well, did you take it as one of those angels message?"

"Yes."

"Did he get in a trance in England?"

"Yes. One evening he went into a trance and my mother came and called me. So we went downstairs and he was lying there with eyes closed and talking in Latin. He said he would meet the Pope and he also said that he was told that mother is not too well."

"Was this trance after the incident when the first accused had said at the picnic that your mother was not well?"

"Yes."

Mr. Bandaranayake asked, "He did not say he was asked to meet the Archbishop of Canterbury?"

"No."

Mr. Marapana asked, "Was mother upset by the statement that she was not well?"

"Yes, she was."

Munilal said that his father, who was at Mihiri's house, went into a trance during which he said that the angel had told him that Russel was ill.

He said that his father was a diabetic and that he controlled his diabetes both through his diet as well as by drugs.

"Somewhere in April 1978 when my father and I went on a picnic in Wales, we stopped at a Chemist shop. While I bought a pair of sun glasses my father bought 100 tablets of the anti-diabetic drug Euglucon and I paid £10.00 for it. I saw the label on the foil of the tablet cover and that is how I identified what it was."

Munilal said he got agitated on hearing that his mother had got unconscious and was taken to hospital. He had got that information from his wife who phoned him on their wedding anniversary.

When he telephoned the Vicarage and asked his father "How are you managing and who is looking after mummy?" he had replied, "We are looking after her." Munilal asked his father by saying "we" whom did he meant, he kept silent. It was then Munilal asked him whether it was Dalrene, and Munilal had said angrily, "I don't want her to look after my mother. She should leave within 24 hours otherwise I will have to come down and throw her out."

Munilal said that he travelled 300 miles from London to Cardiff to inform Mihiri. It was thereafter that he gave three telephone calls to Rev. Edison Mendis and one to the Vicarage.

Mr. Munilal Peiris, cross examined by Mr. R.I. Obeysekera, said a few days after his father came to England, he went into a trance. Mr. Peiris said that he could not remember having mentioned this to the police.

"When I made this statement to the police, the trance was important, but if I had not mentioned it, it might have been because it slipped my mind. I got together all the facts I knew, and reflected on these before making my statement to the police. I could not remember having discussed the three calamities with my sisters," he said.

Mr. Wickramasekera asked "How many statements did you make to the police?"

"One."

"Did you inform the authorities in Sri Lanka when you came down, that you had this information?" asked Mr. Obeysekera.

"No."

"Did you consider important the trance where your father spoke about your mother's illness?"

"Not at that time."

"I put it to you, that you have not mentioned a word about these trances to the police in your statement?"

"Maybe."

"Were you aware that there were arrangements being made to get your sister married on her arrival in Colombo?"

"My sister did mention there was a proposal."

"And details were given to you?"

"Yes."

"Have you been present at the Thursday afternoon services at the church?"

"Yes."

"Have you assisted in these services?"

"I have."

"There were people who appeared to be relieved after these services?"

"Yes."

"Was there a bed in the church?"

"Yes."

"You have seen people who were alleged to be possessed of the devil lying on this bed."

"Yes."

Mr. Bandaranayake asked, "Did your father ever say that someone, some supernatural being helped in these exorcism ceremonies?"

"He used to say a number of prayers, and one of these was to St. Michael."

"By exorcism, you mean your father had some power to drive out spirits?"

"That is what he said. My father had mentioned that he was very ill when he was young, and he was given the power to cast out spirits."

Continuing the cross examination Mr. Obeysekera asked, "Your father was a cripple and he was completely paralyzed around 1950."

"I have heard that."

"Your father's dead god mother and Aunt Aurelia Peiris had appeared to your father and thereafter he got cured and came to have powers of healing?"

"I have been told so."

"Do you recall some years ago a Dutchman having sent your father an air ticket, and your father having healed this man?"

"Not to my knowledge."

"Your father was a diabetic?"

"From what I gather, a mild one."

"He used to take anti-diabetic pills?"

"Yes, occasionally."

"You spoke of an incident where your father went to a pharmacy?"

"Yes."

"Is it possible that the Euglucon he bought was in a foil?"

"It is possible."

"I am suggesting to you that your father and Father Edison Mendis were not on the best of terms."

"Not to my knowledge."

"Are you aware that finally one party took the other to Court?"

"I am aware that my father and Rev. Edison Mendis were on opposite sides, and that my father opposed the unification of the church."

Munilal said that he could not recollect whether his father had made any allegations against Rev. Edison Mendis based on information given by Malrani. He said his uncle continued to be on cordial terms with his father and also visited the Vicarage. To his knowledge, there had not been any jealousy between the two priests.

He said that on his anniversary, 20th of January, he had received a call from his uncle and aunt and certain information was given to him. This information disturbed him so he drove to Cardiff to discuss it with his two sisters, and following this he phoned his father at the Vicarage.

He said that between 20th and 30th January he had made about five phone calls, but could not remember whether on any of these occasions his uncle had told him that his mother (Mrs. Peiris) had been taken to see Dr. D.J. Attygalle.

Mr. Obeysekera asked, "Did your uncle tell you that your mother had been taken to see Dr. E.V. Peiris?"

"If I remember right, I asked him to take her to him."

"Did he tell you or not that he had taken her to see him?"

"Yes, towards the end of that month he did."

"Malrani did not tell you that your mother was unhappy living at Mihiri's?"

"No, as far as I can remember, my mother was not unhappy there."

"If Malrani had told you anything about Mihiri's attitude toward your mother, you would have remembered?"

"Yes."

Referring to the discussions the family members had about the situation in Colombo, Mr. Obeysekera asked,

"You had detailed discussions with them about what was going on?"

"Yes."

"You also got to know your father had been taken into custody?"

"Yes."

"Who told you?"

"I subscribed to the '*Ceylon News*' and I came to know through that."

"Up to this time, your uncle had not told you?"

"No."

"So when you got the news you passed it on to Mihiri and Malrani?"

"Yes."

"Did Malrani tell you when she had heard about it?"

"She heard from Mihiri."

"You said that Mihiri was already aware. You did not ask her why she did not tell you."

"No."

"You say now that your sister called you from Cardiff to verify the story?"

"Yes."

"*Ceylon News* comes about a week after the day of publication?"

"Yes."

"So the news was about a week old when you got it."

"Yes."

"Did you see a copy of the inquest proceedings?"

"I did not."

"Did you all discuss Russel's death?"

"I cannot remember if we went into great detail about it."

"Did you get to know about the arrest of the second accused?"

"Yes."

Cross examined by Mr. Cecil Goonewardena, Munilal said that shortly prior to his departure to England, he and his wife held a dinner for their relatives and friends, and he named a few of these people. He said that Dalrene and Russel Ingram were present at this dinner as they were considered their friends.

Mr. Bandaranayake asked, "Was there anything belonging to you, left at the Vicarage?"

"Yes. I remember a tape recorder."

He said that at this time he had nothing against Russel or Dalrene, but had accepted the Ingrams as friends. Up to this time Dalrene had worked for his father for about a year and a half.

Mr. Goonewardena asked, "You noticed no improper conduct between Dalrene and your father?"

"I did. I did notice an over familiarity."

"But you still considered them as friends?"

"Yes, I tried to keep an open mind," he said.

Giving one instance of Dalrene being overfamiliar, he said that whenever he went to the Vicarage Dalrene used to come up to him and ask if he would like a drink or something to eat. He said he did not like this attitude as he wanted to be free in his own mother's home. When asked to give another instance of Dalrene being over familiar he said he did not like the way she used to run the house.

"Was she the house-keeper at this time?" asked Mr. Bandaranayake.

"She more or less acted like it."

"You said that Chandrakanthi had a disagreement with Dalrene and wanted to leave?"

"Yes."

"Do you know how much she paid as a boarder?"

"I am not aware."

Munilal said that at that time Chandrakanthi was a teacher at St. Michael's. He said that Chandrakanthi had a problem with Dalrene and he had to sort out. It was regarding the quality of the meals.

He said that he first came to know Russel Ingram sometime in 1976. At that time he did not have a job. He had been employed in Kandy and had lost his job. He said his father was instrumental in obtaining a job at the 'Three Acre Farm'.

Mr. Bandaranayake asked, "When you gave an instance of overfamiliarity, you referred to your going to the Vicarage and the second accused coming forward and offering you drinks etc. By this do you mean she was being forward?"

"What I meant was that my mother was there."

Mr. Goonewardena asked, "Your father was writing a book called 'Damn the Bloody Exorcist'?"

"Yes."

"And Dalrene was typing the manuscript?"

"So I understand."

"It was at this time your father got a job for Russel Ingram?"

"Yes."

"After Thursday prayer meetings, there was a little social affair where the people came to the Vicarage for a drink?"

"It was not a habit. Sometimes people used to drop in."

"Apart from writing this book your father was appointed Grandmaster for the consecration of the Bishop of Colombo?"

"I cannot remember him being appointed Grandmaster, but he was asked to organize this."

"Bishops came from all over the world for this occasion?"

"There were some Bishops from abroad."

"And there was a small Secretariat at the Vicarage to deal with this?"

"As far as I know there were only two people doing it?"

"Did you attend the ceremony?"

"Yes."

"Was it a success?"

"Yes."

"Are you not happy your father was able to do such a big ceremony?"

"Yes."

"During that time Russel Ingram and Dalrene stayed at the Vicarage?"

"Yes."

"In connection with the work of the consecration?"

"I am not aware, but it could be due to the work."

"Russel Ingram used to drink heavily?"

"I do not know."

"Did he take alcohol?"

"He has had a drink in my presence."

"After your father and mother went to England, you and your wife dropped in at the Vicarage?"

"Yes."

Munilal further said that there were many helpers in the church. There were also people who used to take holy water. He said that Dalrene was one of the many helpers at the Thursday services.

"How old was Chandrakanthi?" asked Mr. Goonewardena.

"I do not know."

"When your mother and father were going abroad, Chandrakanthi's parents were naturally worried about their daughter, but your father and mother went and spoke to them and said they should not worry as there is a Mr. and Mrs. Ingram staying at the Vicarage?"

"I cannot remember."

The cross examination was then concluded and Mr. Tilak Marapana re-examined Mr. Munilal Peiris.

"You said the second accused came to the Vicarage around August 1976 and she took part in the Thursday services?"

"Yes."

"When you first saw her, what role was she playing?"

"I think she used to sell medals. There was a stall for medals, and I think she was in charge of this."

"As time went on, what other functions did she do?"

"She was in charge of the holy water. When people got possessed she used to get the altar ready."

Munilal said that when he moved out of the Vicarage he used to go there whenever he could for the services, and took a back seat in the activities. There were many people helping, but towards the latter part he saw only one person helping in everything.

"Who was this person?" asked Mr. Marapana.

"Dalrene Ingram."

"You were asked if Russel Ingram was a hard drinker, and you said it was not to your knowledge."

"Yes."

"At your dinner party did you serve liquor?"

"I must have."

"Was Russel Ingram drunk?"

"Nobody was drunk."

"Whenever you went to the Vicarage did you notice that Russel Ingram was drunk or boisterous?"

"No."

Mr. Bandaranayake asked, "You have never seen him drunk?"

"No."

"Did you know if he was a regular drunker?"

"No."

"About the end of 1976 you offered Dalrene a job?" asked Mr. Marapana.

"Yes."

"Why?"

"I did not know she was being paid at the Vicarage, and Russel Ingram was getting a small salary and as she had three children, and as I could have secured the job I asked her."

"And she declined the offer?"

"Yes."

"Thereafter on any occasion did she remind you of that offer?"

"Not as far as I remember."

The Court then released the two witnesses – Munilal Peiris and his sister Malrani Dodangoda as they were no longer required by the Court, and they were free to return to the United Kingdom.

The next witness, Dr. J.G.C. Peiris, was a general practitioner in the United Kingdom. He was the third and the last witness who had come from Britain to give evidence.

Examined by Mr. Marapana, Dr. Peiris said that he was residing in England and prior to this he has been a Medical Officer in Sri Lanka. While in Sri Lanka he had acted as the family physician for the family of Rev. Mathew Peiris. He had on several occasions treated Rev. Peiris and his wife for minor ailments. Mrs. Eunice Peiris had throat infection and flu, but was never a diabetic patient. He recollected that somewhere in 1960s Mrs. Eunice Peiris had a lump in one of her breasts and she had to be operated. This was not considered to be cancer. After this operation, Dr. Peiris said that he had been in Sri Lanka for about six years before going to the UK and during this period he had no occasion to treat Mrs. Peiris regarding her lump in her breast.

He said that in March 1979 he came for the Centenary Royal-Thomian cricket match and had stayed until the end of March or early April. On his annual visits to Sri Lanka, he always made it a point to visit Rev. Mathew Peiris's family and on this trip also he visited them.

At that time Mihiri had informed him that Mrs. Peiris was in hospital. He had met Rev. Peiris about a week to ten days before Mrs. Peiris died.

Mr. Marapana asked, "Did you have occasion to discuss Mrs. Peiris's illness with him?"

"Rev. Peiris described the illness to me. Dr. Ernie Peiris had wanted some blood tests done at Glass House, and as he could not afford a private hospital, he admitted her to the General Hospital."

"Was there any talk about diabetes?"

"He asked if Eunice was a diabetic and he also asked if there was any connection between the puffiness of her stomach for which she was first treated, and the cancer of the breast, to which I replied that she did not have a cancer."

Mr. Bandaranayake asked, "When the operation was done in the 1960s was Rev. Peiris in Sri Lanka?"

"He was there when the operation was done."

"So he had the opportunity of knowing it was not a cancer?"

"Yes."

Dr. Peiris said that in March 1979 he saw Mrs. Peiris in the General Hospital. Rev. Peiris asked him what he thought and he said to him that it seems to be a hypoglycaemic coma. He asked him as to how this could have come about.

Dr. Peiris said, "I replied that it is possible by one of two ways. Either Mrs. Peiris would have taken an anti-diabetic drug or somebody would have given it to her. I also told him that it would be difficult to prove whatever she had taken by herself or whether it had been administered to her by someone. At that stage Rev. Peiris made a request of him to give him a certificate on an affidavit to the effect that Mrs. Peiris was a highly depressed person and was hypochondriac who has taken to treating herself with drugs for imaginary diseases."

He had said that he would get the affidavit drafted by a lawyer, and then take it to him for his signature.

Mr. Wickramasekera asked, "Were you willing to sign such an affidavit?"

"No, I was not."

Dr. Peiris explained that a hypochondriac was a person who had imaginary ailments all the time.

"Mrs. Peiris was not such a person?" asked Mr. Bandaranayake.

"Mrs. Peiris was worried but not such a person."

"She was not taking any medicines?"

"No."

Mr. Bandaranayake asked, "Did you ask him why he wanted this?"

"No."

Mr. Marapana asked, "At the funeral of Mrs. Peiris was there any conversation regarding the matter?"

"No."

"Did you tell him you were not prepared to sign?"

"It came as a shock to me."

Dr. Peiris said that he had then avoided meeting Rev. Peiris as he was not prepared to sign such a document.

Mr. Bandaranayake asked, "If you signed such a document would it be untrue?"

"Yes."

"Had you occasions to bring any medicines down to Sri Lanka for Rev. Peiris?" asked Mr. Marapana.

"Yes. His daughter Mihiri used to send parcels, and on one occasion she said there were some medicines. On one occasion at his birthday party he also asked me to bring him some Euglucon as he needed it."

Dr. Peiris said that Mihiri had sent this through him. He said that Euglucon was an oral anti-diabetic drug.

He said that he had not met Mr. Ingram but met Dalrene as she was working for Rev. Peiris.

Dr. Peiris said that Rev. Peiris told him that Russel Ingram had died of rare islet tumour of the pancreas, and even called it a medical rarity.

Mr. Anil Obeysekera, Counsel for Rev. Peiris cross examined Dr. Peiris who said that he had been the Church Warden for nearly three years at the Kynsey Road church. He however said that he did not take part in the Thursday services. He said that he was not aware that Rev. Peiris went into trances until he came to Sri Lanka and read the papers.

"You have known the first accused from childhood?" asked Mr. Bandaranayake

"Yes."

"At the time you saw Mrs. Peiris in the General Hospital did you have any hope of recovery for her?"

"To me? No."

Mr. Weerasekera asked, "When Rev. Peiris told you he had ordered his daughters not to come to the Vicarage, was Mrs. Peiris alive?"

"Yes."

Dr. Peiris said that he was aware that Rev. Mathew Peiris was a diabetic.

Dr. Peiris was then dismissed by the Court, as he had completed giving his evidence.

The next witness, Mr. Alexander Parker Ingram, 62-year-old father of the late Russel Ingram giving evidence said that he was a retired railway engine driver.

Answering questions of Mr. Tilak Marapana, he said that all his sons including Russel Ingram were healthy persons and there was never an occasion to have a family doctor because his children did not fall ill. He said that Russel had his schooling at Wesley College where he represented the school in the Stubbs Shield Inter School Boxing Tournament. He had also played cricket and athletics and that he was a good sportsman. After leaving school he played cricket at club level for the Borhas Cricket Club. He said that Russel also visited Mount Mary's Railway Sports Club at Welikada.

He said that on 9th June 1978, he visited the Vicarage as Dalrene informed him that Russel was not well. He found Russel sick in bed. He asked Russel what was wrong with him. He replied, 'Daddy, I can sleep, sleep and sleep'. Rev. Peiris then said, 'No man, he is having some pancreatic disorder. An operation has to be done. There is no other treatment.'"

Mr. Ingram said, "Rev. Peiris prepared Russel's food and even fed Russel. He prepared something like mincemeat and fed Russel. Food was prepared specially for my son. My son took one or two spoonfuls in a disgusted mood."

He said that at about 8 p.m. on the 10th June Rev. Peiris was in his bedroom on his bed, which was in the room next to where Russel was. Rev. Peiris was lying on the bed motionless and he thought he was dead. Mr. Ingram looked at Rev. Peiris, and Dalrene told him that "Father was in a trance".

Mr. Ingram said that the first accused was making sounds which gave him the impression that he was in conversation with someone. Dalrene put off the light and lighted a red bulb, like a night lamp, so that there was sufficient light in the room to observe what went on. Mr. Ingram said that the Rev. Peiris mentioned the name 'Michael' and while stroking his abdomen said "Pancreas, pancreas". This went on for 20 to 25 minutes and Dalrene and Russel were there with hands on Rev. Peiris's body. Then Dalrene brought a bandage and some rectified spirit and took the palm of Rev. Peiris on to her thigh and starting rubbing the palm with spirit saying, "This is the place where the wound is". Mr. Ingram said he was very close by but did not see a wound on the palm and there was no blood on the palm.

"On the following day Rev. Peiris told me that he conversed with angels and that he was given very bad news that there was a crisis. I remained at the Vicarage for about 4 days because of Russel's condition. On 10th June, the first accused pulled out about 4 pills and a capsule from his pocket, and gave it to Russel who started sweating about 10 minutes after consuming it. The first accused had said that Dr. Weerasena had prescribed these pills and that they were no medicine, but just like Disprin. I accepted this statement. That day by evening Russel was out of bed. The first accused fed him liver and he ate about a spoonful," Mr. Ingram said.

"Russel's condition was fluctuating, sometimes drowsy, sometimes all right. The four days I was there a doctor did not visit. When I saw the first accused giving the pills, the second accused would have been in the kitchen. I asked the first accused to take Russel to the General Hospital but he said they would mess the case up. Also the first accused said that sugar, carbohydrate and glucose were poison for Russel and that rice was bad for Russel. To an extent I believed the first accused and Russel had faith in him. One day Russel became boisterous and took a knife and tried to attack me but later quietened down and went to sleep. His behaviour was quite irrational. I have seen the first accused sitting by Russel praying and with a stethoscope. The first accused was also constantly phoning people and giving the impression he was speaking with doctors," Mr. Ingram said.

"I noticed a familiarity in the behaviour of the first accused Rev. Peiris and the second accused Mrs. Dalrene Ingram during my stay at the Vicarage. However, Dalrene appeared to be distressed over her husband Russel's illness and was crying bitterly," stated Mr. Ingram.

"One day when I went to the Railway Club to pay a bill, my friends told me my son had died," he said.

At this point he wept and then turned and looked at the two accused.

The Court was adjourned for 15 minutes and when the Court resumed he said, "I met my wife and eldest son and they said that they had a call at 8 a.m. that Russel had died. I later came to know that he had died at 3 a.m. but no effort was made by anyone to inform us. I went to the mortuary and asked mortuary keeper to allow me to see the body. He asked me who I was and I said I was the father. He then said 'I have been given instructions not to allow anyone other than the wife of the deceased to see the body'. Just then the door opened and a friend of mine who worked at the hospital came and he took me in to the mortuary. The drawer was opened and I saw my son and I could only see his face"

He broke down shook his head from side to side and wept again while describing to Court how he kissed Russel's face at the mortuary.

He said that he was told that the second accused had claimed the body, which was taken to the Vicarage.

He said he was present in the cemetery to identify the remains when Russel's body was exhumed on 30th April 1979.

At the conclusion of Mr. Ingram's evidence-in-chief, the Court noticing the demeanour of the witness inquired whether he could stand the cross examination straightaway. Mr. Ingram replied that he was totally upset emotionally and that he would like time relax. The Court then adjourned for the day.

Cross examined by Mr. Obeysekera next day, Mr. Ingram said that his wife Cora told him that whenever Russel came home he used to sleep for hours and that Russel was drowsy. On the day he went to collect his pension Russel told him he could sleep, sleep and sleep. He could not remember whether he made a statement to Police that Rev. Peiris told him that sugar was bad for Russel.

Answering questions of Mr. Obeysekera, Mr. Ingram said, "I never tried to paint a different picture at the instance of the police. I could not remember whether he read newspaper reports regarding the opening of the case in this Court. I am not used to Court procedure. I may have read paper reports on sensational matters."

"Russel was not a hard drinker. He was only a moderate drinker. He was never an alcoholic but a social drinker. Russel took drinks with his friends too. When Russel was in Kandy he lost his job. It was over some sort of shortage of cash. Russel was taken to police custody and was remanded. He did not know whether his wife bailed him out," he said.

Mr. Ingram said that when Russel was ill at the Vicarage no doctors had examined him because all the doctors "came over the phone."

When Mr. Obeysekera said, "I am putting it to you that you are not speaking the truth," Mr. Ingram replied, "You can put it to me in any way but I am speaking the truth."

"Don't think that your indignation would make you appear a truthful witness. You are a hardened engine driver."

"But not in the Court."

Mr. Marapana said, "Now he is only a passenger!"

Mr. Obeysekera suggested to Mr. Ingram that his wife Cora Ingram had told the City Coroner, Mr. Walter Perera, who held the inquest into Russel's death that she suspected her son had been poisoned. Mr. Obeysekera said that this was done in an effort to get the body of Russel. Mr. Ingram said that his wife did not ever think of using the statement she made to the Coroner just to get the corpse of her son. Mr. Ingram also flatly denied that he was lying when Mr. Obeysekera said that, what Mr. Ingram had said had happened at the General Hospital, when Russel was admitted was untrue. Mr. Ingram said that he was telling the truth. He said that Rev. Peiris had warned a lady doctor not to give glucose.

As Mr. Ingram told Court that he was tired, the Court adjourned half an hour early. On a number of occasions Mr. Ingram told Court that he was under oath and was speaking the truth and that he had no Court experience earlier and knew little of Court procedure.

He told Court that since he had to attend Court he could not draw his pension.

When Mr. Ingram told Court that if in re-examination he is asked to narrate once again the tragic circumstances in which he saw his dead son Russel, it would give him a knockout punch like during previous day's proceedings.

Mr. Ingram also agreed to produce in Court his personal diary in which he remembers to have made an entry about Rev. Peiris's trance. Mr. Bandaranayake, who directed the witness to produce his diary, assured him that the Court will only look at the relevant entry. Mr. Ingram if so desired could bandage the rest of the pages of the diary so that his personal entries will not be divulged to anybody, Mr. Bandaranayake said. The Court gave him time on Monday to draw his pension.

At the end of day's hearing Mr. Bandaranayake told Ingram, "Speaking for myself you have every right to be indignant if any outrageous suggestions are put to you."

Mr. D.W. Wanigasekera, a Colombo businessman, the next witness for the prosecution, was questioned by the State Counsel Mr. Ananda Amaranath.

He said that that he came to know Rev. Peiris around September 1975 through a friend. He attended the Thursday services conducted by Rev. Peiris at St. Paul's Church, Kynsey Road. He came to know Rev. Peiris and his wife as time went on.

He attended those services regularly up to the end of 1977. After the service the priest used to bless people at the statue of Lady Walsingham.

"Some people fainted and others became boisterous at the altar. Then they were carried away by helpers to the vestry of the church where the priest attended on them. The priest conducted ceremonies connected with exorcism. As time went on my wife and I developed a friendship with the priest and his family," he said.

Describing events at the Vicarage, he said that Dalrene not only attended the Thursday services but also functioned as a helper. He also had seen Dalrene prepare and serve tea in the Vicarage and taking part in many other roles also. Later she also worked as a typist under the priest. She was typing a manuscript of a book the priest had written on exorcism.

"Rev. Peiris was strong willed, humble and pushy. Rev. Peiris was a very learned person in Christianity. He however did not display knowledge of other disciplines. As for Mrs. Peiris, I could say that she was a very humble, kind, obliging, good natured, good hearted, good lady," said Mr. Wanigasekera.

"Would you say that she was a devoted wife?" asked Mr. Amaranath.

"Though I am not entitled to say it from what I have seen, I could say that she was."

"During this period did you observe anything unusual?"

"I can't understand what is meant by unusual."

"Then I shall be more specific. Did you see an over familiarity between the priest and the second accused?"

"I would not say it over familiarity. By nature the priest is very familiar with people. By Western standards that type of conduct is acceptable."

Mr. Bandaranayake asked, "Did Rev. Peiris exceed the limits of familiarity?"

"No," said Mr. Wanigasekera. He also referred to standards of familiarity associated with younger and older generations. The familiarity the priest showed did not mean anything, he said.

"Did the first accused develop a particular attachment to the second accused?" asked Mr. Amaranath.

"I am unable to answer that question."

Questioned further by Mr. Amaranath, Mr. Wanigasekera said that during the period under reference Dalrene and her family were living at Athurugiriya. He had also seen Rev. Peiris giving car lifts to Dalrene and other members of the family and Rev. Peiris anxiously awaiting Dalrene's return to the Vicarage.

Mr. Amaranath said, "You have told us that the second accused was playing a multifaceted role?"

Mr. Goonewardena, Counsel for Dalrene intervened. "What do you mean? He never said so."

"That is what he has already told us. Why are you getting unduly excited about it?"

"It needs lot more to get me excited," quipped Mr. Goonewardena!

Mr. Wanigasekera said that he saw Russel in a sick condition when he called at the Vicarage one day in July 1977. He came to see the priest on that occasion.

Mr. Amaranath queried, "Did you ask him whether he was sick?"

"No, I did not like Russel and his wife at all."

Mr. Wanigasekera said that Rev. Peiris told him that Russel was ill. According to Rev. Peiris, Russel at times ate a lot and at other times ate very little. Mr. Wanigasekera said he wanted to take Russel to hospital, but he felt that the priest did not like to take Russel to the General Hospital.

"I told the priest that I am prepared to take him to a private nursing home and also to meet the expenses."

Judge Wickramasekara asked, "Why did you undertake that?"

"That was through the respect I had for the priest. I had a lot of regard for him and had done many things for him."

Mr. Wanigasekera said that they got Russel admitted to a private nursing home. The priest was the person who gave the history of the patient to the hospital authorities. Russel became boisterous at the hospital on that occasion.

Judge Wickramasekara asked, "Was he a frightened man?"

"Russel had been a crude, bad-tempered and violent man."

Judge Bandaranayake queried, "The adjectives you used to describe him were true of him from the time you first met him?"

"Yes. From that time."

Mr. Wanigasekera said that Russel recovered and was discharged in three or four days.

The defence objected to a certain portion of the witness's statement to police being led in evidence. Hearing submissions of counsel representing both the defence and the prosecution on the objection, Mr. Bandaranayake said that a ruling will be given at a later stage of the trial considering further evidence the prosecution would lead before Court.

Miss Chandrakanthi Dharmadasa, who was a boarder in the Vicarage when the Ingrams were there, giving evidence said that Russel was in perfect health and had no sickness as at the end of May 1978. He was doing a job. He had a brief illness in July 1977.

Miss Dharmadasa said, "A book entitled 'Body, Mind and Sugar' was on the first accused's book shelf during the period that the first accused and his wife had left Sri Lanka on a world tour. Anoma, a boarder, left of her own accord while I left when I heard Mrs. Peiris would not be coming back for some time," she said.

The next witness, Mrs. Therese Bridget Jackson, Dalrene's eldest sister, examined by Mr. Tilak Marapana, said that her father worked in a government department and was now drawing a pension. Her mother who was a nurse too was receiving a pension. In 1959, she married Graham Jackson, who was now a security assistant attached to the British High Commission in Colombo. Her sister Dalrene married Russel Ingram in 1969.

She said she was aware that in June 1978 Russel was warded at the General Hospital, Colombo. He was first at ward no. 44 and thereafter transferred to ward no. 18. She had visited him daily in the evenings.

"On a number of occasions I have noticed Dalrene coming to see Russel. On all those occasions she came with Rev. Peiris. I remember Russel asking Dalrene on one occasion as to where his parents were living at that time. Dalrene had replied that they were residing at the Vicarage. I knew that Russel's parents were not residing at the Vicarage during the time when Russel was warded. I wondered why Dalrene had said that. I have noticed Dalrene bringing soup, milk and coffee to her husband. I did not notice Dalrene bringing any other food. I remember on one occasion Russel telling Dalrene that he was feeling hungry and wanted her to bring roast bread and plantains. Accordingly, she brought about six to eight plantains and roast bread. Russel had consumed all those on that occasion. I felt sorry for him. Russel was not getting any food from the hospital and I thought Russel was not allowed to take any food. Whenever Russel asked for something to eat Dalrene gave it. I questioned Dalrene as to what was wrong with Russel. Her reply was that Russel was suffering from an ailment opposite to diabetes," she said.

"When I asked Russel what was wrong with him he told me that he was tired and drowsy because of the tablets and mixtures given to him. I immediately asked Dalrene not to give him any more tablets and mixtures. Her reply was that Rev. Peiris knew all that. I have been to the Vicarage even after Russel was discharged from the hospital. On one occasion the first accused had brought Russel a plate of rice and wanted me to feed him. I said that Russel's wife was there and to ask her to feed him. My recollection was that there was beef, *wattakka* (pumpkin) and *mallun* (green leaves) with rice. Russel on his own ate a little bit and kept the balance. Immediately after Russel finished eating I noticed Rev. Peiris bringing a cup of ice cream."

"One day I heard Rev. Peiris and Dalrene discussing about Russel's illness. On that occasion Rev. Peiris said that Russel's condition was bad and asked Dalrene where he should be buried after his death. I was surprised as to what made Rev. Peiris to pose that question to Dalrene. This made me think deeply because Russel was all right in the noon and had his lunch."

"The same evening I saw Rev. Peiris bringing a cup of tea to Russel. That was on 16th June. On that occasion before handing over the cup of tea to Russel, Rev. Peiris asked where those medicines were. Dalrene replied 'Why father they are with you.' Rev. Peiris then pulled out four white tablets from his pocket first, and two green tablets and a capsule next. Rev. Peiris then requested me to give those tablets to Russel. I refused to comply with that request stating that Russel's wife was there. When I refused to give the tablets and capsules to Russel I noticed Rev. Peiris himself giving them to Russel. A few minutes after giving the tablets I noticed Russel sweating heavily and wet the bed."

"On 16th July 1978, when my husband and I were in the Vicarage, Russel was carried to a double bed in an unconscious state. Before he became unconscious he sweated and passed urine in the sarong he was wearing. She told Dalrene to get a doctor. Rev. Peiris said that the next day being Monday, he would get Russel admitted to the hospital. Later the same night with her husband's assistance the priest changed the sarong Russel was wearing. The priest provided a urinal tube for Russel," Mrs. Jackson said.

She said she and her husband stayed overnight at the Vicarage and left the following morning, 17th June. Both of them came to the Vicarage on that night also and stayed over the night.

She inquired whether a doctor was consulted because Russel's condition remained the same. Rev. Peiris said that Russel would be taken to the clinic on the following day. On that morning Russel was taken to the hospital in an ambulance. Before he was taken the priest conducted a small service at a make-shift altar by Russel's bedside.

Mr. Marapana asked, "What was this service?"

"According to the Roman Catholic religion, it is a service at which last rites were performed."

She said her sister Dalrene, who was a Catholic at birth, became an Anglican after her marriage. On two occasions she visited Russel in hospital she saw a fat doctor. Dalrene told her that he was Dr. Lakshman Weerasena, one of the doctors to whom the Rev. Peiris had made reference very often in connection with Russel's sickness.

She said that soon after Russel was admitted to hospital, Rev. Peiris and Dalrene went to meet the Food Commissioner to get the ration books of Dalrene and her children changed to the Vicarage address. They got that done that day itself.

Mr. Wickramasekara queried, "Can that be done in a day? There are people who have to wait for months!"

Mr. Marapana replied, "Influential people can!"

She said whenever Rev. Peiris and Dalrene visited Russel at the hospital, Russel was angry with his wife Dalrene.

"Russel was angry with his wife because she was always coming late to hospital during visiting hours. Russel had told Dalrene that his parents living at Athurugiriya were able to come on time but not she, who was staying at Ethul Kotte," she said.

She said that on the first occasion of her visit to ward 44, Russel was conscious and she had noticed that doctors had not taken much interest in him. She said the first and the second accused came together to hospital to see Russel and when she had asked Dalrene what was wrong with her husband, she had said that he was having a slight attack of diabetes.

Answering Mr. Bandaranayake, she said that on the last occasion she saw Russel at the hospital he was in a better condition than when he was at the Vicarage.

She said on one occasion when she was at the Vicarage, the first accused brought a little rice and curry to be given to Russel and asked her to feed him. "I refused to do so saying that that Dalrene, his wife, was there to feed him. When I refused to feed Russel the first accused fed him, but Russel did not eat all the rice and thereafter he was given ice cream. After feeding Russel all of us came out of the room. The first and the second accused then had their lunch. At that time the first accused said that Russel's condition was very low and he might die at any time. I asked why and looked at Dalrene and she put her head sideways in a sorrowful mood."

She said on 16th July, when the two accused were in Russel's room, the first accused asked Dalrene 'Where is that medicine?' Then she replied 'It is with you Father.' Then he took the drugs from the pocket of his cassock.

Mr. Marapana asked, "He put his hand into the cassock?"

"Yes. He took some tablets. Four tablets, white in colour."

"With a covering?"

"No."

"Were they exposed?"

"Yes. He had a small polythene bag and from that he put them on his palm. There were also two green tablets and a capsule."

"Altogether seven?"

"Yes."

"What happened thereafter?"

"He asked me to give it."

"Who asked?"

"The first accused. He kept them on his palm and said 'Therese you give'."

"To Russel?"

"Yes. I said I cannot and said after giving them if he chokes? He was lying down and he had to take them with tea. So I refused and the first accused gave them."

"Why did you refuse?"

"He can get choked because he was lying down."

"You did not suspect anything?"

"No. Because it was for his sickness and it was medicine."

"Russel was conscious at the time?"

"Yes."

"He was up and shortly before that he was talking to you?"

"Yes."

"Russel also heard this conversation?"

"This was in the second room and Russel was in the first room."

"What took you to the first accused's room?"

"I dressed a child's wound and I went to see the little one. They were having tea.

"First accused gave the tablets?

"Yes, and the tea. Russel was up at the time. He drank the cup of tea and the tablets and capsules were also taken. He swallowed with tea."

"Thereafter what happened?"

"Ten or fifteen minutes after that he was in a bath of sweat."

"You continued to be at the bedside?

"I was by the bedside. Then Russel passed urine."

"Where were the first and second accused at the time?"

"They gave tea and drugs and went out."

"When Russel was in a bath of sweat, where were the first and second accused?"

"They were in the dining room."

"Did you call out for them?"

"No."

"How did you know that Russel had passed urine?"

"He had a bedsore at the back of the spine and he was struggling. I think it was smarting and then he passed urine and I saw. I went and told Dalrene that Russel passed urine and was struggling and asked, why did you give the tablets?"

"What was Dalrene's answer?"

"She did not answer."

"At the time the first accused was trying to give tablets did the second accused tell him not to give the tablets?"

"No."

"When the first accused was at the lunch table discussing about the grave did the second accused say she will discuss the grave with the Ingrams?"

"No."

"When you told the second accused that Russel was struggling etc. what did she do?"

"She came into the room and felt Russel's head. I asked why this is. She came with some clothes in hand. Then gradually he was breathing."

"Was he gasping for breath?"

"Yes, like that. I told her try to get a doctor and show him and do not keep him like this."

"You were talking to the second accused?"

"Yes, she said 'Father will get the doctor'."

"Then what happened?"

"They did not take any notice. The Father said, 'We will see. We will see'. When I was there they did not get down a doctor. I left at 4.30 as my husband had to go to church."

"After Russel urinated what happened thereafter?"

"They did not change his bed clothes. At that time my husband had gone to the church and I sent a message. I came back about 6.30 p.m. and he was in the same condition. Until then no doctor came."

"Did you change the bed clothes?"

"No, they were not changed until my husband came."

"Was he conscious?"

"No after he gave the tablets he went off. As he got the tablets he got into a bath of sweat and became unconscious and passed urine. With the sweating he passed urine."

"Did he have fever at the time?"

"I cannot say. We did not take the temperature."

In answer to a question by Mr. Bandaranayake, Mrs. Jackson said that she never saw a stethoscope in the Vicarage.

She said that Rev. Peiris told her that Russel's condition was very low and that he might pass away at any time and that he will not recover. Rev. Peiris also said if Russel dies he wanted to bury him in his ground. Mrs. Jackson said, why not in Ingrams grave (their mother's grave). Then Rev. Peiris said, "No, no, he can be put in my grave."

Mrs. Jackson said, "On the day Russel died, shortly before Russel's body was brought, Rev. Peiris walked up to the kitchen and asked for Dalrene's hand to put a ring. Rev. Peiris put a band ring, which was very much similar to a wedding ring, on Dalrene's third left finger and asked her not to worry. He blessed and kissed her. He also told Dalrene 'Very soon I will also be like you' and went away tapping her shoulder."

"Dalrene at that time had Russel's ring on the same finger. She gave her hand. She did not tell anything. With the priest's ring, she was wearing double rings on the occasion," she said answering Mr. Bandaranayake.

"Did she remove the ring?"

"No".

"What did you do?"

"All what I did was to refrain from extending my sympathies to Dalrene at her bereavement because it was more a wedding than a funeral!"

"Why do you say so?"

"Just imagine Sir, putting wedding rings at a funeral!"

She also said that she had not seen that ring before nor did it belong to their family.

Mrs. Jackson said that she had later come to know that Russel's mother had made a complaint to the Coroner that she suspected foul play in the death of Russel.

Cross examined by Mr. R. I. Obeysekera, she said that the ring the priest put on Dalrene's finger was just like a wedding ring.

Mr. Obeysekera asked, "The priest saw you at the time?"

"Besides me there were several others like Mrs. Koch and Mrs. Wanaguru.

"What the priest was supposed to have said was within the hearing of all others also?"

"Yes."

"Were you taken back?"

"Why not? That was why I did not want to sympathize with Dalrene."

She said she considered the whole episode a mockery. She told what she saw to her husband.

"So, what did your husband say?" Mr. Obeysekera asked.

"He did not take it seriously and said that such things happen almost everywhere!"

She said that after Russel's funeral she had nothing to do with Dalrene. She however attended the seventh day alms giving.

Mr. Bandaranayake asked, "What do you think the priest meant when he told Dalrene 'Don't worry, very soon I will also be like you'?"

"What he meant was Mrs. Peiris will also die soon."

Mr. Obeysekera asked, "The things you mentioned to Court as regards what the priest was purported to have said, are not in your Police statement. What you have stated to Police is that the priest kissed and blessed Dalrene on the occasion. Did the priest kiss her?"

"I do not know that. I however did not see it. I may have said he kissed."

"Does tapping mean kissing?"

"No."

"I put it to you that your story about the priest putting a ring on second accused's finger in malicious concoction?"

"No, it is not made up. It is true."

On one occasion Russel had told her that 'they were giving me tablets'. This made him tired and drowsy. When Russel said that 'they were giving me tablets' he meant Dalrene and Rev. Peiris. She then told Dalrene not to give any more tablets to Russel.

It was Rev. Peiris who fed Russel with a spoon. She quite well remembered having told the police about this. On the same afternoon at about 3.30 p.m. Dalrene brought a cup of tea for Russel which was given to Rev. Peiris. Rev. Peiris wanted her to feed that tea to Russel, which she refused to do. In fact she wanted Dalrene to feed Russel. She had told about this to the police.

After the Requiem Mass, Dalrene stayed with her sister at Wattala.

Cross examined by Mr. Cecil Goonewardena, Mrs. Jackson said that she was aware that her sister had been charged with conspiracy along with Rev. Peiris with the murder of Mrs. Peiris and Russel Ingram.

She did not tell the police that the three children were sleeping on a mat while Dalrene was lying on the single bed on 16th June. Rev. Peiris was seated on a chair in the same room on the day in question.

Re-examined by Mr. Marapana, she said that she noticed the tablets being given to Russel by Rev. Peiris on the evening of 16th June. Few minutes later Russel became unconscious and started sweating. Russel's parents visited the hospital almost daily. Her recollection was that the parents were residing at Kadawatha and not at the Vicarage.

It was seven days after the death of Russel her sister had gone to Wattala to stay with another sister.

To a question by Mr. Wickramasekara, she said that she had seen Russel at social parties. She said that Russel took alcohol, and he could stand any amount of drinks. She said however much he consumed liquor he was sober! Russel daily visited the Railway Club at Mount Mary.

Mr. Bandaranayake asked. "What happened to the ring which you said was put on Dalrene by the first accused?"

"I do not know sir."

"Where was Russel buried?"

"At Kanatta."

"How was he dressed?"

"Full suit."

"What was the colour of the suit?"

"I cannot remember," she said.

Dr. P.A.P. Joseph, retired Senior Surgeon of the General Hospital, Colombo, giving evidence said he was now the Medical Consultant of the State Plantations Corporation.

Examined by Mr. Tilak Marapana he said he had first come to know the first accused in late November 1974. He said in July 1978 he received a call from the first accused.

Dr. Joseph said that the first accused informed him that he had a lodger who had symptoms for which he took him to various doctors who were confused. He however did not mention the name of this lodger.

"He mentioned by name Dr. Lakshman Weerasena, who had told Rev. Peiris that the symptoms were baffling. I asked him how old the lodger was and he said thirty two years. I asked what the problem was and Rev. Peiris replied that the patient became violent, excited and at other moments drowsy and stuporose."

"I asked him if he had noticed whether these symptoms appeared in the morning when the patient awoke and he said 'Yes, quite right'.

I asked him whether the patient felt relieved after his breakfast and he said 'Quite right'. I asked if he noticed that when the patient was hungry the symptoms appeared and when food was taken the patient felt relieved and he said 'Quite right'. I next inquired if the patient was diabetic and he said 'No'."

"He asked me what are these symptoms due to and I said that in my opinion it was due to low blood sugar. There was a moment of breathless silence. He next inquired as to what was the cause of the low blood sugar. I told him I could not answer that question as he was not a diabetic, but the only thing I could recall was that an islet cell tumour of the pancreas. He then said, 'Do you know that my visions have led me to the pancreas?' Thereafter he asked me for information on the islet cell tumour and in the course of the conversation I was struck by the knowledge that Rev. Peiris had as a layman about the pancreas and diabetes. It was quite remarkable for a layman. He next asked me what advice I would give and I said he should be admitted as the case called for careful study."

"He wanted the patient admitted under Dr. U.S. Jayawickrama, Visiting Physician, General Hospital, Colombo, stating that Dr. Jayawickrama was a personal friend of Dr. Dayasiri Fernando, a surgeon, who was his nephew. I said it would be all right. He then asked me for a favour. 'Could you please give me a letter for admission?' I told him that it was my practice not to give any letters without examining the patient. Father said very well then, the next day I will show you the patient, and the conversation ended," said Dr. Joseph.

"Did you visit the Vicarage?" asked Mr. Marapana.

"The following day I was having my lunch. The telephone rang. My wife answered the call and she told me that Father Peiris was on the line. Frankly I had forgotten Father Peiris as I had a busy day. Father Peiris told me 'We are waiting for you'. I told Father Peiris that I was having my lunch, and that I would come. I did not finish my lunch, but proceeded to the Vicarage. I was met by Father Peiris and he told me that the patient was violent, boisterous in the night and that he was resting, and showed me a closed room. I saw a lady and some children in the Vicarage. On this occasion I did not see any other male present."

On a question from Mr. Bandaranayake, Dr. Joseph said that he was not shown into the room where Russel was supposed to have been resting. Father had stepped out of the Vicarage onto the pathway, and it was here that the whole conversation took place. Father rushed out to meet me," Dr. Joseph said.

Dr. Joseph added that on several occasions the first accused had rung him up and given him progressive reports on Russel Ingram. He had however appeared to be dissatisfied with the treatment given to Russel at the General Hospital.

"When I asked him in what way are you dissatisfied, he said the patient was transferred from one ward to another," said Dr. Joseph.

Mr. Marapana asked, "Did you eventually come to know that Russel had been discharged from the hospital?"

"On 15th July 1978 I received another call from Rev. Peiris and he stated, 'A hell of a thing has happened. Russel has discharged himself from the hospital and he is here (meaning the Vicarage)'. I replied that was extremely foolish of him. He then wanted me to come to the Vicarage and give him my medical opinion. I accordingly went. I was introduced to Russel Ingram's wife, the second accused, and also to Russel Ingram's father and then I was taken into a small study room. There Rev. Peiris courteously served me with a little brandy. Through politeness I took it. He next led me to a room. Meanwhile Russel Ingram's father and the second accused remained in the study. Father Peiris was by my side when I saw Russel emerging from the toilet."

Questioned by Mr. Bandaranayake, Dr. Joseph said that this was his first and last glimpse of Russel alive.

Dr. Joseph said, "As Russel emerged from the toilet his gait was slow and unsteady. He was then put in a bed. I noticed that he was emaciated. I asked him why he left hospital and he did not answer.

He appeared dull and apathetic. He gave me the impression that he did not want to be disturbed. I examined his chest. I then set a test. I asked him to subtract seven from hundred and he replied ninety three. When I asked him to subtract seven from ninety three he said it could not be done."

Dr. Joseph said that Russel had seemed to wrack his brains and had then said it could not be done.

"I must also say that when I questioned Russel the first accused answered. It is an irritating habit which I normally do not tolerate, but in respect of Rev. Peiris I kept quiet. I told Russel that it was foolish of him to have left hospital and that he should eat well and take plenty of glucose," Dr. Joseph said.

Mr. Ramanathan asked, "Was the first accused present when you said take plenty of glucose?"

"Yes."

Mr. Wickramasekera asked, "When you told Russel to take plenty of glucose did the first accused say anything?"

"Not a word. Not a hum."

Dr. Joseph said when Russel died the first accused had rung him and asked him to be a pall bearer at the funeral.

"On visiting the funeral house there appeared to be a studied hostility. Rev. Peiris appeared to be giving orders, like a General. I followed the coffin to the adjoining church and I was uneasy, so I sympathized with Alex Ingram and left the Church," said Dr. Joseph. He said that the people of the Vicarage behaved peculiarly, and he felt hostility among the people present.

On 18th March 1979 he said he came to know that Mrs. Peiris had been hospitalized. He had been at Union Chemists around 9.30 a.m. or 10.00 a.m. and the first accused had also been at the chemists.

"He tapped me on the back and asked me 'Have you heard of a bedsore in the occiput?' (*Occiput is the back of the skull*) I said, 'No father'. He said 'You know my wife is having a bed sore in the occiput and she is a vegetable at the General Hospital, Colombo.'"

The first accused had then told Dr. Joseph that he had been accused of having something to do with his wife's condition and said that it was actually due to an overdose of anti-depressants. The following day Dr. Joseph said he had read the obituary notice of Mrs. Peiris in the newspapers.

Mr. Marapana asked, "Can an overdose of anti-depressant drugs cause low blood sugar?"

"No."

In answer to Mr. Bandaranayake, he agreed that if a layman spoke of 'hypoglycaemia' he could either speak of hypoglycaemia caused by a tumour or by administration of a drug. He said that a temporary diagnosis of an insulinoma was normally done by a physician and then transferred for surgery. The immediate treatment for hypoglycaemia was glucose and that too came under a physician.

Cross examined by Mr. R.I. Obeysekera, Dr. Joseph said, "I was not aware that the first accused was a diabetic. I am aware that some persons who have various ailments like to study them. The first accused's knowledge for a layman was surprising as he was technical. There were many paper backs and quack literature on hypoglycaemia in the United States. With all my experience I felt Rev. Peiris's knowledge about the pancreas, hypoglycaemia, diabetes and islet cell tumours was astonishing. However, the first accused never told me that he was a diabetic."

Dr. Joseph said that pancreatic tumours were rare but it was a well known clinical entity and there were over 500 reports published. Dr. Joseph said 'factitious hypoglycaemia' could only be detected by medical or para medical people.

When he gave his statement no one probed the date on which Russel discharged himself, and he attached no significance to what the first accused had told him at the Vicarage.

Re-examined by Mr. Marapana, Dr. Joseph said that had he examined a patient and diagnosed hypoglycaemia he would have advised that the patient be hospitalized immediately. On 15th July after he examined patient he prescribed plenty of glucose and if his advice was followed, the patient would never have gone into a hypoglycaemia coma. He was never aware that Russel Ingram was admitted to the Durdans Hospital.

Rev. Edison Mendis, brother of Mrs. Eunice Peiris was the next witness. Senior State Counsel Mr. C. R. de Silva asked him, "Your sister was ill. Did anyone try to get a doctor?"

"Father Mathew was making a call to Dr. Weerasena and I heard him saying 'So you want me to give her a high protein diet?' 'No glucose or sugar?' "

"Did you see her having any food that day?"

"Yes, Father Mathew gave her some liver."

Rev. Mendis said that on 28th January 1979, was his sister's dinner party. He said he cannot say when he last visited the Vicarage and that he did not see the second accused at the Vicarage on 30th January 1979. Rev. Mendis further said that he felt that his sister was overlooked at this party.

Mr. de Silva asked, "What is the last sacrament given to a dying person is the Anglican Church?"

"Holy Communion."

"Is Holy Communion given when a person is dying?"

"Yes."

"After she was removed to the General Hospital did you not inform her children as to her condition?"

"I did so. I sent a cable to Mrs. Mihiri Wickramasinghe, my niece, informing that mummy's condition is critical."

Cross examined by Mr. Cecil Goonewardena, Rev. Mendis said, "I have not made any false statements under any circumstances."

Mr. Goonewardena quoting the commandment "Thou shalt not bear false witness against thy neighbour", said, "Please answer these questions truthfully." Rev Mendis said that the suggestion made by the counsel is not correct.

In answer to Mr. Wickramasekara he said that his sister Eunice attended her last social function on 26th January 1979.

The next witness was Mrs. Myrtle Mendis, wife of Rev. Edison Mendis.

Examined by Mr. C. R. de Silva, she said that Mrs. Peiris, who was the Vice Principal of St. Michaels, Polwatta, was to return to Sri Lanka for the school term at end of April 1978.

Mr. de Silva asked, "Did Rev. Peiris say anything about her stay in England?"

"I cannot remember. She came monthly to see her grand children when they were here. She was looking quite rosy when she returned from England."

Mr. Wickramasekara asked, "Was she aided when she got into the jeep in which they travelled?"

"I cannot remember at all that she was helped to the jeep. When I visited the Vicarage, Eunice was not as cheerful. She did not talk so much. When I visited I can remember she was sleeping in a sofa."

Mr. Bandaranayake asked, "Were you aware that she was taking any medicine?"

"I cannot remember. When I went to Durdans, she was not unconscious. She really had not known how she had fallen ill. Rev. Peiris was very quiet. I volunteered to stay in the hospital. There was no special attendant. I was the only person who waited in hospital."

Answering further questions of Mr. de Silva, she said, "If a member of my family were ill, Rev. Peiris who was usually very helpful, would have got down specialists and seen that the person received proper treatment. Yet when his own wife was hospitalized, I noticed that this treatment was lacking. I asked him, 'Why don't you get a specialist? If I were ill you would have brought two specialists'."

Mr. de Silva asked why she had said this, and Mrs. Mendis replied "Because he is like that. Very helpful."

She said that on 31st January 1979, Rev. Peiris had phoned her at about 9.00 a.m. He had told her, 'One of you go to Dr. Weerasena and collect a letter and some reports and take them to the Vicarage'.

She had conveyed the message to her husband and he went to the Vicarage, but she did not accompany him. By the time she went to the General Hospital that day on hearing that Mrs. Peiris had been warded, it was around 1.00 p.m. Mrs. Mendis said she went there as her husband had phoned her and said 'she's very bad'. She was in hospital that day until about 6.30 p.m.

On a question from Mr. Bandaranayake, she said she thought Mrs. Peiris would die.

"Why do you say that?"

"Because she was so bad."

Mr. de Silva asked, "What did you observe?"

"She was wet. She was a nice person to look at, but I could not look at her as she was unconscious."

"What did the second accused do when she came to the hospital?"

"She went up to the bed, looked and said 'this is just like Russel'."

"Did she say anything else?"

"She looked at the drip and said 'this is also what Russel was given'."

"From April 1978 right up to the time of Mrs. Peiris's death, have you seen the two accused together?"

"Yes."

"Have you observed anything unusual about the two accused."

"In a sense, yes."

She said that at the time Dalrene was working for the first accused, Dalrene used to treat him as her equal, which few of us did. On a question from Mr. Bandaranayake she said that she did not like the tone of voice used by Dalrene on the first accused, as she was his secretary.

"One day I commented on it to my husband. She said that the two accused were too friendly."

"What were the matters that led to this impression?"

"It was not anything much but there was a feeling and when my sister-in-law came back she did not talk much when Dalrene was there. Maybe I resented it. On the 15th when I went to the Vicarage, my sister-in-law was lying on the bed and Father was seated on a couch. I had a feeling that it was not right. I felt sad for my sister- in-law. I cannot explain."

Mr. Bandaranayake asked, "Woman's intuition?"

She said, "Yes."

Cross-examined by Mr. R. I. Obeysekera, she said that her husband and she had not been informed about the date of Mrs. Peiris's return to Sri Lanka.

"You now know that Malrani did not want you and your husband to know about it?"

"Yes, I read about it in the newspapers. My children had been angry when they had read about this in the papers."

"Mrs. Peiris had told you she was drowsy, weak and dizzy?"

"Yes."

"I am putting it to you that you put it to Munilal that a specialist be called?"

"No."

"I am putting it to you that you and your husband were ill disposed towards the first accused?"

"Never. I was very friendly with the first accused."

"Do you deny my suggestion?"

"I deny it."

Mr. Cecil Goonewardena then cross-examined Mrs. Mendis.

Mrs. Mendis said that on the birthday party of the first accused, the cake had been brought by her. It had been made by her daughter. There had also been two other cakes, one from Dalrene and one from Eunice.

"As Mrs. Peiris was in the UK at this time, she had instructed a close friend of theirs to bring a cake on her behalf?"

"Yes."

Mr. Goonewardena commented, "Some secretaries sit on the lap!"

Mr. Goonewardena said that the day before she was admitted to Durdans, Mrs. Peiris had written to Malrani that 'it is fortunate that Dalrene is there to see to the marketing'.

"Was that the correct attitude Mrs. Peiris had of Dalrene at the Vicarage?"

"I do not know."

"I suggest to you that you have let your imagination run riot and come out with all this?"

"No."

The next witness was Dr. K.U.R.A. Banagala, the then intern medical officer of ward 18, General Hospital, Colombo, with Dr. Bandula Wijesiriwardena and Dr. Mohan de Silva. Examined by Mr. Marapana he said that he saw Russel Ingram for the first time on 25th July 1978. On that day after the examination he did not make an entry that Russel was sweating, because he did not observe any sweating. Thereafter, on 27th July when he examined Russel once again he noticed slight sweating. That night he once again examined Russel and ordered 50% dextrose to be given.

On 28th July he did not examine Russel. It was Dr. Wijesiriwardena who examined Russel that day. With reference to the Fluid Balance Chart (FBC), Dr. Banagala said that there was an entry on 28th July that the patient was given water, 50% dextrose and 500 millilitres of saline. Russel had been given 50% dextrose in the afternoon also along with 10% dextrose. The same night the patient was continued to be on dextrose. At 1 a.m. the following day, Russel was given saline and at 6 a.m. he was given dextrose once again. That was continued at 10 a.m. with 50% dextrose.

Dr. Banagala said he noticed a hypoglycaemic attack at 9.30 p.m. on 29th July and he gave 50% dextrose and the signs have subsided. On 4th August also said he observed an attack and Russel was treated with dextrose and the attack subsided. Dr. Banagala said that there were other occasions where he observed signs of hypoglycaemia, which he treated during this period but did not make an entry in the BHT.

Dr. Banagala stated that Russel was deeply unconscious throughout and that if at the hospital they discontinued the administration of dextrose to Russel, he would not have survived so long.

Answering questions by Mr. Bandaranayake, he said that towards the latter part of July, Russel was more or less a vegetable.

He said on 3rd August 1978 Professor R.A. Navaratne, the Professor of Surgery, who was in-charge of the ward, referred Russel to the Consultant Physician Dr. N. Nagaratnam. Professor Navaratne had informed Dr. Nagaratnam that the patient was still having attacks of hypoglycaemia.

Dr. Banagala was then cross examined by Mr. R.I. Obeysekera.

"Can you say when you noticed sweating, whether the onset of sweating was sudden?" asked Mr. Obeysekera.

"I am unable to answer this question," said Dr. Banagala.

In answer to Justice Wickramasekara, Dr. Banagala said the symptoms could appear depending on the rapidity of the fall of the blood sugar level.

He agreed that when he examined the patient he used to look for sweating as that was a symptom that he had noticed in the patient earlier. He said that the 'suspected' diagnosis of Russel's illness was that he was getting hypoglycaemic attacks due to an insulinoma. They arrived at this diagnosis because of the fluctuating blood sugar levels and the hypoglycaemic attacks he got.

Shown the admission letter given by Dr. P.A.P. Joseph, Dr. Banagala said he had not seen that letter earlier. He had not discussed the case of this patient with Dr. Sheriffdeen nor did he discuss it with Professor Navaratne. However, he discussed it with Dr. Wijesiriwardena, who like him was an intern at that time.

Answering a question of Mr. Bandaranayake, he said that he did not at any time suspect that the sudden drop in the blood sugar levels in Russel was induced by an extraneous factor.

"On 27th July when I examined the patient at about 9.30 p.m., I noticed more sweating than when I examined him in the morning, between 7.30 a.m. and 9.30 a.m. the same day. I noticed the increased sweating half-an-hour after the patient was given Marmite and one-and-a-half hours after milk was given," said Dr. Banagala.

Continuing he said that Russel's clothes were changed frequently and they were brought from home. Even linen was at times brought from home. They would have been brought in a basket. He could not recollect whether he told the Police that he had seen the first accused bringing a basket to the ward. He said he was unable to say whether Russel's father brought any food for the patient.

Cross examined by Mr. Cecil Goonewardena, Dr. Banagala said that he had seen Rev. Peiris with his hand round the waist of Dalrene.

"I am unable to say whether it was in the morning or evening that I saw Rev. Peiris with his hand round the waist of Dalrene. I thought that that behaviour was unusual because it was being done by a priest. If a young man had his hand round the waist of a young woman I would not have thought it unusual."

"Don't you know that old people have a licence to do such things and get away?" queried Mr. Goonewardena.

Dr. Banagala remained silent!

Mr. Marapana remarked, "That is what has been done in this case!"

Mr. Goonewardena told Dr. Banagala, "Have you heard Alexander Pope saying 'That everything is yellow to the jaundiced eye'?"

Dr. Banagala did not answer.

The next witness, Mrs. Leela Manawadu, Staff Nurse of ward 18, General Hospital, Colombo, was examined by Mr. Tilak Marapana.

She said on 29th July morning she had given Russel dextrose. Thereafter, on 31st July afternoon she gave tea and at 4.00 p.m. milk. On 1st August she had not made any entries on the FBC. On 3rd August she had given tea at 8.00 a.m. That was tea supplied by the hospital. She had made an entry in the FBC that tea was given at 8.00 a.m. On 6th August at 8.00 a.m. again she had given tea and made an entry.

She said most of the food given to Russel was what Rev. Peiris brought.

"At times he told me to give food he had brought. There were occasions when Rev. Peiris left the food with the person who was looking after Russel. This person stayed by Russel's bedside but he did not attend on the patient. He was not an attendant. The feed through the nasal tube was usually given by a nurse. I have never seen anyone else feeding the patient but I have observed the bottle, which was used to feed the patient kept unwashed. This indicated to me that someone other than a nurse had used the bottle. If a nurse had used the bottle, she would always wash it," Mrs. Manawadu said.

In answer to Mr. Wickramasekara, she said when a patient who was critically ill was being fed, the nurse would remain until the patient finished taking his food and then leave only after washing the bottle. She said she had never forgotten to wash a bottle after feeding a patient.

In answer to Mr. Bandaranayake, she said she had seen the bottle kept unwashed on two occasions. On both occasions milk had been put into the bottle.

She recalled informing Rev. Peiris that when Milk Board milk was given to patients sometimes their stomachs got upset. He then told her that the milk brought was from a cow he had at home and was carefully prepared for the patient. She denied that Rev. Peiris had told her that he was bringing Elephant House milk.

She said she had seen Dalrene accompanying him to the ward. On occasions when she was on duty she had seen two of them come together during visiting hours? On such occasions she had seen Rev. Peiris bringing food.

Mrs. Manawadu said she had told the doctors that the patient used to sweat after taking meals. She did not inform Rev. Peiris about the sweating. Dalrene never spoke to her about the patient's condition. She further said, "When Russel was warded he was given an intravenous drip. Russel was never restless as he was deeply unconscious. Therefore, there was no chance of the drip coming out as a result of the patient struggling. I have never seen the drip needle given to Russel come out but noticed the clamp closed which meant flow of dextrose into the patient's body had been stopped. The clamp cannot get closed by itself. It has to be closed by someone."

She said that a blood sample was taken before the patient was given dextrose. She told the police, that she took the blood on the instruction of Dr. Wijesiriwardena, but got Dr. Karunakaran to fill the request forms.

She explained that when 'extras' were ordered for a patient, as and when it was supplied by the hospital if it could not be given to the patient, there was no rule requiring them to return such extras to the kitchen. If 'extras' were for some reason not given to the patient, it could be given to another patient. They did not consume 'extras' ordered for patients. If such 'extras' were returned to the kitchen she could not say what happened to them at that point.

Counsel asked, "Does that food disappear from the kitchen?"

"I cannot say that," she said.

She said that she discussed Russel's sweating with the other nurses and then informed the doctors.

In answer to Mr. Bandaranayake, she said that she was present on 18th July when Russel was admitted.

She recalled Dr. Wijesiriwardena informing her that Russel was re-admitted and requesting her to obtain a blood sample. The blood sample was taken around 9.30 a.m. or 10.00 a.m. She said that Russel was quite conscious when he was first in hospital. He was on a normal diet and was walking about, but he appeared to be depressed and preferred to be left to himself. Even then food was brought from outside for Russel, but she did not observe him sweating as he did when he was re-admitted.

She said that Russel was admitted to ward 18 on the first occasion for investigations. A glucose tolerance test (GTT) was carried out and for which the night nurse was required to take a sample of urine from the patient but the test was put off as the patent had failed to give a sample early morning. Thereafter, the patent was discharged and he was asked to report back for a GTT. She further said that she had never seen Russel chatting with other patients. Russel always preferred to be left alone.

Cross examined by Mr. C. P. Illangakoon, junior counsel for Dalrene, Mrs. Manawadu said Russel was discharged on 14th July on the first occasion. It was then that she had said Russel did not talk with her or any of the patients. It was during this time that Russel's mental condition was not normal.

"On the second occasion when Russel was admitted he was unconscious and he remained so till he died on 10th August 1978. The nasal tube should be inserted by a staff nurse supervised by a doctor. Precaution had to be taken to ensure that the tube did not enter the respiratory system. Once the tube entered the stomach it would not affect the patient even if he moved about in the bed. Cleaning of a patient that was unconscious could be done by anyone, once a person was told how to do it. Where Russel was concerned no relatives came forward to sponge and clean him," she said.

"When Rev. Peiris was in the ward with his arm round the waist of Dalrene others too would have seen it as it was during visiting hours I saw it," she said.

Re-examined by Mr. Marapana, she said that she could not ascertain exactly which food was given to Russel when he started sweating. There were times when Russel was given food brought from outside and also given hospital food just before sweating was noticed.

Mrs. Premawathi Sugathapala, a Staff Nurse of ward 18 examined by Mr. Gamini Amaratunge, State Counsel, recalled the first occasion on which Russel Ingram was admitted to ward 18.

"He was quite conscious and took normal food. When I spoke to him he had replied but was rather reluctant to speak. Russel was given normal food brought by Rev. Peiris at different times. Russel was given tea from the hospital. There were times when Rev. Peiris was alone and at times with Dalrene. When he came with Dalrene it was during visiting hours. She recalled Russel after being discharged on 14th July being re-admitted. She saw the patient in an unconscious state after 18th July. On the second occasion Russel was on a liquid diet. The first accused brought him milk, soup, Marmite and *thambili* (king coconut) water at various times. There were times Rev. Peiris had asked them to give drinks he brought. These drinks were given to Russel through a nasal tube," Mrs. Sugathapala said.

In answer to Mr. Wickramasekara, Mrs. Sugathapala said, "Russel's condition worsened after taking that food. She said she had observed Russel was sweating profusely, the pulse rate weakened, became restless, and went into a coma. She noticed these changes on four or five occasions when she had fed the patient with the food brought by Rev. Peiris. One such occasion was on 20th July after she fed Russel with milk at 2.00 p.m. This milk could have been what Rev. Peiris brought."

"I did not make an entry when I noticed changes in the patient but informed a doctor. Milk I gave at 2.00 p.m. was plain milk. What the hospital supplied was tea with milk. When I gave what was supplied by the hospital, I made an entry in the FBC to the effect that tea was given to the patient. I would not say 'milk' if I gave tea with milk. On 20th July about 6.30 p.m., I gave Russel Marmite, which had been brought from home. On 23rd July at about 10.30 a.m., I gave Russel milk. This milk I thought was supplied by the Rev. Peiris. After I gave the milk I noticed that the patient's condition changing. Then I gave him dextrose. After dextrose was given the patient returned to normal even though yet unconscious," she said.

A staff nurse of the ward 18, Mrs. Lasantha Fernando, examined by Senior State Counsel Mr. Gamini Amaratunga said that Rev. Peiris used to bring Russel, milk, soup and Marmite. She said that on one or two occasions immediately after visiting hours, the needle from the dextrose drip used to be out of Russel's arm, and on those occasions the two accused were seen leaving Russel's bedside. She said she re-inserted it into the patient.

On explaining how the needle could have come out she said if someone standing by Russel's bedside had accidentally knocked against the drip, the needle could have dislodged.

Cross examined by Mr. R.I. Obeysekera, she said that she did not tell everything she had done for Russel to the police but had only answered their questions.

He asked "You have not mentioned one word about the first accused bringing Marmite?"

"Maybe."

"You have lied in Court when you said that the first accused brought Marmite?"

"I am speaking the truth."

Mr. Oliver Fernando, a Laboratory Technician of the General Hospital giving evidence described in detail the tests he performed on the blood sample sent to him during the lunch interval between 1 and 2 p.m. on 18th July 1978. The sample he received bore the legend that it was the blood of one Russel Ingram, a patient in ward 18. He tested the sample for sugar. He did the normal recognized test for blood sugar which was generally used in the laboratory. He received a 'nil' value that is, the test showed there was no blood sugar. He was surprised with this result as he had never before had such a result. He said he repeated the test and again got a 'nil' value.

"I then telephoned Dr. Perera, the Head of the Laboratory and informed him of this result. Upon his instructions I repeated the test for the third time and yet again got the same 'nil' result. I telephoned the result to the ward and later prepared the report, which I signed and countersigned by Dr. Perera later," he said.

Dr. Terrence Gamini Raja de Silva, Medical Officer in charge of the Government Hospital, Colombo Central, Maligawatte, who was an intern in ward 47B, General Hospital, was examined by Mr. Tilak Marapana. He said on 31st January 1979 he was the first house officer of ward 47B to see Mrs. Peiris.

He said that he obtained his MBBS in 1978 and was serving his internship at the General Hospital, Colombo. He said that around 12.30 p.m. on 31st January 1979, when he was in ward 49, the BHT of Mrs. Peiris was brought to him and he was informed that a bad patient had been admitted under his Consultant Dr. K.J. Nanayakkara to ward 47B. He then went there and examined Mrs. Peiris. On a number of occasions right upto her death he has examined her. She was unconscious right throughout her stay in the hospital but was never observed going into a hypoglycaemic coma right upto the time of her death.

Dr. de Silva said there was a history of dizziness and giddiness in the patient two or three hours after meals, which was compatible with hypoglycaemia. It was also confirmed by a blood sugar report that she had got a hypoglycaemic coma. On examination, her reflexes were totally absent which was also compatible with hypoglycaemic coma.

"If the patient who was unconscious, had suffered a stroke, would she have lived for seven weeks?" asked Mr. Bandaranayake.

"Very unlikely. She would have died within a few hours or a day or two. If there had been a stroke it would have been revealed at the post-mortem examination. In a case of hypoglycaemia, there would be diffuse death of brain cells," said Dr. de Silva. He also said the fluctuating levels of consciousness of Mrs. Peiris were also not compatible with a stroke.

"The blood sugar report which arrived later also confirmed that Mrs. Peiris had gone into a hypoglycaemic coma. Her pressure remained normal after admission and remained so until death. If she was going into a coma from a stroke, she would have had severe haemorrhage and a continuous headache and thereafter would have gone in to a coma. Mrs. Peiris, according to Rev. Peiris had pointed towards her head while getting into a coma. The patient pointing to her head, as told to him by Rev. Peiris signified nothing to him," said Dr. de Silva.

Cross examined by Mr. R.I. Obeysekera, Dr. de Silva said that when he saw Mrs. Peiris she was being transferred to a bed from a stretcher. He looked at the patient and then spoke to Rev. Peiris. He said the reports given to him by Rev. Peiris were ones taken at Glass House. There were six reports and three of them were dated 29th January 1979.

"I went through the letter of Dr. Weerasena. It was handed over to me by Rev. Peiris who gave the history, which I noted before I examined the patient. I thought I took down the history exhaustively. Everything I felt was relevant was noted down. As a practice I normally take down the history, then examine the patient and diagnose the case. Thereafter, I examined the reports and letters brought by the patient and then compared my diagnosis with any other diagnosis," Dr. de Silva said.

Through experience he had decided to follow this practice and he had found that more often his diagnosis has been correct rather than those of others, added Dr. de Silva.

Shown the letter sent by Dr. Weerasena, he said he could not read it because the handwriting was not clear. As the patient was bad he went through it superficially on 31st January. He said the letter was in the BHT and after treating the patient he would have gone through it again and again.

Dr. Lakshman Weerasena, a private practitioner in Colombo, giving evidence said that he has his own clinic and that he had begun his private practice in 1971 at which time he had been the acting JMO of Colombo.

Dr. Weerasena said that he had come to know the Peiris family through by one Victor Gamalathge, another patient, around 1976. This patient had told Dr. Weerasena that Rev. Peiris was presently being seen by a Dr. Jeffry (J.G.C.) Peiris who was leaving for England, and this patient had asked Dr. Weerasena whether he would take over the Peiris family. Dr. Peiris had also requested Dr. Weerasena to look after the Peiris family. Since that time he was the general practitioner attending to the medical needs of the first accused and his family

He said that Rev. Peiris was a diabetic and he prescribed glibenclamide, which is an anti-diabetic drug to control his diabetes.

He said that drug is known as Euglucon and marketed under different names and the strength of the tablet was 5 mg, and that he had prescribed half to one tablet per day with restricted diet and that he gave him a prescription at that time. On being asked whether Rev. Peiris ever discussed the effects of this drug with him, Dr. Weerasena said that on some occasions Rev. Peiris had complained of feeling hungry, giddy or drowsy and he had asked him to reduce the tablet from one to half and to take some sugar. He said that Rev. Peiris himself used to check his urine.

As far as he could remember he said that Rev. Peiris had brought Russel Ingram, Mrs. Dalrene Ingram and a young girl who had fainting attacks to his dispensary for medication. He said that all clergy, irrespective of denomination, were given free medication in his clinic.

Regarding the ailment Russel had, he said Russel had multiple wounds on his feet. At this time Rev. Peiris had mentioned to him that Russel was an alcoholic. He said he found the sores were due to unhygienic standards. He had advised Russel to stop taking alcohol while taking medication, and had given him some antibiotics. He however did not find clinically that Russel to be an alcoholic.

Mr. Marapana asked, "Can you remember the first accused discussing any other ailment, which Russel had with you, and have you prescribed any medication for any other ailment?"

"No."

"Did you describe to Rev. Peiris that Russel had an organic disorder of the pancreas?"

"No."

"Nor did you express the opinion that only an operation would help him get over that condition?"

"No."

Dr. Weerasena said that he never had an occasion to prescribe any pain killers for Russel. He also said that it would be incorrect to say that Russel continued to get treatment from him from time to time.

Mr. Marapana asked, "On the occasion you treated Russel for the sores, did the first accused inform you that Russel ate a tremendous amount of food, or that at time he could not eat at all?"

"No."

"What ailment did Rev. Peiris have?"

"He was a mild diabetic, and had high blood pressure."

Dr. Weerasena said that there never was any talk about Russel having diabetes. He said that Rev. Peiris had called over at the clinic at least twice a month. He had prescribed Euglucon and asked Rev. Peiris to take half to one tablet a day, which is a very mild dose.

Mr. Wickramasekara asked, "Was this readily available in Sri Lanka?"

"Yes, but in 1977 there was a shortage towards the beginning of the year. This was however only for a short time."

"Did the first accused discuss the effects of the drug with you?"

"I cannot remember that."

Mr. Marapana asked, "When did you prescribe these Euglucon tablets?"

"I would have prescribed it at the very outset of his visits to me."

Mr. Bandaranayake asked, "At the time he was referred to you, was he taking any other treatment?"

"I cannot remember."

Mr. Marapana asked, "Do you remember the first accused coming to you with regard to a wound in his palm?"

"Yes, he came with his wife and he told me that while he was praying he began bleeding from his palm. There was a cloth wrapped around his hand. I asked my nurse to give him a tetanus toxoid. Rev. Peiris got annoyed about this and said it was not necessary."

"Did you look at the hand?"

"Yes. There was a puncture wound on the palm and an abrasion on the other side of the hand."

"Did you examine the palm and see if the wounds were connected?"

"I did not probe into the wound."

Mr. Wickramasekara asked, "If it was an abrasion could it have gone through?"

"No," answered Dr. Weerasena.

He said that the wound was about 1 to 1.5 centimeters in diameter. The nurse dressed the wound. After about a week Rev. Peiris had come again to the clinic and asked him whether he could write down what he had seen (regarding the wound in his palm). He had then begun writing on a narrow letter head, and at this point Rev. Peiris had asked him if he did not have bigger letter heads. When he had said 'No', Rev. Peiris had said that if Dr. Weerasena gave him his block, which he used for printing, he would get some bigger letter heads printed for him as he had a friend who owned a printing press.

"At this time I gave him the block and asked him to look after it carefully. As promised he eventually brought about fifty sheets of the big letter heads, but not the block. When I asked him why he had not brought the block he said he had misplaced it. I kept asking him but up to date I have not yet received it," said Dr. Weerasena.

After he had written down what he had seen regarding the wound on Rev. Peiris's palm, he saw in the newspapers about a week later a story that Father Mathew Peiris was having stigmata, and that a general practitioner had confirmed it. Dr. Weerasena said he had been disturbed about this as he had not said anything about stigmata. When Rev. Peiris had collected the letter he had said he only wanted it for his reference.

Dr. Weerasena said that he had seen Dalrene only on one occasion but could not remember when. This was however after he had seen Russel. He said he remembered having seen Mrs. Peiris shortly after she had come down from the UK in December 1978. She had been brought to the clinic by Rev. Peiris with a history of being unable to sleep and puffiness of the stomach, and Rev. Peiris had told him that Mrs. Peiris had some time ago been operated on for a cancer of the breast. He had wanted to know whether there were any signs of secondaries due to the cancer. When he had examined Mrs. Peiris he had noticed that her eyes were also puffy and had then asked Mrs. Peiris for a urine sample to get a test. He said he wanted this test done to exclude any kidney problems. The test had been done in his presence. The results of the test showed that Mrs. Peiris did not have sugar in her urine. He said that he had not treated Mrs. Peiris for diabetes and had not prescribed any medication for diabetes prior to this occasion. He said that he could never remember Mrs. Peiris ever having a serious ailment.

"I have clinically examined Mrs. Peiris and found that clinically there was no evidence of any secondaries. When asked why she could not sleep, Rev. Peiris said that she was always worrying about her children. After the examination I thought she was anxious as well as depressed. I also prescribed Artane to be taken along with the Stelazine," Dr. Weerasena said. He said Stelazine is a drug prescribed for depression associated with anxiety.(*Stelazine is the trade name of trifluoperazine, an antipsychotic drug, used short term to alleviate severe anxiety and calm disturbed patients and Artane is the trade name of trihexyphenidyl or benzhexol, used to treat symptoms of involuntary movements due to the side effects of antipsychotic drugs.*)

"Muscular spasm is a side effect of Stelazine. So in my practice I prescribe Artane to get over this side effect. Stelazine is the medication and Artane is to get over the side effects. I prescribed these drugs for Mrs. Peiris for a period of two weeks. These drugs by themselves do not have any action on blood sugar. Both drugs I had prescribed could make a patient feel drowsy," Dr. Weerasena said.

Mr. Bandaranayake asked, "At that time was it brought to your notice that Mrs. Peiris was on any anti-diabetic drug?"

"No."

About three to four days later Rev. Peiris came and said he was feeling giddy and that his blood pressure had risen. He had prescribed a drug called Declinax *(Declinax is the trade name of debrisoquine. It is a drug used for treatment of high blood pressure).*

On this occasion Rev. Peiris had told Dr. Weerasena that Mrs. Peiris still complained about puffiness of the stomach, and since he had already examined her he prescribed two drugs for her to take, namely Maxalon and Festal *(Maxalon is a trade name for metoclopramide, which is used to relieve feelings of sickness (nausea) or being sick (vomiting), and Festal is a brand name for a drug containing pancreatin, hemicellulase, and certain bile components. Festal is indicated for use in patients with gastrointestinal problems to help actively digest food - especially fatty meals that require pancreatic enzymes).*

He said that on the first occasion he had ignored Mrs. Peiris's complaint of puffiness in the stomach as he could not see any puffiness. He said that he had never been informed that Mrs. Peiris ever felt drowsy. The next time he had examined Mrs. Peiris was on 15th January 1979.

Mr. Marapana asked, "Did Rev. or Mrs. Peiris say that Mrs. Peiris was having pains in the body, thirst, or dryness of the throat?"

"No."

"Did the first accused ever say that Mrs. Peiris was feeling drowsy?"

"No. If I was told so I would have further reduced the dosage of the drugs."

"Did Rev. Peiris contact you on 15th January 1979?"

. "Yes, in the evening when I was in the clinic he phoned me and said that his wife was unconscious and asked me to come immediately. Leaving my patients at the clinic I went to the Vicarage. At this time Rev. Peiris was present at the Vicarage and it was he who took me to where Mrs. Peiris was lying. When I went I found Mrs. Peiris lying unconscious on a bed and she did not obey commands and responded only sluggishly to painful stimuli. I also found that she was breathing very rapidly. I also tried to record her pressure but I could not even feel her pulse. I then rang the Durdans Hospital from the Vicarage and secured a room for her, instructing the nurse on duty what medication to give her as soon as she was admitted. I ordered 10% dextrose drip and dexamethasone to be given intravenously, to elevate blood sugar and blood pressure. I then rang the Red Cross and asked them to send an ambulance immediately. I did not take her in my car as an unconscious person has to be kept flat."

"When you went to the Vicarage, who was present there?"

"I saw Rev. Peiris, and I also saw Dalrene Ingram and she gave me the directory to get the Red Cross number."

Mr. Marapana showed Dr. Weerasena a prescription, which had been written by him on 10th December. The prescription was for Mrs. Peiris for two drugs, Maxalon and Festal. Dr. Weerasena said that thereafter he had no occasion to prescribe these drugs again for Mrs. Peiris. By perusing the document Dr. Weerasena was able to say that the second visit of Mrs. Peiris was on 10th December.

"You said that Rev. Peiris did not contact you on the morning of 30th January 1979?"

"That is correct."

"You never prescribed a drug called Stugeron over the telephone?"

"No."

Shown a document Dr. Weerasena read "Stugeron 15 tablets as per Dr. Weerasena A/C, father M. Peiris." (*Stugeron, is the trade name for Cinnarizine, a drug commonly prescribed for nausea and vomiting due to motion sickness, vertigo, Ménière's disease etc).* Dr. Weerasena said he did not prepare this document nor had he seen it before.

"Have you ever prescribed this drug, Stugeron to Rev. Peiris?"

"I may have but I cannot remember."

"Had you any occasion to prescribe drugs over the phone?"

"No."

Dr. Weerasena said that he did not prepare this document nor had he seen it before.

"Did the first accused call over at the clinic with the reports of the tests you ordered to be done at Glass House?"

"No."

Dr. Weerasena said that Rev. Peiris met him on 26th January and told him that Dr. E.V. Peiris wanted an extended GTT, ESR and a full blood count on Mrs. Peiris. He gave him a letter to Glass House for the tests. On the 30th he asked Rev. Peiris whether they had seen Dr. Peiris. He asked because Rev. Peiris had told him that Dr. Peiris had wanted them to do the tests. Rev. Peiris told him that they had not seen Dr. Peiris with the reports.

Dr. Weerasena said that on 31st January he gave a letter addressed to the OPD to admit Mrs. Peiris. On the previous day he went to the Vicarage and examined Mrs. Peiris.

At this stage Dr. Weerasena was shown a letter, which he identified as the one he had written. It was addressed to the Medical Officer, OPD requesting him to admit the patient for examination. Dr. Weerasena said he wrote out the letter hurriedly when Rev. Peiris asked him for this letter.

In answer to Mr. Bandaranayake, he said it was Rev. Peiris who had told him about Mrs. Peiris feeling giddy after taking glucose at the

GTT. He admitted that in his letter he had incorrectly stated that Mrs. Peiris had told him she felt giddy. He said that Mrs. Peiris did not tell him that she felt giddy after the GTT when he examined her on 30th January. As he wrote out the letter hurriedly he did not say that the patient was taking the drug 'Mogadon'. However, he mentioned she was on 'Tofranil' (*Mogadon is the trade name of nitrazepam, a hypnotic drug of the benzodiazepine group, such as diazepam, indicated for the short-term relief of severe, disabling anxiety and sleeplessness. Tofranil is the trade name of imipramine, a tricyclic antidepressant, used to treat symptoms of depression*).

When Rev. Peiris phoned him on 30th evening he read out the GTT report and later mentioned it again when he went to the Vicarage. He said he did not look at the report. When the GTT report was mentioned he noticed that the last reading was abnormal and he told this to Rev. Peiris and added that it might be necessary to carry out further investigations later.

Mr. Bandaranayake asked, "If you thought there was something abnormal in the reading why did you not look at the report?"

"Yes, I agree that I should have done that but at that moment I had no reason to disbelieve him."

"These reports are meant for the doctor not for a layman?"

"Yes."

"And you were basing a diagnosis on it?"

"Yes."

"Are you certain that you gave this letter on the 31st?"

"Yes it was around 8 a.m."

Dr. Weerasena said since Rev. Peiris said the letter was needed in a hurry he rushed to his clinic and wrote the letter, which was picked up by somebody.

When he examined Mrs. Peiris for the first time in December 1978 he did not observe puffiness in her stomach and three days later when she complained about puffiness he prescribed some drugs. He said for a patient with puffiness of the stomach he would not request an abdominal x-ray and a serum amylase test straightaway. He would prescribe some medicines initially and if the condition persisted he would refer the patient to someone more competent than himself. He recalled prescribing vitamin B injections for Mrs. Peiris when she was at the Durdans hospital. The fact that he prescribed these injections would reflect in the BHT of the Durdans hospital. The first time he saw Mrs. Peiris after she was discharged from Durdans on 2nd January was on 30th January 1979.

"When he phoned you on the 27th morning he read out the GTT report to you?"

"Yes."

"Did you tell Rev. Peiris not to mention the word 'depression' to his wife? That is between the 15th and 17th?"

"I did not."

"Did you further tell him that if the word is mentioned it would aggravate her blood disease?"

"I did not."

"Did you discuss with the first accused any sugar imbalance that was supposed to be affecting Mrs. Peiris?"

"No."

"Or did you order a special x-ray of the stomach of Mrs. Peiris?"

"No."

"You said the first accused phoned you at your clinic at 5 p.m. on the 30th?"

"May be later than that."

Dr. Weerasena said that on the evening of the 30th the first accused had read out the GTT report to him over the phone and also said that Mrs. Peiris was drowsy. He had requested Dr. Weerasena to visit her at the end of his day.

Dr. Weerasena said, "When I arrived at the Vicarage at around 9.00 p.m. on the 30th, Mrs. Peiris was seated in bed and may have been in the process of having her dinner. When I asked her how she was feeling she said that she was extremely drowsy. Then I took her blood pressure and examined her lungs and heart. Since her only complaint was drowsiness I requested Rev. Peiris who was there in the room to stop the drugs Tofranil and Mogadon prescribed by Dr. Sathananthan, as Mogadon is normally prescribed for lack of sleep. Since the patient was drowsy, I wanted both drugs stopped and I requested Rev. Peiris to inform Dr. Sathananthan that since she was drowsy, I had ordered her to stop taking them."

Mr. Bandaranayake asked, "Could the drowsiness have been due to other causes as well?"

"Yes."

"Were you informed on that occasion or did you notice a slur in the speech of Mrs. Peiris?" asked Mr. Marapana.

"No."

"Did the first accused on the evening of the 30th inform you that Mrs. Peiris had been feeling faintish in the morning?"

"I cannot remember."

Dr. Weerasena said that she did not complain she was feeling faintish and she was not found in a bath of perspiration.

"On that occasion would you have expected her to be unconscious just three minutes afterwards?"

"No."

"Did he on this occasion inform you that she used to feel giddy?"

"Rev. Peiris mentioned that when glucose was given."

"Did the first accused or Mrs. Peiris tell you on the 30th evening that she was having aches and pains in her body, a marked thirst or loss of appetite?"

"No."

"There was no question of you having said that you would have a letter ready to admit Mrs. Peiris to hospital?"

"Yes."

"When did you hear from them thereafter?"

"On the 31st morning around 7.30, the first accused rang me at my home and informed me that Mrs. Peiris was ill and he tried to get a room at Durdans but since there was no room available, what I would advise. I then suggested that she be admitted to the General Hospital and also requested Rev. Peiris to inform Dr. E.V. Peiris whom he had consulted regarding her recent illness, that I had requested admission to General Hospital."

"The first accused asked me for a letter of reference to the General Hospital. I said it should be ready in half an hour. I hurried to the clinic and wrote the letter stating the drugs already being taken by Mrs. Peiris and also about the GTT and about her feeling giddy two to three hours after taking glucose, as mentioned by Rev. Peiris. During the course of the telephone conversation of the 31st morning it was not mentioned to me that Mrs. Peiris was in an unconscious state. He never mentioned that her condition was one of drowsiness to unconsciousness or that she was having a fluctuating level of unconsciousness. He did not request me to come to the Vicarage and examine her."

"Was the letter you made out ever collected from you by Rev. Peiris?"

"I later came to know that it had been collected around 10.30."

Dr. Weerasena said that on 1st February, Rev. Peiris rang him up possibly in the morning and said that Mrs. Peiris had been admitted to ward 47B of the General Hospital and asked him to speak to Dr. Nanayakkara and also said that Mrs. Peiris was very ill.

"He did not say that she was unconscious?"

"No."

"It was only after you visited the General Hospital that you came to know that she was unconscious?"

"Yes."

"On this occasion you met the House Officer?"

"Yes, I actually first met the lady doctor and I asked for Mrs. Peiris. The lady doctor said that she was lying on a bed next to the House Officer's desk. I then found Mrs. Peiris with a drip in progress. Then I asked the Senior House Officer Dr. Sarath Wickramasinghe how Mrs. Peiris was and also asked for Dr. K.J. Nanayakkara. The lady doctor said that he was in the male ward. It was here that I met the Senior House Officer who informed me that Dr. Nanayakkara had just left and I then asked the senior house officer the condition of Mrs. Peiris. He said that she had been admitted on 31st January 1979, around 12.30 in the afternoon in an unconscious condition. He also said that Rev. Peiris had objected to the house officer giving Mrs. Peiris dextrose. I said I had seen the patient on the 30th evening and that she had been only drowsy and that I had requested a stopping her drugs, which Dr. Sathananthan had prescribed. I also told him I treated Mrs. Peiris on 16th January 1979 and she had made an almost immediate recovery after administration of 10% dextrose and inquired from him what the patient's blood sugar was on admission to hospital. He told me that it had been very low. Subsequently I met Dr. Nanayakkara at his residence."

"On the 6th or 7th February, Rev. Peiris gave me a call and said that there was still no diagnosis about Mrs. Peiris's illness. He said

'What is the meaning of this? They (the doctors) have informed the police.' I then told Rev. Peiris that it is common practice that when a person is admitted unconscious to a hospital with no proper history, poisoning could not be ruled out and the police post is informed in such a situation."

Mr. Bandaranayake asked, "Until the first accused told you, did you know that the police were informed?"

"No, I did not know."

Dr. Weerasena said that every few days Rev. Peiris used to ring him and complain about there not being a diagnosis as yet. He had again gone to see Mrs. Peiris at hospital and she was still unconscious. After seeing the patient and about to return to his clinic, he met Rev. Peiris just coming into the ward. Rev. Peiris asked about the condition of Mrs. Peiris and he said she was very ill. At this stage Rev. Peiris asked Dr. Weerasena that if Mrs. Peiris was still unconscious could this have been due to the drugs prescribed by Dr. Sathananthan, namely Mogadon and Tofranil. Dr. Weerasena said he was disturbed about this as Rev. Peiris seemed to be accusing Dr. Sathananthan of having given Mrs. Peiris drugs that were too strong.

Dr. Weerasena said that he had told Rev. Peiris that if an overdose of the two drugs were taken the patient would be unconscious, but the blood sugar would not be low. Dr. Weerasena had also asked the first accused whether Mrs. Peiris could have accidentally taken Euglucon. The first accused had then said that he would have to return to the Vicarage and check up.

"But I did not hear from Rev. Peiris thereafter until the day that Mrs. Peiris expired. He rang me up and said that Mrs. Peiris has expired and to look for details of funeral arrangements in the newspaper," Dr. Weerasena said.

Mr. Marapana asked, "When you asked whether his wife had accidentally taken Euglucon what was his reaction?"

"Surprise."

"He used to ring you every two to three days right up to the time his wife died?"

"Yes."

"But after this particular conversation he did not ring you till the day Mrs. Peiris died?"

"Yes, that is correct."

"On the very first visit in early December when the first accused and his wife came to the clinic was there any talk about the first accused having been directed by an angel to bring Mrs. Peiris to you for treatment?"

"No."

"When you visited the Vicarage on 15th January 1979 was Mrs. Peiris unconscious?"

"Yes."

Dr. Weerasena then mentioned the other diseases which could bring about a state of hypoglycaemia and said that there was no trace of these other diseases in Mrs. Peiris.

Mr. R.I. Obeysekera then cross examined Dr. Weerasena.

"You said your busy hours were from 9.30 a.m. to 12.30 p.m. and from 5.30 p.m. to 8.30 p.m.?"

"Yes."

"Do you have a system of cards where you keep a history of the patients?"

"Yes. Originally I had a card for every patient but I discontinued this practice as I did not have anyone to look after this system for me. I later asked the patients themselves to keep their own records on the notes that I made."

"Mrs. Peiris or Russel Ingram however, did not have a card or a file of their own?"

"No."

"You do not have a note which aids you before this Court?"

"No."

"If you had a note, your evidence would have been of greater accuracy?"

"Yes. I have a very good memory and even remembered my patient's names after meeting them on one occasion."

"You said in your examination in chief that you had not made certain statements to the first accused regarding drugs, you also said that you did not prescribe certain drugs?"

"That is correct."

"You were asked whether you were shown the GTT report and you said 'No'?"

"Yes."

"Do you remember being asked by the police whether you ordered a serum amylase test?"

"I cannot remember, and as far as I remember there was no need for it."

Shown a document by Mr. Obeysekera, which stated "Please conduct a GTT on this patient", Dr. Weerasena said it was not his handwriting or his signature and that it was a forgery. Dr. Weerasena said that he would never write an order for a test without mentioning the name of the patient.

At this stage, Mr. Bandaranayake pointed out that there were two spelling mistakes in the document.

Mr. Obeysekera asked, "It is similar to your handwriting?"

"It is similar, but not mine. It is dated 29th, but I did not write this letter on that date, as I did not see the patient. On this letter there was no patient's name mentioned, and this is something I would not have omitted."

At this stage, the Court asked Dr. Weerasena to write and sign five times a passage from a book, which the Court provided, and also write and sign the contents of the questioned document. These specimens along with the original letter were to be examined by the Examiner of Questioned Documents as directed by Mr. Bandaranayake. He directed that the report be furnished by 11th April.

(Dr. Lakshman Weerasena informed me that the letter sent to Mr. A.D.H. Samaranayake, the Examiner of Questioned Documents, was reported as a forgery.)

Cross examined further by Mr. Obeysekera, Dr. Weerasena said that the psychiatrist Dr. Sathananthan had told him that he had no privacy to talk with Mrs. Peiris as Rev. Peiris was present on all these occasions.

Mr. Obeysekera asked, "You said that Rev. Peiris was a diabetic and that he used to take half to one tablet of Euglucon daily?"

"Yes."

"In your statement made to police, you have said, 'As far as I can remember Rev. Peiris was taking one Euglucon tablet daily.' Did you say this?"

"Yes."

He said that he prescribed Euglucon to the first accused at the first visit to his clinic with Victor Gamalathge in 1976. He denied that when he visited Mrs. Peiris at the General Hospital, he had told Dr. (Miss) Pinto that he had received an anonymous telephone call asking him 'not to shield the priest'.

Mr. Obeysekera showed a letter addressed to him and signed by Dr. E.V. Peiris. Dr. Weerasena denied that it was given to him. He said the letter shown to him by Mr. Obeysekera was not taken from him by the police. If the letter was handed over to him it should have been with him. The first time he saw that letter was in Courts.

In his letter to Glass House, Dr. Weerasena said he requested a GTT up to four hours. He wrote out exactly what Rev. Peiris said Dr. E.V. Peiris wanted done. Dr. Weerasena denied that he signed a letter addressed to Glass House on 29th January, requesting an x-ray and a serum amylase test. The letter shown to him was a good forgery. He recalled giving the block from which his letter heads were printed to Rev. Peiris. He gave him the block and told Rev. Peiris to be very careful with it. Along with the block Rev. Peiris took a letter head from his table. Thereafter Rev. Peiris never returned the block to him, even though he asked for it. The letter heads were printed and given.

"On my arrival at the Vicarage on 15th January, I found Mrs. Peiris unconscious. I made arrangements for her to be admitted to Durdans private hospital. I did not accompany the patient as I have left two patients seriously ill in his clinic and had to attend to them. If I did not have those patients and had had the time to accompany Mrs. Peiris I would have done so. I gave instructions to the nurses on the telephone from the Vicarage in regard to Mrs. Peiris and then gave further instructions after visiting Mrs. Peiris that evening. He asked them to stop giving Artane and Stelazine, not because she was drowsy, but because she was unconscious. When I visited the nursing home later that evening Mrs. Peiris was conscious. I asked her what had happened. She could not remember what had happened to her shortly before she fell unconscious. She recovered after dextrose was administered. This was another reason for his opinion that Mrs. Peiris had become unconscious due to induced hypoglycaemia," Dr. Weerasena said.

Mr. Obeysekera asked, "Did you tell the police of your instructions that these drugs should be stopped because Mrs. Peiris was drowsy?"

"Yes, if it is so recorded. My memory would have been fresh at that stage. Therefore I accept it."

"Did you on the 15th get a history of Mrs. Peiris becoming drowsy?" asked Mr. Bandaranayake.

"Yes."

"From whom?"

"Rev. Peiris. He said she became drowsy by day and fell unconscious in the night."

In answer to Mr. Bandaranayake, he said when Mrs. Peiris was discharged from Durdans on 21st January, he gave Rev. Peiris a letter addressed to Dr. E.V. Peiris setting out the patient's condition and the treatment given during her stay at Durdans.

Dr. Weerasena, in reply to Mr. Bandaranayake said a serum amylase test or a stomach x-ray on Mrs. Peiris would have made no difference on the patient or on the diagnosis as she was not suffering from pancreatitis.

He said he did not discuss the diagnosis with Dr. Pinto when he visited General Hospital. He however spoke to the Senior House Officer and questioned the delay in admitting Mrs. Peiris when he had sent the letter as early as 8 a.m. He denied prescribing the drug "Stugeron" for Mrs. Eunice Peiris. He said he did not receive a telephone call from Rev. Peiris on the 30th morning. It was only that evening that Rev. Peiris had phoned him and told him to see Mrs. Peiris at the Vicarage. He said he had never mentioned to Rev. Peiris or to the late Mrs. Peiris about not taking any sugar at any time.

In answer to the Bandaranayake, Dr. Weerasena said it was not possible for a person to feel giddy after taking glucose. In fact glucose was given to offset giddiness.

Mr. Bandaranayake asked, "Is it unusual for people to feel giddy during an extended GTT?"

"No."

"If it is not unusual why did you mention that the patient feels giddy after glucose in your letter to the OPD?"

"Because I felt it would require further investigations."

He did not go through the BHT because it was unethical for private doctors to go through BHTs at the General Hospital. Dr. Pinto did not tell him that doctors suspected poisoning. Dr. Weerasena denied that when he visited Mrs. Peiris at the General Hospital, he had told Dr. (Miss) Pinto that he had received an anonymous telephone call asking him 'not to shield the priest'.

Mr. Obeysekera asked, "You cannot say why Dr. Pinto has made this claim?"

"I cannot speak for her evidence," Dr. Weerasena replied.

Later, he had met Dr. Nanayakkara at his (Dr. Nanayakkara's) residence in the evening and had discussed the condition of Mrs. Peiris. He said that in view of what Rev. Peiris had told him about the results of the extended GTT, he suggested that a further investigation was necessary but never suggested hospitalization.

He said that the block, which he had given Rev. Peiris only contained his name, and that in order to get the rest of the script, which the letter head contained, he had given Rev. Peiris a letter head as a sample.

He said that Mrs. Peiris had complained that she could not sleep and had a puffiness of the stomach. Rev. Peiris had visited him about two days later and he had prescribed two drugs for Mrs. Peiris, who had not come to the clinic on that occasion. He said that he had not however observed the puffiness of the stomach which Mrs. Peiris complained about.

Mr. Obeysekera asked, "On 30th March 1979 at 11.45 a.m., when the police questioned you at your clinic you stated 'I examined Mrs. Peiris thoroughly. I observed a puffed stomach, this was my only observation.' You have told the police you 'observed a puffed stomach'. Do you deny saying this?"

"I may have said it."

"Refreshing your memory now, the position is that you did observe a puffed stomach?" asked Mr. Bandaranayake.

"Yes."

Answering a question of Mr. Obeysekera, Dr. Weerasena said he prescribed Stelazine and Artane to Mrs. Peiris.

"You prescribed Stelazine as an anti-depressant?"

"Yes."

"Is there any difference between an anti-depressant and a mood elevator?"

"I would not say that."

"You would not describe Stelazine as a mood elevator?"

"No."

"The drug Stelazine which you prescribed is not an anti-depressant as you say, but is a major tranquilizer?"

"In my practice I have used it as a mild anti-depressant drug."

"You say that small doses act as an anti-depressant?"

"Yes."

"In your statement to the police did you describe Stelazine as a 'mood elevator', did you say this?"

"I did not. I did not use those words. I cannot remember having said this."

"If it is so recorded could you have said it?"

"I may have."

"A tranquilizer and an anti-depressant have different or opposite effects on patients?"

"Anti-depressant connected with anxiety could be treated with a tranquilizer."

"What was the anxiety?"

"She was worried about her children."

Mr. Bandaranayake asked, "Had she just returned from England?"

"Yes."

"Did she tell you about her anxiety?"

"Rev. Peiris said it. I asked her, but before she could reply he said, 'She is always worrying about her children'."

"Are you relying on your memory about this?" asked Mr. Obeysekera.

"Yes."

"On 15th January when you went to Durdans you said you looked at the medical history of Mrs. Peiris?"

"Yes, to see if the emergency drugs I had prescribed over the phone had been administered, and also to see what observations the House Officer had made."

"You gave instructions to omit Artane and Stelazine?"

"Yes, for the reason that at certain instances these drugs could have been continued in the hospital. So, I mentioned this as these drugs could have been given to her at the hospital."

"Artane and Stelazine were drugs prescribed by you?"

"Yes."

"Is it your position that the drugs should not have been continued after about 20th December?"

"Yes."

"If it had been given after that time, on your evidence, it would have been without your authority?"

"Yes."

"When you went to Durdans and read the history you realized that she is on Artane and Stelazine and you gave instructions 'omit Stelazine and Artane'. Why did you not at that stage add that if given after this date it would have been done without your authority?"

"You do not write these things on a BHT."

"You extended these drugs between the 15th to 20th?"

"As far as I can remember, no."

"I am suggesting to you that you have extended the usage of these drugs right up to the time of Mrs. Peiris being admitted to hospital on the 15th?"

"I may have."

"Did you read Dr. Attygalle's observations on the BHT?"

"Yes."

"On the 16th you wrote a minute to Dr. Attygalle, which was written on the BHT?"

Dr. Weerasena was then asked to read this minute, which said, "This patient had been depressed for some time, and she was on Stelazine 2 mg three times a day and Artane 1 mg twice a day. She had been very drowsy this morning and when I saw her had rapid breathing and low blood pressure. Please advise."

"Dr. Sathananthan was the psychiatrist you referred your patients to?"

"Yes. Also to Dr. Nalaka Mendis."

"You referred Mrs. Peiris to Dr. Sathananthan."

"Yes."

"Artane is prescribed to offset the side effects of Stelazine?"

"Yes."

"Would it not be correct to say that Artane is prescribed only when it is thought Stelazine might have side effects?"

"In my practice it is prescribed."

"You will not agree that Artane is given only where the dosage of Stelazine is not mild?"

"I do not agree. There are some patients who even with a mild dose get these side effects."

"Artane itself has side effects. It can make you drowsy?"

"Yes."

"You said that Mrs. Peiris had puffiness under her eyes when you first examined her?"

"Yes."

"You tested her urine?"

"Yes."

"She may have told you she had puffiness under the eyes?'

"She may have."

"One of the side effects of Artane is thirst?"

"Yes."

"Did she complain to you of thirst?"

"As far as I can remember, no."

"On any of the four occasions you saw her did she complain of thirst?" asked Mr. Bandaranayake.

"As far as I remember, no."

"You were asked by Hema Weerasinghe of the police on 3rd March 1979, 'Did Mrs. Peiris at any time complain to you of an abnormal thirst and display a chilly tongue?' Your answer was 'She never complained or showed me a red tongue but she did complain of thirst.' Do you admit having said that?" asked Mr. Obeysekera.

"Yes."

"And you admit you were speaking the truth?"

"Yes."

"Here again, but for the statement being shown to you, you would not have remembered on your own independent memory?"

"Correct."

"Dr. Sathananthan had spoken to Mrs. Peiris and obtained a history from Mrs. Peiris?"

"I cannot say that."

"Now as far as you know there was no impediment to Dr. Sathananthan talking to Mrs. Peiris alone?"

"I cannot remember as I was not present. He told me he got a scrappy history."

"Did he say he was unable to talk to Mrs. Peiris alone?"

"He did mention that Rev. Peiris was there and he did not have the privacy to talk with Mrs. Peiris due to this."

"Did you have occasion to talk with Dr. Sathananthan about the symptoms of Mrs. Peiris's illness?"

"Yes."

"What you have told the police is that Dr. Sathananthan had no opportunity at all to talk with Mrs. Peiris as Rev. Peiris was on every occasion by her side?"

"I remember making the statement but I cannot remember saying the words 'every occasion'."

Mr. Wickramasekera asked, "If the police have recorded it, would you say it is so?"

"Yes."

"On the evening of the 15th you requested the nurse at Durdans that 10% dextrose and dextamethasone be given to Mrs. Peiris on admission?" asked Mr. Obeysekera.

"Yes."

Answering a question of Mr. Obeysekera, Dr. Weerasena said that there were three kinds of hypoglycaemia, namely, reactive, spontaneous and induced.

"You said you examined Russel Ingram in 1977?"

"Yes."

"You said you observed his general condition."

"Yes, his uncleanliness and I was also told by Rev. Peiris that he was an alcoholic."

"From your observations of Russel, his unkempt condition, did he look an alcoholic?"

"I did not say he looked an alcoholic."

"Did he appear to be uncaring about his appearance?"

"I cannot remember."

"Ordinarily when you get an unkempt patient and there is an allegation that he is an alcoholic, the two would click in your mind?"

"Yes."

"Were you impressed about what Rev. Peiris told you about the stigmata?"

"When I saw him first in 1977 regarding this, I did not. That is why I asked the nurse to give him a tetanus toxide. As I saw Rev. Peiris, he said he had been praying and suddenly he found blood on his hand."

"At that time you thought this was a tall story?"

"Yes, at that time."

"Did you ask him if he struck his hand anywhere?"

"Yes, but he said 'No' and when I asked the nurse to give him a tetanus injection, he protested and said that it was of great religious significance and asked for a sterile dressing."

"What happened after this?"

"He came a few days later and asked if I could write what I saw."

"Did he show you the hand on the second occasion, and were you impressed?"

"There was a little bleeding and he was given another sterile dressing."

"You knew he was doing exorcism?"

"Yes."

"Did you go for the Thursday meeting?"

"Yes, with one or two of my family members."

Dr. Weerasena said that his brother had bad dreams and someone had told him that Rev. Peiris could cure it. So he had taken his brother to the church.

He said, "I drafted a letter regarding the wound on the palm of Rev. Peiris. But Rev. Peiris said he wanted a typed copy, and on a subsequent date, he brought a typed letter to my clinic while I was working and as I had no cause to think he would distort the letter, I signed it without reading it. I trusted him."

He said he came to know about the letter only after a newspaper had carried a story about Rev. Peiris's stigmata. This news item stated that he had certified Rev. Peiris's stigmata.

At the end of the day's proceedings, Rev. Peiris addressing the Court from the dock said that since he had been remanded the Anglican Prison Chaplain had not been visiting him. The trial was adjourned with the Court directing a letter to the Anglican Prison Chaplain to visit the two accused, who are now in remand and they wished to have the Blessed Sacrament administered to them for Easter.

On 8th June, Mr. Tissa Bandaranayake said that his brother judge, Mr. D.C.W. Wickramasekara had received a 'love letter' from an anonymous fan. He said it contained mostly filth and the abuse was directed mainly at him (Mr. Bandaranayake) for questioning the nurses.

"The Court could not be intimidated. The letter showed a degree of vulgarity which unfortunately prevailed among misguided people. The Court would challenge the writer to come forward and be identified so that it could explain the reason for questioning witnesses. This was, not with the idea of taking sides, but in order to assist justice. The Court was therefore compelled to challenge this secret adversary to come forward," he said.

Mr. Cecil Goonewardena said, "It reminds me of what a distinguished Supreme Court Judge in the old days said in his farewell speech that in retirement he would miss the anonymous letters he used to get, while in service!"

Dr. (Miss) Rosemary Kanthi Pinto, who was an intern in ward 47B, General Hospital, Colombo, was examined by Mr. C.R. de Silva, Senior State Counsel.

She said that Dr. Nanayakkara, Consultant Physician, was in charge of the ward and Dr. Wickramasinghe was the Senior House Officer of the ward.

Dr. Terrence de Silva used to come to this ward when she was off duty. She recalled that Mrs. Eunice Peiris was admitted around 12.30 p.m. on 31st January 1979. The Medical Officer at the out patients department had seen the patient at 12.15 p.m. When Mrs. Peiris was admitted, she was off duty.

Dr. Pinto said, "I came to the ward around 2.30 p.m. Mrs. Peiris was on a drip then and was unconscious. I examined the patient after reading the BHT where Dr. Terrence de Silva had made notes. At the time I examined Mrs. Peiris, Rev Peiris was there. He told me about Mrs. Peiris's condition. At that stage Dr. Wickramasinghe, Senior House Officer also came to the ward. Rev. Peiris told me that Mrs. Peiris had been unconscious since the previous night with intermittent periods of consciousness. He told me that Mrs. Peiris had returned from abroad recently and after a GTT she had felt drowsy and weak. At that time I did not take a detailed history and when Dr. Wickramasinghe came, I left and attended to other patients. When Dr. Nanayakkara came to the ward I went with him to see Mrs. Peiris. Rev. Peiris then gave a detailed history to Dr. Nanayakkara," said Dr. Pinto.

Continuing she said, "When Dr. de Silva came to the ward around 3 p.m. he told me about the patient's condition and the treatment given. Dr. de Silva told me that Rev. Peiris had asked him not to give dextrose, but he had given a saline drip and added dextrose to it because he did not want to displease Rev. Peiris. Dr. de Silva also told me that an Anglican priest had admitted a person to hospital earlier and that person had died of hypoglycaemia. He said they identified the priest who brought the earlier patient as the same priest who brought Mrs. Peiris that evening. Dr. de Silva and I informed Dr. Nanayakkara about this."

"We could not exclude poisoning by an overdose of a drug and therefore, decided that the patient should be kept under close observation. We also decided not to give the patient any prepared food brought from outside. We moved the patient to the bed near the nurses' table and put up a 'No visitors' board. This step was taken in consultation with other doctors."

"That evening Rev. Peiris asked me whether they required anything for the patient. I asked him to bring a catheter. I asked him why the patient was not brought in the previous night as she has been unconscious for nearly 18 hours. Rev. Peiris told me that he had tried to get an ambulance and failed, so he could not bring her because he was alone and could not leave her alone at home and go to get a taxi. I did not question him further as I felt he was annoyed by my questions."

"I asked Rev. Peiris whether the patient had been on any anti-diabetic drugs. He replied that the patient was not a diabetic and had not taken any anti-diabetic or any other drugs. In answer to further questions he had told me that there were no diabetics at home and there were no anti-diabetic drugs at home. He also told me that his wife Mrs. Peiris was a good Christian and would not commit suicide," Dr. Pinto said.

"I gave instructions to the nurses not to give the patient prepared food brought from outside. Dr. de Silva told me that he had sent blood samples. We received reports that evening," she said.

Shown the pathologist's report Dr. Pinto said that the report showed that there was 30 mg% of glucose in blood. She said this reading was very low.

In answer to Mr. Bandaranayake, she said, "Mrs. Peiris was shifted to a bed close to the nurses' table before oral feeding was started on 4th February. Feeding was done through a nasal tube. Mrs. Peiris was given Marmite. A bottle of Marmite was brought by visitors. Only prepared food was not accepted from visitors. The Marmite bottle was an unopened one. Even milk was accepted from visitors as long as it was unopened."

Dr. Pinto said that the dextrose drip was discontinued after 7th February and the patient was put on a liquid diet.

"Rev. Peiris used to come to see the patient and remained outside but there were times when she had seen him by the bedside praying. Only on the first few days visitors were not permitted but later visitors were allowed at her bedside. I can remember Dr. Weerasena visiting Mrs. Peiris on two occasions. Dr. Weerasena told me that he knew the patient personally and asked me about Mrs. Peiris's condition. He also told me that he had given the letter for admission. I saw an admission letter in the BHT. I told Dr. Weerasena that the patient's condition had been diagnosed as hypoglycaemia and her condition was poor," Dr. Pinto said.

In answer to a question by Mr. Bandaranayake Dr. Pinto said she had told Dr. Weerasena that they suspected poisoning and he was surprised.

"According to the BHT I have examined Mrs. Peiris at 11 p.m. on the 31st January. Mrs. Peiris was unconscious and responding to pain. I ordered a blood transfusion and Mrs. Peiris did not react adversely to it. Next morning I saw Mrs. Peiris again. She was unconscious. I observed certain movements of the eyes suggestive of brain damage. On the same day I examined Mrs. Peiris at 3.30 p.m. and 10.45 p.m. All unconscious patients were turned on their side and physiotherapy was given and secretions were sucked out from the lungs. This was done for Mrs. Peiris also. When a patient has pneumonia, secretions from the lungs were observed. At that stage the patient did not have fever suggestive of pneumonia."

"On 3rd February I observed muscle twitches on the left side. There was twitching in the left facial muscles and in the left arm. This condition could have been due to brain damage. Thereafter, Dr. Nanayakkara examined the patient. I wrote down what he said – the patient was unconscious, showed response to painful stimuli and had twitching movement of left arm and face."

Dr. Pinto said that Mrs. Peiris was given dexamethasone and hydrocortisone on admission to hospital on 31st January. She was continuously given these drugs till 12th February when it was stopped. Although dexamethasone and hydrocortisone were given, there was no appreciable change in the patient. After admission Mrs. Peiris's blood pressure had dropped but thereafter it picked up.

Dr. Pinto said that Mrs. Peiris's jugular vein pressure was normal. She explained that the observation of the jugular vein pressure being normal showed that there was no heart failure. She said the patient's blood was tested daily for glucose, urea, electrolytes and others.

At this stage Mr. Bandaranayake said that the Court would not be taking into account any findings of the tests unless the original reports on those findings were produced in evidence.

"On 7th February after examining Mrs. Peiris I ordered a GTT to be done the following day. Mrs. Peiris was kept fasting for 10 hours and in the morning I drew the first fasting blood samples. Around 5 a.m. on the 8th she gave the patient 50 mg of glucose, after she had drawn a fasting blood sample and taking a urine sample. The glucose was diluted in 100 millilitres of water. Thereafter, every half hour she drew blood from the patient and also collected urine. After three hours the blood was drawn hourly," Dr. Pinto said.

In answer to Mr. Bandaranayake, she said in between the drawing of blood she was not given water. If necessary, water could be given during the test. She said eight samples of urine and blood were taken in all. She made out a request form and handed the samples personally to the laboratory for testing.

She had treated this as a special case and the laboratory also did a favour by doing the test on the same day. The reason for treating that test as a special one was because she wanted to exclude insulinoma as early as possible. She recalled Dr. Nanayakkara, the Consultant Physician obtaining the report from the laboratory, if she remembered right, the next day, she said.

Mr. de Silva asked, "Did you find anything abnormal in the report?"

"The pathologist commented there appeared to be a delayed absorption and lowered renal threshold. The fasting blood sugar level appeared to be within normal values. The GTT report did not show an insulinoma situated anywhere in the system. On 8th February, I examined the patient and made my observations on the BHT. She was unconscious and there was no significant difference in her condition. I continued to examine the patient practically daily until the patient died on 19th March," Dr. Pinto said.

She said nasal feeding was first started on Mrs. Peiris on 4th February. Marmite was the first feed given through the nasal tube. This was at 9 p.m. By that time Mrs. Peiris had been moved to a bed close to her table. On 8th[h] February, for the first time dextrose was given to Mrs. Peiris through the nasal tube. Dextrose was administered through nasogastric tube for the last time on 11th February at 5 a.m. During the whole period the patient was not given any prepared food brought from outside. She said on 10th February, a bed sore was observed and the patient's face was swollen. This could have been due to the bed sore on the head.

Answering a query by Mr. Bandaranayake she said she had not recorded on the BHT that oxygen was given to the patient. There were times when oxygen was given without recording on the BHT. She said all bad patients were given oxygen. She thought Mrs. Peiris too was given oxygen on the last day but there was no record of that fact. Oxygen was given to bad patients if there was difficulty in breathing. She explained that a respiratory difficulty has not been recorded anywhere in the BHT. The patient had no difficulty in breathing during her stay in hospital.

"At no stage I found that the patient was clinically hypoglycaemic. I did not find the patient sweating at any time," Dr. Pinto said.

Answering a query by Mr. Bandaranayake she said that the visitors were allowed to bring the choice of food they wished, but if the visitor asked they would suggest Marmite, soup and milk foods.

On 17th February she observed that Mrs. Peiris was having diarrhoea. This could have been the result of an infection as there were other diarrhoea patients in the ward. She was treated for diarrhoea and on the next day she had not made any observations in the BHT with regard to the diarrhoea. On 20th February Mrs. Peiris had fever. This could either be due to pneumonia or the bedsore or both. Dr. Pinto said if a patient was lying conscious without any treatment, pneumonia could have set in as a necessary consequence. On the 25th she observed that Mrs. Peiris had bedsores on the back. She explained that right throughout Mrs. Peiris was given antibiotics but the deterioration of her condition could not be arrested.

"I did not observe the patient having meningitis or encephalitis. Except for signs of brain damage, there were no signs of infection of the brain. She died on 19th March at 9.30 a.m. When I examined her around 8.30 a.m. her pressure was low. From then onwards her condition deteriorated. There were bed sores all over her body and there was an offensive smell due to the bed sores," Dr. Pinto said.

Mr. Bandaranayake asked, "At anytime did the patient recover consciousness fully?"

"No," said Dr. Pinto.

After the patient died Dr. Pinto said, she informed the police post at the hospital and requested a judicial inquiry. She stated on the BHT that the cause of death could not be given. She also made a minute to the office for the patient's relations to be informed.

Former Senior House Officer in ward 44, Dr. (Mrs.) Anula Wijesundera giving evidence said that she had MBBS and MD, and at the time of giving evidence she had acquired the MRCP (UK) also. She confirmed that Russel whom she saw at 2.45 p.m. on the 26th of June was unconscious. She approved of the treatment that had already been administered by Dr. (Mrs.) Ruwanpathirana - normal saline and dextrose. Dr. Wijesundera said that she had seen Dalrene feeding Russel in hospital and that Dalrene visited Russel in both stages of his hospitalization. She said that uraemic coma or kidney disease was not the cause of Russel's state of unconsciousness on the 26th June 1978.

The next witness, Dr. Bandula Wijesiriwardena, the Registrar to the Professor of Medicine, was examined by Mr. Tilak Marapana. Dr.

Wijesiriwardena said that in 1978, he was an intern medical officer at ward 18 of the General Hospital. It was a surgical ward and Dr. Sheriffdeen was a Senior Lecturer attached to this ward.

On 3rd July 1978, a patient named Russel Ingram was brought to ward 18 from ward 44 for examination. He had the opportunity to see this patient with Dr. Sheriffdeen, who examined the patient for the first time on that day. He stood by the side of the bed. He said that if he remembered correct the patient was not quite conscious.

Rev. Peiris, who made a self-introduction, gave an account of the patient's illness. He said that he used to observe the patient at home and had noticed that the patient was losing consciousness and his pulse rate was rapid and had irregular respiration. He also said he used to place the crucifix on the abdomen and found it vibrating, which made him believe that there was something wrong with the abdomen.

Rev. Peiris further told them that he had got the blood sugar tested outside and the patient had swinging blood sugar levels. He did not show any reports.

Dr. Wijesiriwardena said that he had not made any notes and was speaking from memory.

He said that Dr. Sheriffdeen agreed to have the patient transferred to ward 18 from ward 44. The patient was subsequently transferred on 5th July and Dr. Wijesiriwardena said he examined the patient and made his observations on the BHT. He said that he noticed the patient was looking well, which indicated that he was conscious. He had also noted some healing bedsores. The patient's lungs were clear and the cardio-respiratory system was normal. The patient continued to be in ward 18 until he was discharged either on 13th or 14th July. The patient was taken charge by Rev. Peiris as he had signed the BHT.

Dr. Wijesiriwardena said that the patient's blood sugar level did not fall during the period he was in ward 18 and while on normal diet. The patient was examined by him on 8th, 11th, 12th and 13th July. He had not made any note that the patient had symptoms of a hypoglycaemic condition. He had noted the patient had no hypoglycaemic attacks.

Mr. de Silva asked, "At the time of his discharge if the patient's blood sugar level was 40 mg%, would he have been discharged?"

"Yes, because he could walk, we did not do a blood sugar test," he said.

In answer to Mr. Bandaranayake, he said that a chronic hypoglycaemic could have a 40 mg% blood sugar level, and still be conscious.

At the time he was discharged, Russel was able to walkabout and was quite cheerful. He had made a note on the BHT that the patient looked comfortable. He was not given any medicines at the time of his discharge nor was he given a prescription to purchase any drugs from outside. He said they did not want to give any medicines as he was required to come back for further medical tests. Dr. Wijesiriwardena further said that the patient was allowed to have a normal diet during his stay in the ward. He did not ask the patient to restrain from eating any particular type of food.

"On 12th July Russel's fasting blood sugar level was 57 mg%. The patient was conscious and was on normal diet. The highest level on that occasion was 105 mg% in one and a half hours," Dr. Wijesiriwardena said. He said that the patient never complained of any signs of hypoglycaemia. He further said that on the day Russel was discharged, a re-admission note was given. It was addressed to the Admitting Officer, OPD. That was done to facilitate the re-admission of the patient for the extended GTT.

On re-admission, the GTT was done in ward 18. On that occasion 50 grams of glucose dissolved in water was given orally. Thereafter, blood was taken, every half-an-hour, five times.

Mr. Marapana asked, "Have you seen the two accused visiting Russel?"

"Yes, on several occasions."

"At what time did they come?"

"Father Peiris used to come outside visiting hours. I have seen him in the ward even around 8.30 p.m. at night. The visiting hours were from 12.00 to 12.30 p.m. and 5.00 to 6.00 p.m."

He said that he had seen the two accused visiting Russel after these hours.

"Did you notice anything unusual between the two accused?"

"Yes, I used to see them coming to the hospital together, and the first accused had his arm around the waist of the second accused."

Mr. Bandaranayake asked, "That means that they were physically close together."

"Yes."

"On three or four occasion I saw Rev. Peiris coming to the General Hospital with his hand around Mrs. Dalrene Ingram's hip. I saw this when Rev. Peiris and Mrs. Ingram were walking through the corridor outside ward 18 where Russel was lying unconscious," Dr. Wijesiriwardena said.

"Russel was readmitted to ward 18 on 18th July. He had been produced first before Dr. Sheriffdeen who had made a minute on the admission card requesting the OPD to admit the patient to ward 18. From the admission card it would appear that Russel had been seen at about 8.30 a.m. on 18th July by Dr. Sheriffdeen. I saw Russel around 9.30 a.m. when I was doing his ward rounds. A nurse told me that a new patient had been admitted. I stopped my rounds and went and saw Russel. On examination, I found that Russel was unconscious and not responding to painful stimulus or obeying commands. He was moving his limbs but his pupils were not reacting to light. I then looked for corneal reflex and found it absent. From that I was able to ascertain Russel was deeply unconscious. The tendon reflexes were absent. The plantar reflexes were also absent and there was no response. This was found out by stroking the sole with a blunt instrument," Dr. Wijesiriwardena said.

He further said that Russel was not anaemic and that he was able to conclude that Russel did not have meningitis, a haemorrhage or a tumour in the brain. He said that he noticed that there was no sweating and the breath had a foul smell. There was no smell of acetone. The smell in the breath showed that the mouth had not been cleaned. Even if the mouth was not cleaned for one day the smell would be there. He said that sweating and rising pulse rate was normally found at the onset of hypoglycaemia and passes off.

In answer to Mr. Wickramasekara, Dr. Wijesiriwardena said when he examined the patient he realized that it was the same patient who was in the ward four days earlier. They were also interested in this patient as he came with an interesting history of an insulinoma.

He said Russel was given two pints of 5% dextrose with 100 milli litres of 50% dextrose added in to each pint. The dextrose was given through a fast drip. He was also given normal saline. Prior to giving this treatment blood was drawn for a test by one of the nurses in his presence and sent for a report immediately.

Mr. Bandaranayake asked, "Was there any one with the patient to give his history?"

"No."

He said he saw Russel at 10 p.m. and he noted that there was a slight improvement as his pupils were sluggishly reacting to light and there was response to painful stimuli. Thereafter, on a number of occasions he has examined Russel.

Dr. Wijesiriwardena said, "Russel continued to be unconscious right throughout his second stay in ward 18. Russel was continuously maintained on a dextrose drip. But none of them proved effective. Food was given in the form of nasal feeding during Russel's second stay in ward 18. At 9.30 a.m. on 26th July, Russel had rapid pulse and sweating and he was given 50% dextrose and the signs have subsided. On 28th there have been three separate attacks I observed at 8 a.m., at 3 p.m. and at 10 p.m. and on each occasion I gave the same treatment and the signs subsided."

On 3rd August the patient was referred to Dr. N. Nagaratnam, the Consultant Physician of ward 44, by Professor Navaratne. Dr. Nagaratnam had prescribed certain treatment. Dr. Wijesiriwardena further said that up to 10th August there was no marked improvement of the condition of Russel and he died at about 3.20 a.m. on that day.

In answer to Mr. Bandaranayake he said that the patients were given milk, fruits and passion fruit juice and Marmite through the nasal tube.

Mr. Marapana asked, "On the occasion of the second admission, did Russel show any symptoms of getting a hypoglycaemic attack?"

"On some occasions I noticed the patient was sweating and having rapid pulse. When 50 millilitres of dextrose was given the sweating reduced and the rapid pulse rate dropped. This almost confirmed that the patient was getting a chronic hypoglycaemic attack," Dr. Wijesiriwardena said. He said if there was a very big tumour in the pancreas it could activate the excess secretion of insulin in the patient even when the patient was given 50% dextrose and the patient could get a hypoglycaemic attack.

He said that Rev. Peiris told him that when he placed his crucifix on the abdomen of Russel, it had vibrated, indicating to Rev. Peiris that Russel had a stomach ailment.

Dr. Wijesiriwardena said at the hospital the first accused used to talk to him frequently about the patient's illness, especially when Russel was admitted a second time to the hospital. He said that the first accused had asked about the condition of the patient and whether he would recover. He had also seemed to know a lot about insulinoma and once asked if an insulinoma could be missed during a post-mortem.

Questioned by Mr. Bandaranayake, he said normally when tests are carried out, the reports are pasted on a sheet on the BHT. However, looking through documents given to him he said that there were neither such sheets nor any reports of any tests. The fever chart, diet sheets, urine reports and the FBCs from 26th June 1978 to 14th July 1978 were also not among the documents.

Dr. Wijesiriwardena said after Russel died, Dr. Sheriffdeen carried out a pathological post-mortem examination. Since the diagnosis was that of a very rare disease, they were keen to find out whether the patient had an islet cell tumour in the pancreas and they arranged a pathological post-mortem.

Then the relatives alleged that Russel had been poisoned and wanted a judicial post-mortem.

Dr. Wijesiriwardena said when he found out that Dr. Sheriffdeen had taken the pancreas he told Dr. Sheriffdeen that the arrangements were made for a judicial post-mortem. He then contacted the JMO who informed Dr. Sheriffdeen that a judicial post-mortem could not be held as already a pathological post-mortem had been performed. The JMO then wanted specimens of hair, nails, and stomach contents taken from the body of Russel Ingram and forwarded to him. Dr. Wijesiriwardena said that steps were taken to collect the specimens and they were handed over to the JMO.

After the post-mortem, Dr. Sheriffdeen gave him a tin. Dr. Wijesiriwardena said he had a look into the tin and found a pancreas. He wrote out a requisition form, which was produced by the prosecution (exhibit P20). In that requisition dated 11th August 1978 he wrote "query insulinoma". He said that the nurses would have written the label on the container. It was sent to the pathology laboratory through the medical orderly.

Dr. Wijesiriwardena said that his statement to the police was made on second May 1979 and when questioned by the police on matters he had not made a note of, he had relied purely on his memory. If there was documentation available, he had answered from these.

Mr. Obeysekera cross examining Dr. Wijesiriwardena asked, "When you made your statement to the Police you relied on memory about what Rev. Peiris told you?"

"Yes."

"Did he say he had done tests outside?"

"Yes."

"You have not told the Police that he told you this?"

"I may have not thought it important at that time."

"I put it to you that you are adding to your evidence that he told you this?"

"No."

"Have you ever made a statement to the police before?" asked Mr. Bandaranayake.

"No," said Dr. Wijesiriwardena.

Cross examined by Mr. Cecil Goonewardena, Dr. Wijesiriwardena said that he had actually seen the first accused with his arm around the waist of the second accused.

"I put it to you that is another instance of your adding to your evidence. You have not told the police one word of this."

"I think I did."

"How many times have you seen the first accused walking with his arm around the waist of the second accused in the hospital?"

"Three or four times."

"At what time of the day have you seen them?"

"Around 7 or 7.30 p.m."

Mr. Goonewardena then read from the statement of Dr. Wijesiriwardena "…he used to usually visit before or after visiting hours. I have seen him standing close to Dalrene and talking."

"Do you agree that standing close and talking is quite different from putting his hand around her waist and walking?"

"Yes."

"You have never seen the second accused in a figure-hugging T-shirt and skirt?"

"No."

Mr. Wickramasekera asked, "Did you tell that to the police?"

"I do not think so."

"Either you are being influenced by what you have read or someone is prompting you?" said Mr. Goonewardena.

"I have seen," said Dr. Wijesiriwardena.

He added that on one occasion he had seen the two accused in the back seat of a taxi. He felt there was something unusual about it as they were seated too close. It registered in his mind at that time, as he had heard rumours.

Mr. Charles Sepala, a clerk who was attached to the Education Department in 1979 giving evidence said that in the Colombo South Education Region about 30 teachers retired annually.

He said Mrs. Eunice Peiris was due to retire on 5th August 1978. The Education Department informed the school to which Mrs. Peiris was attached that she was due to retire from service. This was done by the Director of Education, Colombo. On 18th May 1978 the Education Department informed the Principal of St. Michael's, Polwatte to forward the application for her pension. As the application was not received the Department wrote back to the principal asking for Mrs. Peiris's home address.

On 14th March the first accused brought the application for a pension on behalf of his wife.

Mr. Sepala said that he asked the first accused what was wrong with the patient and the first accused told him that according to doctors there had been only three patients up to that time who had suffered from a similar illness as that of his wife and all three had died. The first accused further told him that even his wife was expected to die and therefore he would request the pension matters to be attended to without delay.

Thereafter, the first accused returned to the pensions branch after a day or two with the applicant's service record. On that occasion he inquired from the first accused as to whether he had got the request form certified by a doctor and the first accused told him that the doctor had refused to certify the thumb impression.

Mr. Sepala said, with reference to an application for a commuted pension, should the applicant die before it was paid, then the pension was paid to the applicant's next of kin. He said that the Regional Director of Education, Colombo South, had on 29th March 1979 stopped the payment of a temporary pension.

Dr. S. Sathanandan, the psychiatrist who saw Mrs. Peiris at the Durdans Hospital in 1978, giving evidence said that he was a psychiatrist attached to the Mental Hospitals in Angoda and Mulleriyawa.

Examined by Mr. Ananda Amaranath, Senior State Counsel he said that he saw Mrs. Peiris when she was referred to him by Dr. Weerasena. When shown the BHT, he read the referral note of Dr. Weerasena.

"*Dear Satha,*

This patient has been depressed for the past two weeks or so. She was on Stelazine and she became very drowsy. Please see and advice.

Thanks.

Lakshman"

"How do you examine psychiatric patients?" asked Mr. Bandaranayake.

"I take the history first, and in this instance I remember getting the history from Mrs. Peiris as well as the first accused," Dr. Sathanandan replied. Then he identified the first accused as the person who gave the history.

Dr. Sathanandan said that in his opinion Mrs. Peiris had no suicidal tendency whatsoever when he interrogated her at the Durdans Hospital. He ruled out the possibility of suicide as most unlikely as she had recovered almost completely from her depression on 20th January.

Mr. Amaranath asked, "On 16th January 1979, what time did you visit Mrs. Peiris at Durdans?"

"Around 6.00 p.m. or so."

"On that occasion did the first accused give you the history of Mrs. Peiris?"

"Yes, he told me that Mrs. Peiris had returned to Sri Lanka from England in December 1978 and since then she had been depressed and had not been sleeping well."

"Any other symptoms? That she was drowsy?"

"I do not think that he said she was drowsy."

He said that he got the impression that since early 1979 she had been listless and had sleeping problems.

Mr. Wickramasekera asked, "Did you make a note of the history given to you."

"Unfortunately, no."

Mr. Bandaranayake asked, "Did the patient speak to you?"

"Yes, but Rev. Peiris gave me most of the history."

Mr. Amaranath asked, "Did the first accused attribute this condition to any events which might have occurred before this?"

"Yes, as a psychiatrist I tried to find out if there was anything which could have brought about these symptoms."

He said that the first accused and Mrs. Peiris had told him that Mrs. Peiris's daughter had returned to Sri Lanka to be engaged and for some reason the engagement had not taken place, and the daughter had gone back. The first accused said he felt that Mrs. Peiris was upset over this.

"I remember they said that a bridal dress had also been brought down and they had apparently made all preparations," he said.

Mr. Amaranath asked, "When you examined Mrs. Peiris, were you aware that she had been admitted to Durdans in an unconscious state."

"No, I was not aware."

"Did you ask her if she had taken an overdose of drugs?"

"Yes, I asked her as Dr. Attygalle said that it could be due to anti-depressant drugs. Mrs. Peiris said she did not take an overdose, and that it was the first accused who gave her the tablets."

"At this time you were aware of the dosage of the drugs?"

"Yes."

"Was it a large or small dosage?"

"Small."

He said that he thought that it was after he had examined Mrs. Peiris alone, that the first accused had told him about him giving Mrs. Peiris the tablets. At the end of his examination he had come to the conclusion that she was suffering from an endogenous type of depression. This he explained was a type of depression normally seen in elderly people where depression comes on suddenly. The depression itself, he said, could be connected to a physical defect. He had then prescribed an anti-depressant called Tofranil and a sleeping tablet called Mogadon. Mogadon, he said, was non-addictive and not a barbiturate.

Reading his observations from the BHT, he said, "Patient appears brighter, depression less, no suicidal thoughts, slept well last night, appetite good." According to an entry on the BHT he had ordered a urine test to exclude the possibility of diabetes.

He explained that on four separate days he had examined this patient and remembered the first accused being present on most of the occasions. Following each examination of the patient, he thought that she was improving in her condition and on 20th January, he decided that she was in a fit state to be discharged.

"Were you satisfied that she had made a complete recovery?"

"Almost complete recovery."

Mr. Nimal Soysa, a receptionist at Glass House said that on 29th January 1979 morning, the first accused came with Mrs. Peiris for an appointment. He called the first accused into the Reception Room. The first accused said that he wanted GTT, ESR and a full blood count done for his wife. He did not show any letters from a doctor. Shown the P11 and P22, requests for blood tests in the Court, he said that he was seeing them for the first time. Mr. Soysa said that after the blood is drawn, the patient was asked to sit in the lobby or verandah for a while until it is time for next sample of blood to be drawn.

"Sometime after the test started, the first accused made a request for an 'Extended GTT' over four hours. I charged him an extra Rs. 40.00 and amended the bill," he said.

He said that if a patient knows what test he wants done, they do that without a doctor's letter. If a doctor's letter is shown, they will write on their report "*At the request of Dr...*" He said that he charged half-rate as the first accused was a priest.

Mr. Harridge, a laboratory technician of Glass House, giving evidence said that he was the laboratory technician the day Mrs. Peiris came for the GTT.

"There was an appointment for a GTT for a lady named Eunice Peiris. I got to know of it that morning from the Reception. I came downstairs to the cubicle and found the working sheet, looked at it and called the patient who came in from the Reception area with the first accused. I have seen the first accused before as I had earlier worked at the Cardiology Unit of the General Hospital, Colombo, next to which is situated the St. Paul's Church, Kynsey Road," he said.

"Either a doctor or one of the supervisors drew the blood from the deceased. When the first sample was taken at 8.30 a.m. I marked that fact on P24. I labeled the bottle with that sample. That was the fasting blood sample drawn. Thereafter, I administered glucose to the patient. The first accused was helping the patient and was playing the more prominent role asking question from me and telling the lady what to do. He did all the talking. She appeared weak and sick and hardly spoke. When I called out her name, she walked into the cubicle with the first accused from the verandah about 10 yards away. She went to the toilet room and gave specimens of urine. After the initial fasting blood sample was drawn and glucose was administered, the patient was asked to sit in the verandah until next sample was drawn. The test began at 8.30 a.m. and ended at 12.30 p.m. During the test, after the first hour, but before two and half hours, the first accused told me that he had given a call to his doctor, Dr. Weerasena, and that Dr. Weerasena wanted an extended GTT done over four hours. So I spoke to the doctor-in-charge, who charged an additional fee and I proceeded to take blood samples over four hours. I was never shown P11 or P22. If the first accused had shown me those letters or had shown them to the reception at the beginning, they would have ordered an extended GTT over four hours. This the first accused did not do. The first accused knew a lot about GTT and even showed him two blood reports during the test," he said.

He was shown the working sheet P24, which he identified as a document made by him. It contained details of the blood sugar test that was done.

Mr. R.I. Obeysekera cross examining Mr. Harridge suggested that what the first accused told him during the test was that it was a mistake to have ordered an ordinary GTT. He denied this and said that if that were so there would have been no necessity for the first accused to have told him that Dr. Weerasena had stated so over the telephone. Mr. Obeysekera then suggested to Mr. Harridge that what might have actually happened was that the first accused just stated that what Dr. Weerasena wanted was an extended GTT over four hours, but by some mistake Rev. Peiris ordered an ordinary GTT and therefore when he realized his mistake he wanted it extended. He denied this but granted a possibility of error.

Re-examined by Mr. Marapana, Mr. Harridge said that if the first accused had these two letters all he needed to have done was to have shown them to the reception.

Dr. Abdul Haleem Sheriffdeen, Senior Lecturer in Surgery at the Faculty of Medicine, University of Colombo, giving evidence said that there was a Professorial Unit in the Faculty of Medicine to which he was attached and that Unit overlooked ward 18. He said he was a General Surgeon with a special interest in vascular surgery, which was concerned with arteries and veins. He was an Honorary Visiting Surgeon at the General Hospital, Colombo, while his substantive appointment was with the University.

Dr. Sheriffdeen said four wards - 18, 28, 6A and 30C, were overlooked by the Professorial Unit. They were all surgical units. Between 60 and 100 persons were at ward 18 at any given time. The Professorial Unit was a teaching unit and medical students accompanied him on his ward rounds. He delivered lectures during the day for one to four hours and carried out ward teaching as well. He said that since he was a teacher and a practising surgeon he needed to keep abreast of the latest developments in his field.

Dr. Sheriffdeen said he recalled having examined a patient by the name of Russel Ingram in ward 44 sometime before 3rd July. He examined Russel before transferring him to ward 18. He said the examination he conducted was to ascertain any tumour in the pancreas.

"Russel was somewhat drowsy when he was admitted and had a bed sore. He had not shaved for some time and had a beard. Apart from this, he was quite well and was discharged on my orders. While he was being investigated during the period from 3rd July to 14th July, the medication given to him was 'general nursing care'. After an initial GTT, I ordered an extended GTT to be carried out on Russel. The extended test had lasted between five to seven hours. I did not order any drugs to be given to Russel after his discharge. I requested that Russel be re-admitted to the ward for further tests on 26th July," Dr. Sheriffdeen said.

Dr. Sheriffdeen said that when the patient was in his ward he had been given a history of Russel's condition at that time. But he could not recollect the details.

"On 18th July Rev. Peiris came up to me and said that Russel was unconscious again. Rev. Peiris told him that Russel had been unconscious for 24 hours. I gave him a letter to have Russel admitted to my ward. Rev. Peiris said that he waited until Tuesday which was my clinic day to have Russel admitted. I did not give my mind to the explanation given by Rev. Peiris for the 24 hour delay in coming to me, had been a satisfactory one," Dr. Sheriffdeen said.

"When I saw Russel in the afternoon of 18th July, he was deeply unconscious. He has been given a dextrose drip. That was the first time I had seen Russel unconscious. My clinical examination brought me to the conclusion that Russel's brain had been irreparably damaged, probably due to hypoglycaemia. Clinical examination excluded a stroke or haemorrhage. All his four limbs were flaccid. It meant that when the limbs were raised and released they simply flopped down. His pupils were reacting to light and his breathing was normal. The brain damage appeared to me to be generalized. In case of a stroke or haemorrhage the damage is localized. Usually, when one sees a person in a coma one thinks of renal failure, liver failure or a diabetic condition. Clinically there was no evidence of any of these causes. There had been no evidence of an alcoholic coma. He was not jaundiced. His liver was not enlarged and there were no signs of liver failure. I excluded alcoholic coma because there was no alcoholic smell. If a man who had his liver damaged, consumed large quantities of alcohol it could lead to a hepatic coma, which could last for several hours. In Russel's case there were no signs of any kind of alcoholic coma," he said.

Continuing, Dr. Sheriffdeen said, "There were no signs of injuries on the head and I ruled out meningitis as well. But the patient was deeply unconscious. One could not always exclude all poisons by a clinical examination. There were no signs of corrosion on the lips or tongue. There was no diarrhoea or vomiting. Had there been involuntary movements of the eyes and tongue, these could be due to poisoning with an anti-depressant. I have not treated the case as one of poisoning going by the previous history of the patient. I am now able to say that the unconsciousness was due to hypoglycaemia and an irreversible brain damage. If the level of blood sugar is zero for more than two hours it can lead to brain damage. No tests had been carried out on humans but some tests had been done on monkeys, which had proved that conclusion."

Dr. Sheriffdeen said that Dr. Nagaratnam, the Consultant Physician, was consulted because there had been no change in the patient's condition. Considering the brain damage the patient had suffered, it was possible to keep him alive until another system failed, provided the cause for the coma did not recur like for example, an induced coma.

"The immediate cause of death had been pneumonia. Pneumonia could be caused by a lack of medical care. But despite adequate nursing care pneumonia can be caused by aspiration. In Russel's case the pneumonia was caused because of the patient being unconscious and therefore, not able to breathe deeply enough to clear his lungs," he said.

In answer to Court as to what he was expecting as the outcome of treatment, Dr. Sheriffdeen said, "I did not expect the patient to recover. We have kept the vital functions going as best as we could. If he had not been treated, he would probably have died on the 18th July. Russel probably had no immediate medical attention on admission. A patient who had zero blood sugar could not last beyond two hours. Yet in this case when Dr. Karunakaran had attended on him six hours later, he was still alive."

"During Russel's first stay in my ward I had no occasion to meet his wife. On one occasion when I was with a batch of medical students in ward 18, Rev. Peiris had placed a cross on Russel's body and told us that the vibrations he was receiving suggested to him that Russel was suffering from a disease of the pancreas! The diagnosis has been received in a spirit of frivolity by the medical students and me," Dr. Sheriffdeen said.

He said, "In short, he had been requested to do surgery on the patient. Even a deep-seated tumour could be ascertained by a process of palpation. Palpation meant the application of certain pressures. The patient was somewhat drowsy when he was admitted and had a bed sore. He had not shaved for some time and had a beard. Apart from this, he was quite well and was discharged on his orders. I said that the medication given to the patient as 'general nursing care' while he was being investigated during the period from 3rd to 14th July."

"During the second period of Russel's stay in the hospital he had been given daily 10% dextrose infusions. Despite this, he had suffered from hypoglycaemia. It was not consistent that a patient who was getting large doses of dextrose and had had a history of insulinoma should yet have suffered from hypoglycaemic attacks," Dr. Sheriffdeen said.

When Mr. R.I. Obeysekera cross examined Dr. Sheriffdeen he said Russel was transferred to his ward following instructions he gave after examining the patient at the request of Dr. Nagaratnam.

Dr. Sheriffdeen said, "Russel was drowsy when I saw him and therefore, I instructed that he be given 10% dextrose and be turned over regularly to prevent him from getting a bedsore. I also wanted an extended GTT done on the patient and a chest x-ray taken. I presumed it was taken. I also wanted a neurological opinion to exclude a cerebral tumour but I presume that those instructions were not carried out. I made this suggestion when Russel was referred to me by Dr. Nagaratnam. It was the physician's business to decide whether my suggestions should be followed or not."

In answer to Mr. Bandaranayake, he said at that moment he would have thought that an insulinoma was not the only cause for Russel's condition, and therefore thought more tests should be done. He said Rev. Peiris suggested to him that a laparotomy be done on the patient. He said the discussion with Rev. Peiris took place on the second occasion and Rev. Peiris told him about his strong suspicion that Russel's ailment was in the pancreas.

Dr. Sheriffdeen said, "Laparotomy is done only if there is a strong suspicion of an insulinoma. I would not do a laparotomy as a method of detecting an insulinoma. It was more a last resort to detect an isulinoma and even then an insulinoma could be missed. The fact that Rev. Peiris held a cross on Russel's abdomen and said there was something wrong with the pancreas stuck vividly in my mind and it was thereafter that Rev. Peiris suggested a laparotomy."

Dr. Sheriffdeen said he did a pathological post-mortem on 10th August at the General Hospital post-mortem room. He said he took the pancreas out of its 'bed' at the post-mortem and carefully examined it, felt it and then cut it into thin slices with a scalpel and further examined it. He found no abnormality and no tumours. In the course of the post-mortem examination he found a nodule in the duodenum and he took it out and examined it and found it to be normal. Then he wanted the pancreas to be microscopically examined for an insulinoma. He also thought of hyperplasia, adenomatosis and nesidioblastosis. He then put the pancreas and nodule in a tin and walked back to ward 18 and nearing the ward he met Dr. Wijesiriwardena and handed over the tin with the specimens to him with instructions to forward the specimens for histology.

Dr. Sheriffdeen said, "When I had completed the pathological post-mortem Dr. Wijesiriwardena informed me that a judicial post-mortem had been requested on the body of Russel."

Mr. Bandaranayake asked, "There is nothing illegal in conducting a pathological post-mortem if done with consent of relatives?"

"No."

"Had you been aware that a judicial post-mortem was to be done, would you have done a pathological post-mortem?" asked Mr. Wickramasekera.

"No."

Continuing the cross examination, Mr. Obeysekera asked, "If a judicial post-mortem had been done and the JMO had been forewarned about ectopic areas, he would have taken specimens of the organs and sent them for tests?

"That depends on the JMO."

"You only sent the pancreas and part of the duodenum for examination?"

"Yes."

"You did not send any other parts on your own?"

"No."

"I put it to you that the secretions of the tumour do not depend on the size?"

"It is. The larger the tumour, more it secretes."

Dr. Sheriffdeen said that he had sliced the pancreas into small pieces, but it was impossible to say how many pieces as these were usually not counted. He said that he put the pancreas into a tin himself, to be sent for examination.

"What did you speak to Dr. P.A.P. Joseph about?" asked Mr. Obeysekera.

"I remember him asking about the post-mortem findings."

He said doctors probably discussed the question of Russel's condition being induced.

"You said 'induced'. Did you mean self-induced or administered by somebody?" asked Mr. Obeysekera.

"Administered."

Cross examined by Mr. Cecil Goonewardena, Dr. Sheriffdeen said that the nurses did not bring the behaviour of relatives of patients to his notice. He said he could not remember any abnormal behaviour of the second accused in the ward.

"Did Professor Navaratne speak to you about it?"

"No."

"If you suspected that drugs were being given to Russel in his food, you would have taken a serious view of it and sent it for analysis?"

"Yes, if I had a strong suspicion."

Re-examined by Mr. Marapana, Dr. Sheriffdeen said that the last time he had seen Russel before his discharge he had been well, was talking, and he had therefore ordered him to be discharged. He had not ordered any drugs for Russel.

Answering a question from Mr. Bandaranayake he said that he could not attribute natural causes for Russel having gone into a coma two days after being discharged.

Mr. T.A.D. Weerasinghe Perera, giving evidence said that he was on duty during this period in the Medical Faculty and that he took the specimen of pancreas and nodule in the tin with the requisition from ward 18 to the pathology laboratory. He said that he could remember the exact date but he used to take specimens on Mondays, Wednesdays and Fridays. The 11th of August was a Friday so that Monday would be the 14th.

Mrs. Chandrani Kalubowila, a technician in the pathology laboratory of the Faculty of Medicine, giving evidence said that she entered the particulars of the specimen sent by Dr. Sheriffdeen in the pathology laboratory register having checked the specimen and the label. The entry was dated 15th August 1978 and has been entered against the serial number 1988/U78 and the particulars have been entered thus – "Russel Ingram – Pancreas and Nodule".

Dr. (Mrs.) Ganeswari Sri Balasubramaniam, giving evidence said that she was an Associate Professor in Pathology in the Faculty of Medicine, University of Colombo.

She obtained her MBBS (Ceylon) in 1960. After working in different hospitals, she joined the Medical Faculty and was a demonstrator. She then proceeded to England and did post graduate work and teaching in pathology departments at London Hospitals. In 1970, she did a PhD in Pathology from London University. From 1971 to 1977 she was at the Colombo University as a Senior Lecturer in pathology. Between 1977 and 1979 she was in the United Kingdom. As a professor she teaches pathology to undergraduate and postgraduate students and is also a Consultant Pathologist to several hospitals in Sri Lanka.

She said that along with others she does about eight thousand histology samples per year. In the course of her work she has examined over 100 pancreases and tested its tissues for various disorders. She has also personally found an insulinoma of the pancreas and she has also seen another slide containing an insulinoma of the pancreas in an examination done by another pathologist.

Dr. Balasubramaniam said that specimens sent from hospitals were kept in a fixative. Thereafter, the technician would take the specimen and the request form, and check them and keep them for her examination. When the request forms are brought to her she goes through them and then goes to the laboratory and examines the specimens, first macroscopically and thereafter microscopically. She has examined Russel's pancreas and nodule on 23rd August.

Dr. Balasubramaniam said, "I first examined the whole sliced pancreas and the nodule macroscopically by palpation. I am familiar with normal pancreatic tissue and the structure of its various cells. Normal pancreatic tissue was yellowish white in colour. Normal insulin producing tissue consists of two parts the 'Exocrine' and the 'Endocrine'. The exocrine part consists of acini and ducts separated by connective tissue, in which are blood vessels and nerve fibres. The endocrine part consists of 'islands' or 'islets' called the islands of

198

Langerhans, named after the German Scientist who first discovered their existence. These islands consist of two main types of cells, the beta and alpha cells, and also delta cells. The alpha cells secrete the hormone glucagon and beta cells secrete the hormone insulin. Of these cells by far the commonest are the beta cells. These beta cells also act as the glucose sensor cells."

"I was able to identify a beta cell under the microscope. Having examined the whole sliced pancreas and nodule for abnormalities, I found no abnormalities macroscopically, no colour change which is usually seen adenomatosis, no tumours seen or felt. I proceeded to process parts of the pancreas and the whole of the nodule. I made four representative slides from the thicker slices of the pancreas. I expressed the opinion that the pancreatic sections showed no evidence of insulinoma. The condition called hyperplasia occurs in the beta cells which could cause increased insulin activity. Hyperplasia was a generalized condition occurring throughout the tissue and therefore easily observable and differentiated from the normal cell. In hyperplasia, under the microscope the islet is seen to be much bigger than normal and also each individual cell that goes to form the island is larger than normal and also the number of such large cells are more than normal," Dr. Balasubramaniam said.

She said that an increase in the size of each individual cell, as well as an increase in the number of cells that go to constitute an island was not observed in the specimen. Slides were seen under the microscope and the cells and their formations were normal. So the condition of hyperplasia in her opinion did not exist in the pancreas.

Dr. Balasubramaniam then went on to explain another abnormal condition which could produce enhanced insulin secretion and very much like hyperplasia only more pronounced and this condition too she was familiar with and could be identified.

"This condition is called 'adenomatosis'. 'Hyperplasia' is also adenomatosis in that, in both there is this diffuse condition and proliferation of cells, but in adenomatosis the proliferation is more marked than in hyperplasia and is seen in a formation known as the 'tumourlet formation'. Further, the colour of tissue changes in adenomatosis to pinkish or purplish from the normal yellowish white. I observed no such colour change. Again, in adenomatosis the tissue is usually firmer than the surrounding tissue. I did not feel such a presence. Adenomatosis was not there in Russel's pancreas," she said.

"Yet a third abnormality of the cells producing increased insulin and observable under the microscope and with which I was familiar, is called 'nesidioblastosis'. In nesidioblastosis, there is a proliferation of the lining of the ducts. This lining is known as 'epithelium'. So this condition consists of proliferation of the epithelium tending to form a tumour. This condition was not present in Russel's pancreas. The nodule found by Dr. Sheriffdeen in the duodenum was also processed and examined and found to be merely a lymph node. That was just lymphoid tissue present all over the body and quite incapable of secreting insulin," Dr. Balasubramaniam said.

Dr. Balasubramaniam, cross examined by Mr. R.I. Obeysekera, said that slides were normally prepared by a technician.

"Preparation of slides takes about twenty four hours and is handled by the technician under the supervision of the pathologist. The technicians are qualified and trained in the department and they used a process to make slides that have been used for more than one hundred years all over the world. Only the machines are new and automatic. After my macroscopic examination, I further sliced the pancreatic tissue into pieces that could get into the machine, i.e. 10 to 12 micro centimeter. The section is about 1.5 centi meter in length and width. I took areas for preparation more from the body and the tail of the pancreas," Dr. Balasubramaniam said.

Dr. (Mrs.) Sujatha Kumudini Ruwanpathirana giving evidence said that she was a House Officer in ward 44, General Hospital, Colombo. Examined by Mr. Tilak Marapana, she said that on 26th June 1978, while she was on duty a patient in an unconscious state was brought in on a trolley at 2.30 p.m. She said that the letter was also brought along with the patient. The patient was accompanied by Rev. Peiris and some others.

Rev. Peiris handed over the letter signed by Dr. P.A.P. Joseph, and volunteered the case history, which she wrote down. Rev. Peiris told her that the patient was Russel Ingram and that he was thirty two years old. He said that he knew the patient from almost his childhood and that he knew the ailment. The patient had a history of abnormal behaviour periodically and on the last occasion, patient has been in a stupor and unconscious for twenty hours. This was recorded on the BHT. Rev. Peiris also said that the patient's blood sugar varied and at times the patient was excited and at times drowsy. He said that when dextrose was administered the patient became violent and homicidal!

When she told the nurses to administer 10% dextrose drip to Russel, Rev. Peiris had flared up and said, 'Are you mad? Sugar is poison in this case.'

Dr. Ruwanpathirana asked, "Are you trying to cause further brain damage?" Rev. Peiris had then remained silent.

She said she prescribed 25 mg Largactil if the patient became violent, and remembered clearly what Rev. Peiris told her about the patient becoming violent when dextrose was given. (*Largactil is the trade name of chlorpromazine, a low-potency antipsychotic drug and in the past was used in the treatment of both acute and chronic psychoses, including schizophrenia and the manic phase of bipolar disorder.*)

She felt the patient was in a critical condition and ordered samples of blood to be taken for tests and thereafter ordered a 5% dextrose drip and a dextrose injection.

Answering a question of Mr. Bandaranayake, she said that there was no history of the patient having taken alcohol or drugs. She said as the patient was deeply unconscious she assumed the patient was hypoglycaemic. After the urine report was received she decided the patient was hypoglycaemic and she proceeded with the treatment of dextrose drip and injection.

Then the Senior House Officer Dr. (Mrs.) Anula Wijesundera arrived and she also recorded the observations on the BHT. She said the patient's condition required immediate treatment and she attended to that rather than first recording her observations.

"Russel responded to the treatment and I ordered a further blood sugar test. He became fully conscious around 8 p.m. that day, although he did not obey commands. He was also drowsy and very apathetic."

Justice Ramanathan asked, "The only treatment given was glucose and by 8 p.m. the patient was conscious?"

"Yes. The blood sugar report stated the sugar level was 40 mg%. This was fairly low. The report was pasted on the BHT but was now missing," she said.

Mr. Marapana said that he would not be relying on that report.

"Up to that time Russel did not show any signs of being boisterous. Russel was reluctant to take meals and therefore, was kept on a dextrose drip. No drugs were given. On 27th and 28th June he was allowed solids. Thereafter, he was on a liquid diet," she said.

In answer to Mr. Wickramasekara, she said that to some extent she was guided by the letter sent by Dr. Joseph. She could say that the patient made a dramatic response to dextrose as he had been unconscious for twenty hours. She recalled that Russel always appeared to be disinterested. When she spoke to him, although he could talk he did not say anything.

Dr. Ruwanpathirana said that at about 5.45 p.m. on 3rd July Russel was transferred to Ward 18.

Dr. N. Nagaratnam, MBBS, MD, FRCP, a Senior Consultant Physician, General Hospital, Colombo, examined by Mr. Marapana said that he was also a Consultant Physician to the Sri Lanka Air Force holding the rank of Wing Commander.

He said he examined Russel on 20th July and on the 3rd August in ward 18, as Dr. Sheriffdeen asked him to do so.

He said that Russel was unconscious throughout and that on 3rd August, he found that the condition of pneumonia had set in and also that the patient had suffered brain stem damage. He said that the initial hypoglycaemic condition could have initiated it and that the post-mortem finding of pneumonia was consistent with his findings.

"I felt there was something going on, which was inducing hypoglycaemic attacks while Russel was in an unconscious state. He was either having an insulinoma, or he was being given some extraneous substance," he said.

He said all that could be done for him was to maintain nutrition, to give adequate nursing care and turning the patient from side to side to avoid bed sores, remove any secretion from the lungs and meet infection with drugs. He said that a patient in a continued state of unconsciousness was prone to pneumonia or inflammation of the lung brought about by infection. He explained the different types of pneumonia, such as primary pneumonia, where an organism affects primarily the lung, secondary pneumonia, as a complication in lungs and aspirated pneumonia, which is the result of aspiration of infected material.

Dr. Nagaratnam said that he ruled out unconsciousness caused by cerebrovascular accident which is the interruption of the flow of blood to the upper part of the brain resulting from thrombosis or embolism, meningitis, which is an infection to the covering of the brain, coma caused by liver or kidney failure, and alcoholic coma or corrosive poisoning or other poisons. He said considering all the information available to him from both hospitalizations, information from the point of history, physical examinations done by him, laboratory data and the patient's response to a certain line of treatment, he is of the opinion that the patient's coma was due to hypoglycaemia.

Dr. Nagaratnam said that a diseased liver is enlarged and can be felt and liver disorders are clinically observable. There is pain, puffiness, swelling, jaundice etc. None of such signs or symptoms was present in Russel. There were no signs of cirrhosis or hepatitis, and no vomiting. He said that a non-diabetic should never use Euglucon tablets as it could reduce the blood sugar to dangerous levels.

"A non-diabetic in the condition in which Russel was, could become hypoglycaemic by taking just 2.5 mg of Euglucon. Such a person who goes into a coma after taking 2.5 mg of Euglucon could recover on his own or after taking meals or dextrose, but there was also the possibility of the person not recovering at all and succumbing to it. If about four tablets of 5 mg Euglucon were given to a person in the condition of Russel, I would think the drug would be active fairly soon, that is within about ten to fifteen minutes. Russel was not a diabetic," he said.

"Does this drug act faster or slower if given in combination with another drug?" asked Mr. Bandaranayake.

"It could act faster. If Euglucon was given along with propranolol, it could lower the blood sugar faster. Propranolol was given in cardiac conditions. It is pink in colour. There were times when vitamin B was also prescribed for diabetic patients. As a physician, I have special experience in treating diabetic patients. I have prescribed Euglucon for the last ten years and also other present day diabetic drugs. If the glucose level was high at the time Euglucon was given, it would take some time for symptoms to show," said Dr. Nagaratnam.

Continuing, he said that he would expect the drug given crushed, to be absorbed faster on an empty stomach. "Euglucon was not soluble in water. If a Euglucon tablet was put into a glass of water it would not dissolve. When a tablet gets into the stomach it would disintegrate, meaning it would break into small particles. This process of disintegration in the stomach could take about ten minutes. If the tablets were crushed and given the time taken for disintegration would probably be less than ten minutes."

"Once the Euglucon starts acting, how long would it remain active in the body?" asked Mr. Marapana.

"It has been worked out that if 5 mg of Euglucon were given to a young non-diabetic, the action would begin in about fifteen minutes, and could last for about twelve hours. If 5 mg were given to a diabetic patient the sugar would come down but with every meal the sugar level could rise again. This would be the result even with non-diabetic persons. If a large amount of Euglucon was given and the amount of glucose taken in was inadequate, the person could have recurrent attacks of hypoglycaemia," Dr. Nagaratnam said.

In answer to Mr. Wickramasekara, Dr. Nagaratnam said that a normal person who was non-diabetic should not take Euglucon at all as Euglucon could reduce the blood sugar to dangerous levels. He said even for diabetic patients the dose was adjusted by a trial and error method. Explaining further he said that doctors normally started a patient on a very small dose. A person in the condition of Russel would become hypoglycaemic if he took 2.5 mg of Euglucon.

In answer to Mr. Bandaranayake, he said he was unable to say whether Euglucon would dissolve in boiling water.

Dr. Nagaratnam said, "When a person takes Euglucon for the first time, the effects of the drug on him would remain for about twenty four hours. When a person in the same condition as Russel goes into a coma having taken 2.5 mg of Euglucon he could either recover on his own or as a result of meals or dextrose or else he could succumb to it. From 18th July to 9th August Russel had been on dextrose continuously but despite continuous infusion of dextrose he had got frequent attacks of hypoglycaemia. This could have been due to the dribbling effect of stored Euglucon in the body. If Russel had been given a fairly large dose of Euglucon at about 9 a.m. on a particular day, it was possible for the patient to get four or five hypoglycaemic attacks within the next twenty four hours. This was also possible even if dextrose was being continuously given."

Dr. Nagaratnam said the first symptoms of hypoglycaemia could be dizziness, giddiness and lethargy, which could be followed by sweating, palpitation, slurring of speech, tremors, agitation and anxiety, aggressiveness or violent behaviour.

"It was very unlikely that if Russel had been exposed to Euglucon or any other anti-diabetic drug during the period 14th to 18th July that the dribbling effect of the stored drug could bring about attacks during the period of twenty two days from 18th July to 9th August. It was too long a period for the dribbling effect to take place with so much dextrose being given. The hypoglycaemic attacks during the second hospitalization of Russel Ingram were due to natural causes such as the secretion of insulin from an insulinoma or the result of some anti-diabetic drug given through a nasal feed," Dr. Nagaratnam said.

Cross examined by Mr. R.I. Obeysekera, Dr. Nagaratnam said he saw Russel Ingram on 26th June at about 3.30 p.m. in the ward. He had also spoken to Russel's father on that occasion.

Shown the book "Hypoglycaemia" by Marks and Rose, Dr. Nagaratnam said he had not read it.

He agreed there were some conditions that could bring about rebound hypoglycaemia. He would not say the conditions were the causes, but there was an association. He explained that in bronchial asthma, for instance, hypoglycaemia may or may not occur. Some of the other conditions with which hypoglycaemia had an association was epilepsy, migraine and vertigo.

Dr. Nagaratnam said that an insulinoma could be very small and could be single or in multiples. In his thirty years career as a doctor he had never come across an insulinoma and therefore it must be very rare. There had been one or two cases reported in this country.

He said that with a 'nil' reading of blood sugar, a patient could survive for about three hours.

In the case of a non-diabetic, even a 2.5 mg dosage of Euglucon could bring about a fair drop in the blood sugar level. The drop in the blood sugar depended on the dosage given. The drop in the blood sugar of a normal person would be about 60 percent if a 2.5 mg. dose was given. The drop would occur in about three to four hours. Even if the dosage was larger the period in which there would be a drop in the blood sugar would not appreciably differ.

Dr. Nagaratnam said that when a person has suffered irreversible brain damage there was no possibility of the patient's primitive reflexes being revived. Brain damage could be caused basically from lack of glucose and oxygen. These two conditions could operate together or independently. The brain like any other organ could react only in a limited manner. In the case of Mrs. Eunice Peiris brain damage could have been caused due to a lack of glucose in the brain cells and a lack of oxygen caused by blood not flowing into the brain due to a fall in pressure. He said he did not see Mrs. Peiris in the hospital. She was not his patient. He was only giving his interpretation on the diagnosis made by other doctors.

Mr. Aubrey Raymond, Managing Director of A.F. Raymond Ltd., examined by Mr. Tilak Marapana said he was the Managing Director of the firm of undertakers.

He said he had known Rev. Peiris for the last fifteen years, chiefly because he used to come with parishioners to place orders. He recalled that in 1978 Rev. Peiris came to his firm and placed an order for Mr. Russel Ingram's funeral. He had asked them not to take orders from anyone else. The funeral was held at the General Cemetery, Kanatta. The body was taken to their firm to be embalmed and then brought back to the Vicarage. His firm also undertook to insert the press obituary notice. This was given by Rev. Peiris. The obituary notices appeared in the Daily News and Daily Mirror.

In answer to Court, he said Rev. Peiris had on earlier occasions placed orders for Parishioner's funerals.

The order for Rev. Peiris's wife's funeral was also placed at his firm. He recalled Rev. Peiris phoning to say his wife had expired. That was on 20th March 1979. The funeral was at Moratuwa. In connection with that funeral he sent the bill to Rev. Peiris but it was not settled. Sometimes after his wife's funeral Rev. Peiris told Mr. Raymond he was undergoing difficulties and he would settle the bill later. As he knew Rev.Peiris he had said it was all right. The bill amounted to Rupees 840.

He recalled sometime after Mrs. Peiris's funeral, Rev. Peiris phoning to inform him that there would be an exhumation of Russel Ingram's body and asked him what would be found when the grave was opened. He felt that Rev. Peiris wanted to know whether there would be any remains. This was eight to ten months after Russel was buried. He had told Rev. Peiris that this was difficult to say. In a body that had undergone a post- mortem they normally embalmed each section separately.

In answer to questions by Mr. Bandaranayake, Mr. Raymond said, "Many people had asked me similar questions even before Rev. Peiris. Normally after a post-mortem the brain was removed and put into the abdomen along with the intestines. This was done at the JMO's office and when the body was taken by the undertaker, the parts in the abdomen were removed and buried in the cemetery. In this case I would not say whether Russel's brain had been removed in this way. In cases where the probable cause of death was known a partial post-mortem was done and the brain would probably remain in the skull and the undertaker would embalm that too."

Cross examined by Mr. R.I. Obeysekera, he said he did not try to force Rev. Peiris to settle the bill of Rupees 840. He said Rev. Peiris used to have a Requiem Mass on All Soul's day at the Anglican Chapel, Kanatta. There was the Anglican burial order whereby when a body was exhumed under the order it was known as 'disturbing the dead.'

Mr. Cecil Goonewardena, Senior Counsel for Dalrene said he had no questions to ask Mr. Raymond.

Mr. Piyal Weeraman, a Director at Independent Newspapers, Russel's immediate superior, giving evidence said Rev. Peiris spoke to him and asked him to give Russel a job. Mr. Weeraman obliged Rev. Peiris and employed Russel in a probationary capacity on 3rd November 1977 in the firm's advertising department and confirmed Russel in his job on the first of January 1978.

Mr. Weeraman said that Russel was quite healthy and participated in the activities of the Social Club and he was a member of their Cricket Team, which played at club level. He said Russel did his work competently, to the satisfaction of his employer, and was generally regular in his attendance. Russel was a well dressed person and that he met the public on behalf of his firm.

"Russel was not an alcoholic and I never found him drunk in office," said Mr. Weeraman. He told the Court about the leave Russel has taken from the 1st January up to the 9th June 1978 when he became unconscious.

Mr. S. P. Arumugam, a cook (*Appu*) at St. Peter's Church, Fort, who earlier worked at the Vicarage, Kynsey Road examined by Mr. C. R. de Silva, said that there used to be an old woman who came to the church regularly. On 19th January 1979, Rev. Peiris asked him who she was. He told Rev. Peiris that she was the woman who came to the church verandah daily and asked Rev. Peiris whether he had not seen her before. Then Rev. Peiris scolded him for allowing the woman to come there saying he had brought a prostitute. Rev. Peiris then chased her away.

"The old woman left hurriedly and I too tried to run but Rev. Peiris shouted to me not to run, that he would hand me over to the police. I went to the police station and made a statement. Rev. Peiris too had made a complaint against me and thereafter dismissed me. I could not say why a false complaint was made against me. Prior to my dismissal there had been an advertisement for a church cook. A parishioner told me this, so I knew I was going to be replaced but I stayed on," Arumugam said.

He has seen that woman earlier begging near the post office and Rev. Peiris too had helped her. At the police station he was kept in a cell for some time and released after his statement was recorded. After this incident he had no animosity against Rev. Peiris. Even Rev. Peiris knew that what he had done to the witness was wrong but he was not angry with Rev. Peiris. He confirmed that he had filed action against Rev. Peiris in the Labour Court.

"After Mrs. Peiris returned, I had occasion to speak to Mrs. Dalrene Ingram. I went into the kitchen to speak to her and also met her in church. Though I have seen Mrs. Peiris in the kitchen when I went there, I have not seen her and Dalrene together in the kitchen. There were occasions when I inquired about Mrs. Peiris and Dalrene said *'oki'* was inside and ill. This reply was given a few days after Mrs. Peiris returned. I did not go in to see Mrs. Peiris," he said. (*'Oki'* is a disparaging word used for a woman).

In answer to Mr. Bandaranayake, Arumugam said several people came to the Vicarage but he could not say whether they were doctors.

"When Mrs. Peiris was in hospital, Dalrene and her children stayed at the Vicarage. After Mrs. Peiris was admitted to hospital, when I inquired about her Dalrene told him that Mrs. Peiris (*'Oki'*) was not dead, but that she was waiting to eat at her almsgiving. During the time Dalrene came and went, there were occasions when she came in the absence of Mrs. Peiris. One Sunday, Rev. Peiris officiated at morning service when he indicated he would be away in Batticaloa. After service Rev. Peiris told me to close the church and leave. Soon after Dalrene came and asked for Rev. Peiris. I told her that Rev. Peiris might have gone to Batticaloa. Then Dalrene went towards the Vicarage and he saw Rev. Peiris at the Vicarage when he went for tea. Rev. Peiris told him not to go anywhere and to keep the church open till evening. That same evening Rev. Peiris went out with Dalrene. Rev. Peiris inquired whether I had kept the church open and I lied, saying I had. Later that day Mrs. Peiris and Malrani who had gone out on Friday morning returned to the Vicarage," Mr. Arumugam said.

"Before Rev. Peiris went on the trip to London, he introduced me to the Ingrams and said that they would be in charge of the Vicarage until he returned and asked me to look after the church and the garden. Rev. Peiris called Dalrene 'Darling' when he spoke to her, but in the presence of Russel or Mrs. Peiris he called her Dalrene," Mr. Arumugam said.

He further said that when Rev. Peiris and Dalrene were alone in the Vicarage all the doors and windows were closed. He did not tell Mrs. Peiris or Malrani that Rev. Peiris and Dalrene had remained in the Vicarage. He then recalled using a small lorry at Rev. Peiris's request in which Dalrene and the witness travelled to a place off Ethul Kotte.

They transported some goods from a house where Russel's family lived to the Vicarage. Either on the way there or when returning, Dalrene was saying her prayers.

Arumugam said that he had never seen Russel after liquor. If he had stated to the police that for some reason Russel started drinking heavily he said he would accept it. Russel may have consumed liquor but he did not know about it.

He said that he had been summoned to the ASP's office at Gregory's Road to make a statement to Inspector Crusz in connection with this case on 23rd February 1978. He was required to answer questions and if he tried to say something on his own the police officer shouted at him. At the end he was asked to sign it.

Mr. Hema Weerasinghe, Superintendent of Police, Narcotics Bureau, examined by Mr. Marapana said that in March 1979 he was the ASP in charge of the Crime Detective Bureau (CDB) Headquarters, which supervised the work of CDB units at all police stations. He was also the ASP in charge of the Narcotics Bureau and the City Homicide Squad. All murders in the city of Colombo were routed through the local CDB to the City Homicide Squad.

The first intimation they had of these murders was on 5th March 1979. He had got some papers from Inspector Malcolm Crusz of the Maradana police. At the time they received the information, Mrs. Peiris was still alive and it was not yet a case of homicide. The information was that Mrs. Peiris had been admitted to hospital and it was either attempted homicide or attempted suicide and also that there had been a previous death in similar circumstances of one Ingram who lived in the same place as Mrs. Peiris.

On 19th March they were informed that Mrs. Peiris had died at the General Hospital.

Mr. Bandaranayake asked, "Had anything been done by your unit between 5th and 19th March?"

"Inspector Crusz had recorded some statements and I discussed the investigations made so far with him."

"Had anything been done in regard to Russel Ingrams death in similar circumstances?"

"Yes. I asked Inspector Crusz to get the BHT of Russel Ingram," Mr. Weerasinghe said.

Questioned about the inquest proceedings in respect of Mrs. Peiris's death, Mr. Weerasinghe said he was present when the post-mortem was conducted by Dr. S. Subramaniam, the JMO, assisted by Professor H.V. J. Fernando.

"On 19th March, preliminary evidence had been led by Inspector Lambert Perera, OIC, and City Homicide Squad. On 23rd March, I recorded Mrs. Mihiri Wickramasinghe's statement. I led evidence of Rev. Peiris and Mihiri Wickramasinghe at the resumed inquest on 24th March. Earlier, I recorded a statement by Rev. Peiris. I had the evidence of Rev. Peiris because he was closest to Mrs. Peiris and had provided medication to her during her illness. I thought he was the best person to speak about it. Rev. Peiris did not show any reluctance to give evidence. At the inquest it was held that Mrs. Peiris had pneumonia and prolonged unconsciousness and a further report was to follow," Mr. Weerasinghe said.

Mr. Bandaranayake asked, "Between 5th and 19th March did any police officer go to hospital and see Mrs. Peiris?"

"Inspector Malcolm Crusz had gone and Dr. Terrence Silva had stated that she would die. At that stage it was not a matter for the homicide squad. But we kept the file as Dr. Terrence Silva had said she would die."

Mr. Marapana asked, "On 5th March you were certain that the patient would die?"

"Yes," replied Mr. Weerasinghe.

"At the inquest I did not read out any charges to Rev. Peiris. I did not tell him of any allegations against him. As far as I was concerned no offence had been committed at that stage and the police were conducting investigations with an open mind," Mr. Weerasinghe said.

In reply to Mr. Wickramasekara on the exhumation of Russel Ingram's body, Mr. Weerasinghe said that there was no dispute that the body was that of Russel. They had examined the records at the cemetery and identified the grave in which the body had been interred. There was also a plaque on the coffin bearing Russel Ingram's name. Mr. Weerasinghe was also questioned on searches he had made at the Vicarage on two occasions having obtained a search warrant from the magistrate.

"Rev. Peiris was present and consented to the search on both occasions. In the course of the first search on 3rd April 1978 I recovered several documents. ASP Gamini Weerasinghe who was in the search party made a sketch of the Vicarage while I made a sketch of the vestry. On 4th April, I visited the Vicarage and recovered the book, "Body, Mind and Sugar". Rev. Peiris gave it to me from a book case in the hall. In the second search we were looking for prescriptions and letters written to Rev. Peiris and by him. We recovered 14 documents and a stethoscope. The documents included a prescription by Dr. Lakshman Weerasena dated 10th December 1978," Mr. Weerasinghe said.

Continuing he said that a competent group of police officers were assigned to the case. Inspector Sabaratnam was one of them and he was conversant in all three languages but worked in English.

"By about May 1979 surveillance was kept by the investigating team on the movements of Rev. Mathew Peiris and Dalrene Ingram. At this time Rev. Peiris was residing at the Vicarage. On 3rd May I kept surveillance near Colonial Motors at Union Place where Dalrene was working. At about 5 p.m. Inspector Crusz who was on foot surveillance near Colonial Motors, reported to me that Dalrene had gone in a car being driven along Union Place towards Eye Hospital Junction. I followed that car, which turned into Dharmapala Mawatha and stopped near Cinnamon Gardens post office. Dalrene who was next to the driver got off, crossed the road to 'Osusala' and walked direct to a Blue Renault Dauphine parked in the premises. Rev. Peiris was in the driver's seat. He was dressed in a T shirt. As soon as Dalrene got in, this car took off, past Lipton's roundabout. Near Albert Perera Mawatha, Nugegoda, the car stopped and Dalrene got off. She spoke a few words to Rev. Peiris and walked down Albert Perera Mawatha with two of her children who had come to meet her. Rev. Peiris then drove towards Nugegoda. We lost track of him thereafter as we were following Dalrene at the time," Mr. Weerasinghe said.

Mr. Cecil Goonewardena cross examined Mr. Weerasinghe who said that during the course of the investigations the case was well reported in the national press. Asked whether prior to the arrest of the Dalrene it was reported in the press whether she was a likely suspect, Mr. Weerasinghe replied that there was speculation as to whether there was to be a second arrest.

Mr. Goonewardena asked, "There was a good dialogue between the investigating team and the press and handouts were given?"

"There was a poor dialogue and there were no handouts given. In fact, the press had complained about it," replied Mr. Weerasinghe.

"After the death of Russel Ingram, an inquest was held and Mrs. Cora Ingram gave evidence before the Coroner. The death certificate issued by Dr. Sheriffdeen was produced and the Coroner returned an open verdict," Mr. Weerasinghe said.

In reply to a question by Mr. Goonewardena whether any further inquiries were conducted into the death of Russel by the police at this stage, Mr. Weerasinghe replied in the negative.

Mr. Bandaranayake asked, "At the early stages, which death was the police concentrating on?"

"Mrs. Eunice Peiris's death."

"As far as the death of Russel was concerned, the matter was a closed chapter before Mrs. Peiris's death?"

"Yes. There was only the statement of Mrs. Cora Ingram that she suspected her son Russel may have been poisoned."

He said that Malrani, the daughter of Rev. Peiris, had not in either of her statements to the police said that Dalrene had acted as the mistress of the house on Christmas day.

"What she had in fact said was "Dalrene had helped in the preparation of lunch and helped to lay the table?"

"Yes," replied Mr. Weerasinghe.

The next witness was Mr. Malcolm Crusz, who was the OIC Bambalapitiya. He said that he was at the time attached to the CDB of the Maradana police station. He said that at about 5.45 p.m. on 5th February 1979 information was received from the hospital police post that Mrs. Eunice Peiris had been admitted to hospital in an unconscious state.

"On receipt of this information I proceeded to the hospital and found Mrs. Peiris lying in bed in a state of coma. I then spoke to Dr. Terrence de Silva and recorded his statement. Subsequent to recording the doctor's statement, I proceeded to the Vicarage to speak to the patient's husband Rev. Mathew Peiris. He was present at the time. There were some other people also. I questioned him and tried to find out how Mrs. Peiris had come to be unconscious. He said he would come the following day to make a statement. He came to the Maradana police station the following day at around noon and was questioned for about one and a half hours. I then went with him to the Vicarage and searched his room and recovered 22 drugs. He consented to the search," Mr. Crusz said.

Mr. Bandaranayake asked, "Did you have a warrant?"

"No. He consented to the search."

"Where exactly did you find the drugs?"

"On a bedside table."

"Were they bottles and were they labelled?"

"These were bottles. Some were labelled. I took these drugs into my custody and produced them before the JMO."

He described the 22 drugs he recovered from the Vicarage. Among them were anti-diabetic drugs, iron tablets, some cream and two Disprins.

"I then informed my immediate superior of the progress and continued with the inquiry. Then one Alex Ingram came to the police station on 1st March. I was not present at the time. Subsequently I contacted him and recorded a statement."

Mr. Crusz said that immediately after Russel's death there was no material evidence to take anyone into custody. He said that it was only after Mrs. Eunice Peiris's death that everything came out and investigations were begun into Russel's death. Even though an 'Open verdict' was returned into Russel's death, no investigation was initiated.

Answering Mr. Marapana about surveillance, Mr. Crusz said that he stood at a bus stand near Colonial Motors and pretended to be reading a newspaper while waiting for Dalrene. He saw Dalrene ride out in a car from Colonial Motors and he had followed her in another car. He confirmed what Mr. Weerasinghe said earlier.

Cross examined by Mr. R. I. Obeysekera, Mr. Crusz said normally before starting investigations the police did a study of circumstances leading to the case. He said he questioned Rev. Peiris on 5th February at the Vicarage for about 45 minutes. Rev. Peiris had wanted to come to the police station the following day to make a statement. As there were people at the Vicarage at that time he allowed Rev. Peiris's request.

Mr. Crusz said that he recorded Arumugam's first statement on 23rd February 1979 at the Maradana Police Station. The statement had been recorded in English and read over in Sinhalese to Arumugam. He said that Arumugam understood Sinhala very well.

Mr. Obeysekera asked, "Did you put any pressure on Arumugam in any form?"

"No. The statements made by Arumugam had been voluntary statements. Arumugam had not mentioned to police that he was abused by Rev. Peiris over the purchase of some kerosene oil in the presence of some respectable people of the church. Arumugam had made four statements to the Police. No reference had been made of

Dalrene caning the children. In his second statement, no reference had been made that children were on the roof of the Vicarage," Mr. Crusz said.

Cross examined by Mr. Cecil Goonewardena, he said that in the statement recorded on 3rd April, Arumugam had not mentioned about Mrs. Peiris's illness. He had also not referred to Dalrene and the children being in the front room while Rev Peiris was in the second room.

Re-examined by Mr. Marapana, Mr. Crusz said that it was necessary to record full statements from Arumugam as there was evidence on investigations conducted.

Dr. S. Subramaniam, the JMO, Colombo, at the time of the deaths of Russel and Mrs. Peiris, was the JMO Jaffna when he came to give evidence on 2nd September.

Examined by Mr. Tilak Marapana, Dr. Subramaniam said that from the time he graduated in 1961, he had worked as a house officer, and an acting DMO from 1962 to 1965. From 1965 to 1968 he was an acting JMO Jaffna and then JMO Jaffna.

He said from 1969 to 1972 he was in the United Kingdom doing postgraduate studies. He had degrees of MBBS, MRCP (Forensic Medicine, UK) and Diploma in Medical Jurisprudence. He had twenty years experience as a JMO.

He said before Mrs. Eunice Peiris died he had examined her in ward 47B of the General Hospital, Colombo on 6th February 1979 at the request of the Hospital Police Post. He said that she was unconscious and then the diagnosis was suspected hypoglycaemia and he found nothing contrary to that diagnosis when he examined her.

"On 20th March I conducted a post-mortem examination on Mrs. Peiris. The body was identified by her daughter Mrs. Mihiri Wickramasinghe and a brother Rev. Edison Mendis. Before performing this post-mortem I perused the bed head ticket and familiarized myself with the patient's history. The appearance of the body was that of an ill-nourished female of about 59 years. There were also bed sores on the head and various parts of the body. At the post-mortem I examined the brain and found the distributing blood vessels were normal and internally they showed no signs of disease.

(After the dissection of the formalin preserved brain, Dr. Subramaniam added the following to the post-mortem report. "Increased subdural space with collection of fluid in the subarachnoid space. Softening of brain all over being marked over the frontal lobes and the hippocampal region. Uncal regions were very soft. Cut surface showed thinning of the cortex over the frontal, parietal and temporal regions. There was mild dilatation of ventricular system. Cerebral blood vessels were normal and free of atheroma. Histopathology showed diffuse subcortical degeneration being marked in the temporal lobe.")

Mr. Marapana asked, "If the unconsciousness was attributed to a Cerebro-Vascular Accident (CVA) would you have expected to find signs of that?"

"Yes, a CVA occurs when a blood vessels ruptures and the effect of the rupture would be visible. If it was a blood clot it would be present. Also the area of the brain which suffered would show degeneration."

Mr. Marapana asked, "In the case of a patient who died after being unconscious like Mrs. Peiris, do you keep CVA in mind when you do a post-mortem?"

"Yes."

"But there were no signs in this case that a CVA had occurred?"

"No."

Mr. Bandaranayake asked, "Did you look for such signs of a CVA?"

"Yes."

"Where is the pituitary gland situated?" asked Mr. Marapana.

"In the base of the skull."

"Did you consider the pituitary to be relevant to be examined in the case of Mrs. Peiris?"

"Yes."

"Your conclusion as to the cause of death was 'pneumonia'?"

"Yes."

"The pneumonia was an inevitable consequence of a prolonged unconscious state?"

"Yes."

Dr. Subramaniam said that he had found a thrombosis in the left calf vein. This condition, he said, also arose as a result of the prolonged immobilization of the person.

"Was there any consequences arising from this thrombosis?"

"No."

Mr. Wickramasekara asked, "Was it in any way directly or indirectly the cause of the death of this lady?"

"No," Dr. Subramaniam said.

Mr. Marapana asked, "At the end of the post-mortem examination you made out the report which sets out the observations you made and your opinion?"

"Yes."

"And you have said 'In my opinion death was due to pneumonia and pulmonary oedema due to brain damage'?"

"Yes."

"What are the organs that you looked carefully to either confirm or eliminate this opinion?"

"The unconsciousness in this patient could have been the result of hypoglycaemia and as such all causes that might give rise to hypoglycaemia had to be looked for either to establish or eliminate. The organs are the pancreas, liver, adrenal glands, pituitary gland and the thyroid gland. These are looked for specifically to see for any abnormalities. The only abnormality found was the damage to the brain cells which could have been caused by hypoglycaemia. This damage to the brain would have been permanent and have occurred before death. In this patient I found no signs of a stroke."

"I did not find anything to suggest a diabetic or hepatic coma. I considered a brain infection, but the meninges were normal and there was no adhesion of the membranes. When I examined the chest I found pneumonia in both lungs. The diffuse brain damage was possible due to hypoglycaemia resulting from the ingestion of a hypoglycaemic agent like glibenclamide. Damage to the brain cells would have occurred before death. I carried out histological examinations of the pancreas and found it to be normal. There was no tumour or hyperplasia. I satisfied myself that there was no insulinoma outside the pancreas. I also examined the liver and the heart and found them to be normal. I did not find any traces of cancer in any part of the body," Dr. Subramaniam said.

He said that the cause of death was pneumonia and pulmonary oedema following prolonged unconsciousness due to diffuse brain damage caused by hypoglycaemia, resulting from ingestion of a hypoglycaemic agent like glibenclamide.

Continuing he said, "My post-mortem did not find anything contrary to the clinical diagnosis of hypoglycaemia. The only abnormality other than in the lungs was damage to the brain cells. This was consistent with hypoglycaemia. The prolonged damage to cells showed it as a result of the lack of glucose. However I could not find any cause for the hypoglycaemic condition."

In answer to Mr. Bandaranayake he said he did not find any tumour in the pancreas, cancerous growth or other malignancy anywhere in Mrs. Peiris's body when he performed the post-mortem.

Dr. Subramaniam said that among the 22 items of drugs produced before him by Inspector Malcolm Crusz, there were 10 tablets of Betanese and 5 tablets of Euglucon, both anti-diabetic drugs. (*They are trade names for glibenclamide.*)

Mr. Bandaranayake asked, "What strength were these tablets?"

"I have not mentioned it, but they were 5 mg tablets," Dr. Subramaniam said.

On 30th April 1979, Dr. Subramaniam said he was present at the General Cemetery, Kanatta, when Russel Ingram's body was exhumed. It was identified by Alexander Ingram, the deceased's father.

"The body was packed with saw dust showing it had been embalmed. On doing the post-mortem I found the brain and other vital internal organs were not there. Therefore an opinion could not be expressed. Prior to the exhumation of the body, I was aware of the case of Russel Ingram. This was on the day after Russel had expired and when the doctor in charge of the case had come with an AJMO and consulted me. I was asked by the Coroner at the time Russel died to do a post-mortem."

He said he consulted Dr. Sheriffdeen and other Medical Officers of ward 18 to be present at the post-mortem and was making arrangements to convey to Dr. Sheriffdeen the time the post-mortem would be held. However he could not do the post-mortem as a pathological post-mortem had already been done. He said that he did not receive any stomach contents, particles of hair or nails from Russel Ingram's body to be forwarded to the Government Analyst.

Shown the book titled "Body, Mind and Sugar", Dr. Subramaniam said he had read it after the investigations in this case commenced. He agreed that the book was written in simple language and could be understood easily by laymen. It dealt with the pancreas and hypoglycaemia among other things. It also dealt with the treatment for hypoglycaemic attacks, blood sugar levels and glucose tolerance tests. He knew that this book had been in the possession of Rev. Peiris, and had been taken into the custody of Superintendant of

Police Hema Weerasinghe during the investigation into the Vicarage deaths.

In answer to Mr. Bandaranayake, Dr. Subramaniam said the book gave laymen a very good account of various disorders of the pancreas in relation to hyperinsulinism. He said that the book had been first published in 1951. "That was just after insulin was identified and treatment of diabetes with insulin started," he said.

Cross examined by Mr. R.I. Obeysekera, Dr. Subramaniam said that he performed the post-mortem of Mrs. Peiris and the brain and the pancreas had been subjected to histological examination. He said he was not a histopathologist.

Mr. Obeysekera asked, "When the brain was subjected to histopathology, Dr. H.R. Wickramasinghe was present?"

"It was discussed with him."

"Was he present at the post-mortem?"

"No."

"But he was there when the brain was sliced?"

"Yes."

"He is a neuropathologist?"

"Yes."

"Was he called by you?"

"Yes."

"On what basis did you call in Dr. H.R. Wickramasinghe?"

"Whenever slides of importance have to read by me, I consult him so that he too could give an opinion."

"You admit his specialty in that field?"

"Yes," Dr. Subramaniam said.

He said that Dr. Wickramasinghe also had a look at the slides prepared by him for histology because the analysis of slides could be a specialized function. He said Dr. Wickramasinghe had more experience than him in reading slides of brains.

Answering a query by Mr. Bandaranayake, he said that Dr. Wickramasinghe was working at the General Hospital, Colombo.

"Does he do pathological post-mortems?"

"Yes."

"These pathological post-mortems are for what purpose?"

"The reports go to the ward or the doctor concerned who had treated the patient," Dr. Subramaniam said.

He added that when consulting a person like Dr. Wickramasinghe, that person should have equal or better knowledge to be consulted.

The brain, pancreas, lungs and kidneys of Mrs. Peiris had been subjected to histology. Regarding hyperplasia, he said that prolonged use of an anti-diabetic drug by non-diabetic patient could result in hyperplasia.

Hyperplasia, Dr. Subramaniam explained, is the enlargement of the insulin secreting cells (beta cells) and also the increase in the number of the beta cells in the pancreas. The cause could be the prolonged use of anti-diabetic drugs. An insulinoma he said, could either be single or multiple and even if multiple, may not be generalized.

In answer to Mr. Bandaranayake he said hyperplasia could take if place in a non-diabetic too, if he took anti- diabetic drugs. Such a person would however die prematurely.

Dr. Subramaniam further said that Dr. Sarath Abeysuriya, the Neurosurgeon and Dr. K. J. Nanayakkara, Consultant Physician, had both treated Mrs. Eunice Peiris and were called in by him to be present when the brain was examined. The lungs, kidneys and liver too were subjected to histology. The pancreas could be sectioned very finely even to a thickness of one millimetre. This was more or less done in this case.

Dr. Subramaniam said he excluded islet cell hyperplasia as there was no evidence. He said, "I have seen slides of pancreatic tumours when doing post graduate studies abroad, but had never seen a pancreas with a tumour after that. During the last fifteen years of my practice as a JMO I had occasion to look for tumours of the pancreas."

On a question from Mr. Bandaranayake, Dr. Subramaniam said that in a normal post-mortem all organs of the body are examined. Concentrating on a further examination would depend on the history of the dead person. On a question from Mr. Wickramasekera he said that he concentrated more on the organs of Mrs. Peiris on account of the available history.

Dr. Subramaniam said that the technique in post-mortem was to examine all the organs in the body. Concentration on a particular area would depend on the history of the patient.

In answer to Mr. Bandaranayake he said that at the post-mortem he had examined the pituitary gland carefully and found no abnormalities. He further said that the hypofunction of the pituitary gland could not be in itself diagnosed microscopically but if there was a tumour in the pituitary gland it would have been visible to the naked eye. As he did not detect any abnormality in the pituitary gland he did not subject the gland to histology.

Mr. Obeysekera stopped his cross examination to give way to Mr. Marapana, who on directions by Court would lead in evidence through Dr. Subramaniam, passages from the book "Body, mind and Sugar", on which he would be relying.

Dr. Subramaniam was then shown the book and he read and marked a large number of the passages put to him.

Dr. Subramaniam said that the book titled 'Body, Mind and Sugar' was written by a medical person and a journalist and it gave laymen a very good account of insulinomas and various pancreatic disorders in relation to hypoinsulism. He then referred to various passages in the book in which Mr. Marapana was relying. As directed by Court he read out the passages.

He agreed that there were two kinds of hypoglycaemia, reactive and fasting. Fasting was the insulinoma type of hypoglycaemia. In all cases of hypoglycaemia, the immediate treatment was dextrose to alleviate suffering.

In answer to Mr. Wickramasekara, he said if a patient with reactive hypoglycaemia was brought unconscious to him the immediate treatment would be dextrose. In such an instance if the person accompanying the patient asked him not to give the patient sugar he would consider it to be absurd and think that person was interfering with the treatment.

Referring to a further passage Dr. Subramaniam said that it dealt with functions of the pancreas. He said having referred to a passage relating to insulin shock, that insulin shock arose when there was too much insulin in the system. He explained that it could happen when an overdose of insulin was taken. It could also occur when insulin was secreted as a result of taking an anti-diabetic drug or when there was an insulinoma. The immediate treatment for all this was dextrose.

Answering Mr. Marapana, he said that the drop in the blood pressure could be attributed to a malfunctioning in the pituitary gland.

In answer to the Bandaranayake he said he did not find any tumour in the pancreas, cancerous growth or other malignancy anywhere in Mrs. Eunice Peiris body when he performed the post-mortem.

Mr. P.K. Anthony, a labourer, General Hospital, Colombo, the next witness, examined by Mr. Tilak Marapana, said in July 1978 he was a labourer at the Colombo General Hospital, attached to ward 18. One of his duties was to deliver blood and urine samples to the laboratory. Shown a request form for GTT, he said he may have taken blood and urine samples to the laboratory. He recalled seeing a patient by the name of Russel Ingram in ward 18. He said he could remember the patient Russel Ingram because Christian priests used to visit him.

Mr. R.K. Suresh Chandra, an Attorney-at-Law and Notary Public, examined by Mr. Nimal Gamini Amaratunge, State Counsel, said he was in practice since 1978. He knew the first accused Rev. Mathew Peiris. He had known him for about 10 years. Shown the 'Last Will' of Mrs. Dalrene Ingram dated second December 1978 he said it was attested by him. He drafted that Will. When Mrs. Dalrene Ingram approved her Last Will she was concerned about the welfare of her children. He said the beneficiaries of Mrs. Ingram's Will were her three children. The Will also appointed Rev. Mathew Peiris as the executor and guardian of the children.

In answer to Mr. Bandaranayake, he said when the first accused gave him instructions to draft the Will, Mrs. Ingram was not with him. Thereafter he drafted the Will and took it to the Vicarage on second December. The second accused Mrs. Ingram was also there and so was the first accused. He said he explained the draft to Mrs. Ingram and she approved it. Thereafter it was signed by Dalrene, the witnesses and by himself (witness).

In answer to Mr. Bandaranayake he said it was just a few months before second December 1978 that he came to know Mrs. Ingram. She was introduced to him by Rev. Peiris when he went to the Vicarage. At that time he was not aware that Mrs. Ingram's husband was dead. At the time he attested the Will he was aware that Mrs. Ingram was a widow. He further recalled attesting a signature card for a bank account on 5th. The signature card which he attested was brought to him by Rev. Peiris. The card was to open a joint bank account. He attested the signatures of Rev. Peiris and Mrs. Ingram.

Mr. Suresh Chandra said that Rev. Peiris attended lectures at his classes. He followed Roman law, Legal Systems of Sri Lanka, Criminal Law and Constitutional Law lectures.

Cross examined by Mr. R. I. Obeysekera, Senior Counsel for Rev. Peiris he said the Will was very elementary and the main item was the appointment of a guardian for the children of Mrs. Ingram.

Cross examined by Mr. Champani Padmasekera, Junior Counsel for Mrs. Ingram, he said when Mrs. Ingram approved the Will she was most concerned about her children.

Examined by Deputy Solicitor General Tilak Marapana, the next witness Inspector of Police Lambert Perera said that in May 1979 he had been an Inspector, and was in charge of the Homicide Squad of the CDB. He was also one of the team investigating into the 'Vicarage deaths'. He was presently the Headquarters Inspector of the Badulla Police.

He recalled that on 9th May 1979 he had conducted surveillance duties. He described in great detail how he had kept surveillance on Rev. Peiris and on one occasion followed him. He took Dalrene and her three children to dinner to a hotel. He watched them enjoy an egg hopper dinner. On 14th May 1979 he had again conducted surveillance duty on Rev. Peiris from 1.45 p.m. to 9.00 p.m. in an unmarked car.

"At 6.52 p.m. Rev. Peiris left the Vicarage and drove to the YMBA building at Nugegoda where he picked up the eldest son of Dalrene. Then Rev. Peiris drove towards Nugegoda. Near Mahasen Mawatha, Dalrene was walking on the road with her other two children. She was about 150 yards away from Albert Perera Mawatha. Rev. Peiris, Dalrene and her three children then drove up and stopped at the Supermarket Park. I then sent a Police Constable to watch the car. At 7.00 p.m., Rev. Peiris drove off from Nugegoda towards Pannipitiya and then came back to Maharagama to the Manel Hotel and Bakery. Rev. Peiris had gone into the hotel and Dalrene got off with two of her children and walked along the road. They all had dinner at the hotel," he said.

Cross examined by Mr. R.I. Obeysekera, he said that on 15th May he went back to Raheema Hotel and found out that Rev. Peiris had purchased hoppers and egg *rotis* and left.

He said that Mrs. Jackson's first and second statements were recorded at her house at Ethul Kotte. In the course of Mrs. Jackson's statement she had said "...having put the ring, Father Peiris kissed and blessed Dalrene."

At the conclusion of the testimony given by IP Lambert Perera, Mr. R.I. Obeysekera, Counsel for the Defence, informed Court that they intended to take certain matters of law before the Prosecution leads any further evidence.

He submitted that there were three matters of law concerning the prosecution's prospective further evidence. Two of these matters concerned the admissibility of certain documentary evidence and the other is a matter of procedure concerning the statement of witnesses. One of the matters concerned documentary evidence and questioned of the inadmissibility of evidence given by the accused at the inquest proceedings.

"In regard to that matter we wish the counsel for the prosecution to address us further. In regard to the matter of procedure namely the calling of witnesses, the counsel for the defence wished to know from the prosecution whether the prosecution intended to call Dr. Abeysuriya, who is listed as a witness on the indictment and also whether the prosecution intended to place the report of the Government Analyst on the examination of certain productions sent to him by the JMO Colombo," Mr. Obeysekera said.

Mr. Marapana informed the Court that he did not intend to call Dr. Abeysuriya as a witness for the prosecution and he further informed the Court that he is not able to place the testimony of the Government Analyst as he is confronted with the legal difficulty regarding the voyage of the productions to the Government Analyst.

After eight days of legal submissions by the prosecution and defence, the Bench reserved their order on the matter.

The Trial-at-Bar comprising Judges Tissa Dias Bandaranayake, P. Ramanathan and D.C.W. Wickramasekara refused the application made by the Defence Counsel in regard to the summoning of witnesses.

The Chairman Mr. Bandaranayake said, "We have considered that the submissions made by both counsel appearing for the defence and we are of the opinion that this is not an appropriate case where the Court should have recourse to the sections cited. I therefore refuse the application in regard to the summoning of witnesses. In regard to the admissibility to document P9 we uphold the objection taken by the defence and we hold that the document is not receivable in evidence in this case. Reasons will be stated later".

The next witness IP Cyril Selvaratnam examined by Mr. Tilak Marapana said that in 1974 he was posted to the Colombo Fraud Bureau, which was part of the CDB in Colombo. In 1977 he was posted to the CDB and in 1980 as OIC, CDB. His duties included supervising of all CDBs in the city police stations.

In March 1979 a special team led by Mr. Hema Weerasinghe was appointed to investigate the present case. It was done a few days after Mrs. Eunice Peiris's death. He said that he was a member of this team.

He said that nurse Mrs. Manawadu had mentioned in her statement that she saw the Russel sweating after the food brought by the first accused was taken.

"The witnesses whose statements I had recorded were Mr. Alex Ingram, Mrs. Cora Ingram, Miss Chandrakanthi Dharmadasa, Mr. Russel Jackson, several nurses at the General Hospital, two laboratory technicians, Dr. Wijesiriwardena, Dr. Pinto, Miss Malrani Peiris and Mr. Munilal Peiris. In order to record the statement of Miss Malrani Peiris and Mr. Munilal Peiris, he along with Mr. Hema Weerasinghe visited the United Kingdom and was there during the period 31st July to 18th August 1979. All appointments for this purpose had been arranged by Scotland Yard," he said.

Inspector Selvaratnam said that Mr. Munilal Peiris was questioned by ASP Hema Weerasinghe at his workplace in Essex, England. Mr. Peiris did not say in the course of his statement anything with regard to Rev. Peiris going into a trance while he was in England in April 1978.

Cross examined by Mr. R. I. Obeysekera, Inspector Selvaratnam said two statements were recorded from Miss Malrani Peiris. The second statement was on 13th August 1979 in Cardiff. Her first statement was recorded in April by Mr. Hema Weerasinghe at the Vicarage, Holy Emmanuel Church, Moratuwa.

After the statement was recorded, Miss Malrani Peiris had read it and initialled every page to the effect that the statement had been recorded correctly. The same procedure was followed after her second statement. In the course of Miss Peiris's statements she did not say her mother cried after reading a cable. Miss Peiris did not in any of her statements say that Rev. Peiris had told her it was the angels' guidance to him that Mrs. Peiris should stay back in the UK with the children.

Mr. Munilal Peiris was working in a hospital as a trainee nurse in Psychiatry. He made one statement. He was questioned by ASP Weerasinghe and Mr. Selvaratnam recorded the statement. This statement was recorded at Brentwood, Essex. He had been accompanied to Brentwood by Detective Sergeant Woodingham of Scotland Yard. There was no mention in Mr. Peiris's statement with regard to the first accused going into a trance when he was in the UK in April 1978. Mr. Peiris did not mention anything about a calamity that Rev. Peiris had spoken of.

He said he recorded one statement from Mrs. Myrtle Mendis and another statement was recorded by ASP Hema Weerasinghe. He said that Mrs. Mendis never mentioned in any of her statements that in the course of conversation with Mrs. Peiris, Mrs. Peiris told her that Rev. Peiris had said that the doctors wanted her to take pills.

Mr. Selvaratnam said there was no reference in any petition to the two accused travelling together in a car with children close to Bishop's College or that the car was sporting a Prince of Wales College flag.

Referring to the statements made by Rev. Edison Mendis, he said that Rev. Mendis, had not stated that he phoned the Vicarage on 30th January 1979. Mr. Alexander Ingram, father of Russel did not mention in any of his statements that Dalrene cleaned the palm of

Rev. Peiris by resting the palm on her thigh. He said that Alex Ingram did not state that he saw the first accused getting into a trance on 10th June 1978 at the Vicarage, in any of the four statements.

Mr. Ingram did not state in any of his statements that during a trance the first accused uttered the words 'pancreas, pancreas' or that the first accused said he was guided by the angels as to the treatment. There was no mention about a stethoscope being used by the first accused in any of the statements nor did Mr. Ingram state that the first accused prepared food for Russel or that the first accused prepared food on a stove in the study.

Mr. Selvaratnam said that Mr. Ingram never stated that Rev. Peiris fed Russel Ingram during the period he was at the Vicarage in June 1978, nor was there any mention about Rev. Peiris taking out pills from his pocket, for administration to Russel. Mr. Ingram never stated that Rev. Peiris used to often say that sugar was poison for Russel and rice was bad or that angels said sugar was bad, nor did he state that when Russel was at the hospital in 1978 he had a slur in his speech. Mr. Ingram did not in any of his statements mention that on 9th June 1978 when he visited Russel at the Vicarage Russel told him that he could sleep, sleep and sleep. Mr. Ingram never stated that in June 1978 after an alleged conversation between Rev. Peiris and a lady doctor, Rev. Peiris told him that they were going to give dextrose and that would be Russel's end.

He said nurse Miss Ranaweera had stated that Russel did not speak much with anyone but she saw the patient speaking with Dalrene. He said that there was no allegation of a love affair between Rev. Peiris and Dalrene in any of the petitions, which Rev. Edison Mendis had sent to ASP Hema Weerasinghe. He has also not stated in any of the petitions that when he went to see Mrs. Eunice Peiris on 31st January, she had complained she was too feeble to dial his number.

Inspector Selvaratnam produced five such petitions.

He said that nurse Mrs. Manawadu did not say she found the clamp closed twice and that she informed the doctors about it. She did not state that there was an outsider by the bedside of Russel or that the milk brought by Rev. Peiris for Russel had to be diluted with water on account of its thickness.

Mr. Wickramasekara asked "Did you pose questions to her or did she on her own give a narrative?"

"I questioned her."

In answer to Mr. Bandaranayake, he said there was a possibility that Mrs. Manawadu stated certain things on her own while answering questions put to her. He said Mrs. Manawadu had mentioned in her statement that she saw the patient sweating after the food brought by the first accused was taken.

Mr. Obeysekera then questioned him with regard to the statement made by nurse Sugathapala. He said that she told him that she saw the drip given to Russel clamped.

At this stage the Court warned the defence to be more careful when questioning with regard to contradictions.

Cross examined by Mr. Cecil Goonewardena, Mr. Selvaratnam said that Mr. Ingram has not stated that when he questioned Dalrene at the Durdans, she told him that these people say that Russel was having a condition opposite to diabetes. He said Mrs. Mendis had not stated that the second accused told her that Mrs. Eunice Peiris was admitted to Durdans on 15th January 1979 with high fever.

Questioned with reference to Mr. Graham Jackson's statement, Mr. Selvaratnam said Mr. Jackson did not in his statement mention that when he was at the Vicarage he heard the lock clicking and the bolt being drawn on the door leading to the room in which Russel was lying. Mr. Jackson did not state that his wife told him that pills were given to Russel by Rev. Peiris on 16th July at the Vicarage, nor did he mention anything about a urinal drip or a urinal stand which he saw at the Vicarage. He had also not stated that on 17th July he went to the Vicarage on receipt of a phone call from Rev. Peiris.

Mr. Selvaratnam said that Mr. Ingram did not mention in any of his statements that Dalrene cleaned the palm of Rev. Mathew Peiris by resting the palm on her thigh. Mr. Jackson mentioned in his statement that he was aware that Mrs. Peiris died about a month or two after she returned, under the same circumstances as Russel.

In answer to questions by Mr. Anil Obeysekera, junior counsel for Rev. Peiris, Mr. Selvaratnam said he recorded the statement of the nurse Miss Wimala Ranaweera. In her statement she had stated that she noticed that Russel was sweating after taking a feed. She did not state that bottles in which feeds were given were ever found unwashed nor did she state that passion fruit and king coconut water for Russel was brought from outside.

Mrs. Manawadu did not say that she found the clamp closed twice and that she informed the doctors about it. She did not state that there was an outsider by the bedside of Russel nor that the milk brought by the first accused for Russel had to be diluted with water on account of its thickness.

Mr. Wickramasekara asked, "Did you pose questions to her or did she on her own give a narrative?"

"I questioned her."

In answer to Mr. Bandaranayake, he said there was a possibility that Mrs. Manawadu stated certain things on her own while answering questions put to her. He said he told Mrs. Manawadu that it was suspected that the patient had been poisoned. He said Mrs. Manawadu had mentioned in her statement that she saw the patient sweating after the food brought by the first accused was taken.

Dr. (Mrs.) Manel Panditharatne, a medical practitioner at the Durdans Hospital giving evidence said that she had graduated from the University of Ceylon and passed her MBBS in 1963. After serving one year in the Health Department she had proceeded to England where she had obtained a Diploma in Child Health. After returning to Sri Lanka she joined the Durdans Hospital as a Medical Officer.

She said that Russel Ingram was admitted to Durdans at 6.30 p.m. on 8th July 1978.

In answer to question from Mr. Bandaranayake, Dr. Panditharatne said she recalled someone accompanying the patient, but could not remember whether any person was in the room or outside. She saw the patient on being informed by the Duty Nurse. Prior to this, no other doctor in the hospital had seen the patient. She obtained the history from a person whom she did not know. Although Russel had been conscious, he had not been in a fit state to give his history. She noted on the BHT that Russel had been irrational, disoriented and restless. She said she had found it difficult to examine the patient as he was turning from side to side. When she questioned him, he did not seem to know where he was. She thought the patient had been fairly seriously ill.

Dr. Panditharatne said, "I found nothing abnormal in Russel but he appeared to have a psychiatric problem. I did not get the smell of alcohol from Russel. He remained in the hospital under the care of Dr. Muttiah, a Consultant Physician, and left hospital on 16th July. When he left he appeared to be normal."

Regarding Mrs. Eunice Peiris, Dr. Panditharatne said, "She had been admitted to Durdans on 15th January 1979 under the care of Dr. Lakshman Weerasena. At the time I saw her, she was being given dextrose and dexamethasone intravenously, as instructed by Dr. Weerasena. When I examined I found her drowsy and her blood pressure was 150 over 100. She did not speak but obeyed commands and had responded to painful stimuli."

Cross examined by Mr. Cecil Goonewardena, she said that Russel was alright within a day or two after the medication. She said that the diagnosis of Russel could be described as an agitational condition. She said that she did not get the smell of alcohol from Russel when he was warded at the Durdans Hospital in July 1978.

Mr. Leon Dias, Manager of Osusala, giving evidence said that from about 1977 Rev. Peiris used to buy regularly Euglucon and Sodium

Bicarbonate once every 3 weeks. He said that Euglucon was freely available from about 1977 onwards and it was sold at 16/- per foil and that each foil had 10 tablets of 5 mg strength each. He further said that this drug was in the first schedule of the Foods and Drugs Act and therefore could be sold over the counter without a prescription. He knew the Rev. Peiris well and he usually served doctors and priests before he served the public.

Mr. S. M. Sudusinghe, Managing Partner of New City Chemist, a Pharmacy and Grocery at 889, Maradana Road, Colombo 10, situated within a walking distance of the Vicarage, giving evidence said that he knew Rev. Peiris for over 10 years and that Mrs. Eunice Peiris had an account with him in his shop. Both she and Rev. Peiris used to buy things on this account. Mr. Sudusinghe said that he had sold anti-diabetic Euglucon tablets to Rev. Peiris. In particular he said he sold 50 tablets of Euglucon of 5 mg strength to Rev. Peiris on 12th July 1978. He identified the counterfoil of the bill book produced. This sale has also been entered in the credit ledger, which bears the credit account of Mrs. Eunice Peiris. The counterfoil showed that it has been sold to Rev. Peiris.

Mr. Sudusinghe said that at the end of the month these bills are sent to the Vicarage for settlement in Mrs. Peiris's name. These bills have been paid by Rev. Peiris up to the end of November 1978.

Professor K. Jayasena, Professor of Pharmacology of Peradeniya University who was both a Medical Doctor as well as a Chemist and was presently with the World Health Organization giving evidence said that glibenclamide acts on functioning cells in the pancreas and makes them secrete more insulin. It is sold in Sri Lanka under the trade name Euglucon. Professor Jayasena said that an anti-diabetic tablet can be crushed and put into liquid and it will pass down the oesophagus and will get absorbed in the stomach.

Professor Jayasena cross examined by Mr. R. I. Obeysekera said he was aware that unconscious patients were fed through a nasal tube. He agreed that if any crushed tablet was mixed in some liquid and given to a person through a nasal tube it would go through the tube easily. If Euglucon tablets were ground and put into a watery solution it would settle down at the bottom sooner than if it was put into a thick soup.

Once the drug entered the stomach it would disintegrate. Thereafter part of it could get into the portal blood streams and enter the liver. Then it goes through the hepatic circulation and enters the heart. He agreed that the liver metabolized the drug, which meant that each molecule of Euglucon gets hydrolyzed into two breakdown products. From there it entered the heart and the lungs through the pulmonary vein. Thereafter it gets pumped out into various parts such as the pancreas.

Mr. Bandaranayake asked, "Does it also go into the brain?"

"Yes, but there could only be a part, as Euglucon does not have direct access to the brain. It acts through the pancreas."

Professor Jayasena said he had studied this subject and was aware that the action of Euglucon would take place in about ten minutes or so and if a non-diabetic took Euglucon it could be clinically diagnosed when signs of hypoglycaemia appeared. This would also depend on the amount of Euglucon taken. The other method of diagnosing whether the drug had been taken was a blood test.

Cross examining Professor Jayasena, Mr. Obeysekera referred to an article taken from the 'Archives of Internal Medicine' titled 'Sulphonyl urea induced factitious hypoglycaemia'. Professor Jayasena said he agreed with what was stated in that article. He agreed that if a Euglucon tablet was crushed and mixed with a thick solution like thick soup it would remain in suspension for a long time. The drug 'Mogadon' too would have no effect on the action of Euglucon but if a large dose of 'Mogadon' was given it could put a person into a coma as a result of Euglucon into a deeper coma.

Mr. Bandaranayake asked, "Up to how long after injecting Euglucon or any other anti-diabetic drug could you expect to find traces of it?"

"Probably after five days. If a single dose of about 20 mg was given one would not find traces."

In answer to Mr. Cecil Goonewardena, he said that if Euglucon or any other anti-diabetic drug was given along with food, the traces would remain in the body for a longer period.

Dr. Dayasiri Fernando, who is related to both, Rev. Peiris and Mrs. Peiris, giving evidence said that he was attached to the Professorial Unit of the General Hospital, Colombo and was also a Senior Lecturer in Surgery. He was a Consultant Surgeon at the same hospital.

He said he has come across the book "Hypoglycaemia" written by Marks and Rose when he was in England. He thought this was a standard work and a very good reference book.

Dr. Fernando said that some time before 17th May 1978, Rev. Peiris came and met him at the Accident Ward of the General Hospital where he was working at the time and spoke to him about 'an interesting case'. Rev. Peiris had told him that Dr. P.A.P. Joseph had wanted him to speak to him.

Dr. Fernando cross examined by Mr. R. I. Obeysekera, said he specialized in gastroenterology which involved the whole digestive system including the gall bladder and the pancreas.

Questioned on insulinomas, Dr. Fernando said they could be single or multiple. When one says it was multiple it could be more than one and could be several. Insulinomas could be very small. The smallest recorded is 0.5 millimeters but what is significant is 5 millimeters. Less than 5 millimeters in size may not be functionally significant. All the same it could secrete insulin. But to produce hypoglycaemia, it may not be significant.

Mr. Bandaranayake asked, "If a growth is 5 millimetre, is it palpable?"

"It would be difficult to palpate if it is in a tissue. It may be seen in an organ."

Dr. Fernando said that in most difficult cases he would consult Professor Navaratne, his superior, who was also the Head of his Unit.

Mr. Marapana re-examined Dr. Fernando and thereafter he told Court that he had concluded leading evidence and moved to close the prosecution case when the trial is resumed on 25th October 1983.

Mr. R. I. Obeysekera objected to the defence being called upon to answer the charges.

On 27th October, Mr. R. I. Obeysekera commencing his submissions to the defence application that they be not called upon to answer the changes, said that if a pancreatic tumour was an alternative hypothesis in the case of Russel's death, then there was no question of homicide. Then it was a death due to natural causes as happens during a heart attack.

In the case of Mrs. Eunice Peiris, according to Dr. Sathanandan's evidence she was depressed about matters regarding her children.

"It could be that Mrs. Peiris took one diabetic pill accidently which caused her condition. Dr. Nagaratnam in his evidence had said that one such pill was sufficient to bring the blood sugar level to 30 mg% said doctors gave their mind to the fact whether what the patient had been administered was an anti-diabetic drug. However they did not take follow up action to discover the drug. The knowledge of Rev. Peiris with regard to diabetic and related drugs was understandable as he himself was a diabetic. Even after the death of Mrs. Peiris he continued to buy anti-diabetic drugs," Mr. Obeysekera said.

"The evidence given by Dr. P.A.P. Joseph and Mr. Alex Ingram could not be reconciled. According to the evidence of Mr. Ingram he was asked by Rev. Peiris to go to Dr. Joseph's residence and collect a letter. He met Dr. Joseph and brought the letter at about 12.30 p.m. on that day. Dr. Joseph had said he visited the Vicarage the same day by lunch time. Although he went there, he had said, he was not allowed to see the patient. There was no room for such an inference. If Dr. Joseph did not see the patient why did he give a prescription?" Mr. Obeysekera asked.

He pointed to many lapses on the part of the hospital authorities.

"When the patient was given 50% glucose and the condition was getting worse the hospital failed to take a blood sample and test the blood sugar level. The nurses' evidence given after 8 months of the incident is totally unacceptable. What the nurses so closely observed and suspected was not told to the police or the doctors. Nurse Manawadu had lied in her evidence when she said that she saw the drip clamped. But this was never told even to the doctors. She had told Court when she found an unwashed bottle it was indication that someone else gave the meals."

Mr. Obeysekera further said these were the very nurses who were very busy and sometimes forgot to enter the FBC. Another nurse Miss Sugathadasa had said that she suspected Rev. Peiris when she saw the clamp closed. But this was never mentioned to the police.

He said that a reasonable jury would never convict the accused in this case. When Russel was first admitted to the General Hospital, he had 40 mg% sugar content in his blood and there was no brain injury. He had gained a quick recovery. According to medical evidence a Euglucon pill was effective for only one and a half to two hours. Russel Ingram had been unconscious for two days.

Russel had been unconscious for two days prior to hospitalization according to Alex Ingram's evidence. This could not be believed. He said the medical evidence did not prove that. Mr. Obeysekera said it was not for hypoglycaemia that Mrs. Peiris was hospitalized. Her blood report had not been submitted.

Dr. Nagaratnam had not been questioned in Court regarding Mrs. Peiris's admission to Durdans. Rev. Edison Mendis had not told the children that Mrs. Peiris had mentioned about her being given 7 pills at a time. Rev. Peiris had never said that Mrs. Peiris had an ailment in the pancreas. What he had said was that she was suffering from depression. Mr. Obeysekera said most of the doctors had given evidence relying on memory without any notes and it was dangerous to go on such evidence. Rev. Peiris had told his son that

Mrs. Peiris was feeling drowsy. At that time he had given her some pills prescribed by Dr. Sathanandan. Mr. Obeysekera said Mrs. Pciris was not suffering from hypoglycaemia. He said this being a criminal case there was insufficient evidence to call for a defence.

Mr. Cecil Goonewardena submitted that the Deputy Solicitor General had stated that Dalrene had not asked Eardley Mendis about Mr. Peiris's condition when he arrived at Colonial Motors and that Dalrene did not get an opportunity to inform Dr. Joseph about Russel's condition. Parker Ingram too had not told anything about it to the doctor. Although Dalrene was at the Vicarage when the first accused entered into a trance on 29th December, she was unaware of the things which occurred in a room at night. When Eardley received a message about Mrs. Peiris's illness, Dalrene had informed Rev. Peiris about it. As the Mendises treated Dalrene with suspicion she could not ask Eardley about Mrs. Peiris's condition.

He said there was no proof about any misbehaviour on Dalrene's part. She may have considered Mrs. Peiris's sickness as a natural illness. Mr. Goonewardena thanked the Chief Justice for referring this case to a High-Court at Bar notwithstanding the objections raised by the Attorney General's Department. Mr. Goonewardena said as this was a case of circumstantial evidence, every circumstance had to be proved beyond any reasonable doubt.

"If this was a case before a jury the proceeding would have been stopped by now due to the inadequacy of the evidence. The prosecution tried to base its charges on an alleged illicit love affair between the two accused. They have put the relationship under an umbrella of a strong sexual relationship. But so far the prosecution had been unable to prove a single charge," Mr. Goonewardena said. He cited authorities in support of his submissions.

"There was no evidence to show an illicit sexual relationship between Rev. Mathew Peiris and Mrs. Dalrene Ingram on which the prosecution relies to prove there was a conspiracy between them to get rid of their spouses. The bedrock of the prosecution case was the alleged close association between the two accused and that they were involved in a grand plan to 'remove' Russel and Mrs. Peiris who were an 'obstruction' to the continuation of their friendship. The prosecution had to rely entirely on circumstantial evidence for Court to infer that there was a close association between the two accused," said Mr. Goonewardena.

Citing the judgement 'Queen vs. Liyanage', Mr. Goonewardena said, "It must be proved that the accused had jointly conspired to kill. In considering the evidence in this case the Court must take into account the evidence in regard to the nature of the accused. Mr. Wanigasekera, Rev. Peiris's son Munilal, daughter Malrani, brother-in-law Rev. Edison Mendis, sister-in-law Myrtle Mendis all said that he was a kind hearted and sympathetic person. Dr. J. G. C. Peiris, whom the State called from abroad, said that when helping people, Rev. Peiris made no distinction. It did not matter whether it was a man or woman a spinster or a widow or a divorcee."

Mr. Bandaranayake commented, "He said 'Yes' to a question put by you"

Mr. Goonewardena said, "But that was the evidence and it is in this light that they should view his helping Dalrene. The prosecution case was that he helped Dalrene not for any altruistic purpose but that he was motivated by base sexual impulse. That was the prosecution case if it was to be put in an unvarnished way. We have heard about the stories of King Arthur's Court where every day there was an effort to help a damsel in distress. Wasn't there something of a Sir Galahad in Rev. Peiris when he advertised for an annexe? There was no evidence that he had wanted to purchase a house. It was true that he paid the first month's rent for the annex but thereafter it was Dalrene, who had started working who paid the rent."

"There was no evidence that Rev. Peiris bequeathed any large sums of money to her. By the time Russel died, her in-laws had fallen out with her. She did not come from an affluent family and it was in these circumstances that through sympathy Rev. Peiris had asked her to wait at the Vicarage. There was also evidence that Russel never ran a house except in Kandy. There he lost his job. It was around this time that they began attending the Thursday services with the hope that something good would came from them. Was it unusual for a sympathetic person like Rev. Peiris to help them?" asked Mr. Mr. Goonewardena.

Continuing Mr. Goonewardena said that Rev. Edison Mendis had said that at no stage did Munilal tell him of suspicions he had of a close association between the two accused. Parker Ingram's evidence was that he had seen no impropriety in the behaviour of Rev. Peiris and Dalrene.

Referring to the evidence of witnesses who said they had seen Rev. Peiris putting his arms round Dalrene's waist, Mr. Goonewardena said that was not enough to prove sexual intimacy. Witnesses said they saw nothing wrong in that. Referring to Mrs. Jackson's evidence that she saw Rev. Peiris putting both arms round Dalrene's waist and hugging her while Russel remained ill on bed, Mr. Goonewardena said that when she complained of what she saw to her husband his reply had been that he would have been consoling her. Mr. Goonewardena asked whether such things would have been done openly if the two accused had an illicit love affair.

Referring to Munilal's evidence that there was an over familiarity between Dalrene and his father, Mr. Goonewardena said that Munilal had thought that by Dalrene's act of offering him a sweet drink at the Vicarage was improper.

"Was it not an act of Courtesy on Dalrene's part? Could it be said that she was throwing her weight about? I would have been happy if anyone offered me a drink - a soft drink," Mr. Goonewardena said amidst laughter in the Court.

None of the material adduced by the prosecution had proved any illicit relationship between them. Arumugam's evidence was a litany of lies. Although Arumugam and other witnesses had stated many additional things in Court, not a word of these things had been mentioned to the police.

Continuing his submissions Mr. Goonewardena said that none of the charges against his client Dalrene had been proved. On the question of the alleged sexual motive, which it was said prompted the accused to get rid of their spouses, he referred to the evidence of Mr. Eardley Mendis, a brother of Mrs. Peiris and said that Mr. Mendis had insulted and abused Dalrene and she was compelled to stop visiting Mrs. Peiris in hospital. She could not attend Mrs. Peiris's funeral as by then she was a suspected murderess.

"There was also Eardley Mendis's evidence that Dalrene's lunch was brought from the Vicarage, sometimes by Rev. Peiris. There was also an occasion when Dalrene was not well and Rev. Peiris had taken her some toast. Did this mean that there was some intimate relationship between them? Why should he do this unless through sympathy?" he asked.

"Eardley Mendis has also said he had seen Rev. Peiris and Dalrene talking to each other often on those occasions and once at the Markfed premises. This was done in the open and broad daylight and not in secret. If that was the sort of evidence on which the prosecution wanted them to infer that there was sexual intimacy between Rev. Peiris and Dalrene, one might even be afraid to talk to any woman hereafter! Another example of Eardley Mendis's fertile imagination was when he says he thought there was some relationship between the two accused when he saw Dalrene sweeping the Vicarage dressed in a frock," Mr. Goonewardena said.

"What else is she to wear? I can understand if this witness said this on seeing her wearing a bikini or a swim suit! But, Eardley Mendis was compelled to admit that he had not mentioned a word about a love affair to the police and that he came out with it for the first time in this Court."

Dealing with the evidence that Dalrene brought a cake on Rev. Peiris's birthday, Mr. Goonewardena asked what was wrong in a woman who was helped when she was in difficulty, bringing a cake for her benefactor.

"It was also stated that when Edna Fernando, a sister of Mrs. Peiris was there, when Dalrene cut the cake. What was wrong or sinister in that?" he asked. Mr. Goonewardena pointed out that there had been occasions when the wife of a good friend of his would cut the cake on his (Mr. Goonewardena's) birthday even though his mother was present.

There was evidence that even after this party Edna Fernando had invited Dalrene for her wedding anniversary. Dalrene could not attend. Mr. Goonewardena asked whether such an invitation would have been extended to Dalrene of there was any animosity or ill-feeling or any suspicion of an illicit relationship between her and Rev. Peiris. What had happened in this instance was that instead of being thanked for being helpful to the Peiris family she was being blamed.

Another point that was made was that Dalrene wanted to see that the boarders were sent away in order to continue her clandestine association with Rev. Peiris.

"But what was the evidence? The boarder Anoma left of her own accord while Chandrakanthi Dharmadasa left when she heard Mrs. Peiris would not be coming back for some time. Where is the evidence that they wanted the boarders to leave so that they could live like two love birds," he questioned.

Referring to Dalrene getting a job at Colonial Motors, Mr. Goonewardena said it was important that Rev. Peiris did not get her the job but that she got it through her own efforts. It was Russel's father's (Parker Ingram's) evidence that Russel held Rev. Peiris in high esteem. Mr. Goonewardena said there was not cogent or convincing evidence to show intimacy between the two accused. The evidence of Arumugam was so untrustworthy that it did not bear examination. Court would have to take into account the strong animosity which Arumugam had towards the accused.

"There was no evidence that Russel and Dalrene hated each other. On the contrary they were getting on well. It was important to remember Parker Ingram's evidence that when Russel was ill and they were waiting for an ambulance to remove him to hospital, Dalrene was crying bitterly. It was Dalrene who paid for the ambulance. There was also the unimpeachable evidence of Dr. Anula Wijesundera that she had seen Dalrene feeding Russel in hospital. Dalrene visited Russel at both stages of his hospitalization. Mr. Goonewardena said no adverse inference should be drawn from the fact that Dalrene did not attend on Russel while he lay unconscious. No one else attempted to do so either. It was a job which needed special skill or else if something went wrong Dalrene would have got the blame for it. On all this evidence there was nothing that Dalrene had cooled off towards Russel. There was also no evidence that Mrs. Peiris resented Dalrene's staying at the Vicarage. Mrs. Peiris' letter of 14th January 1978, a day before she entered Durdans in which she says "Fortunately Dalrene sees to the marketing" cuts across Malrani's evidence that Mrs. Peiris did not like Dalrene staying at the Vicarage. This showed there was no hostility on Mrs. Peiris's part towards Dalrene," Mr. Goonewardena said.

Dealing with Dalrene's conduct, Mr. Goonewardena said attempts had been made to tie her up with the charges by introducing the element of hypoglycaemia.

"We now know that Russel's condition had nothing to do with a hypoglycaemic attack. Dr. (Mrs.) Panditharatne said it was a psychiatric condition. What was important was that the prosecution alleged that when Dalrene was asked by Russel's father what was wrong with Russel she replied that it was a condition opposed to diabetes. But not a word of this has been mentioned to the police by Parker Ingram. That is what the prosecution relies on as a false statement by Dalrene; that knowing Russel's real condition she said something untrue."

Mr. Goonewardena submitted that the Deputy Solicitor General who at the commencement described the two accused as lovers had now watered it down as an emotional relationship. He submitted that the evidence led was not sufficient to rebut the presumption of innocence. The evidence was led to show that Dalrene knew that pills were administered and she remained silent. It is on the evidence of Bridgette Jackson the prosecution built the argument that Dalrene was aware that the pills were administered. Her evidence was totally discredited. Rev. Peiris, according to her evidence had the pills himself but asked Dalrene where the pills were. This was made up to rope Dalrene.

"Then the prosecution argued that Dalrene knew about Russel's condition. The two items of evidence placed to support this were unworthy of consideration. The prosecution tried to make capital of the fact that Dalrene informed the Rev. Peiris about the relations trying to take Mrs. Peiris to Moratuwa. Rev. Peiris told his wife the information was given to him by Dalrene. If Dalrene was a conspirator will Rev. Peiris mention her name?" Mr. Goonewardena asked.

"Munilal did not know till 2nd January that Dalrene was at the Vicarage. The defence position is that till Rev. Mendis worked on the children they accepted the position that Dalrene was living at the Vicarage. They never objected to it. There is no case made either on the law or on the fact. All the circumstantial evidence led do not add up to the rebuttable of the presumption of evidence," Mr. Goonewardena.

Mr. Goonewardena referred to what he claimed to be other diabolical lie to tie up his client with the charges and said that her conduct was consistent with the prosecution story being a built up one, after the event. This is proved by the fact that many of the witnesses said things in Court, which they had not mentioned to the police in their statements. It was unsafe to act on such evidence.

Mr. Goonewardena concluded his submissions on 31st October.

Mr. Marapana commenced his submissions when the trial was resumed on first November. He replied to the defence submissions of the application by them not to be called to answer the charges against them.

Mr. Marapana referred to the evidence relating to the events that took place on the morning of 30th January 1979. He said that according to Rev. Edison Mendis, he had given a call to the Vicarage to ascertain Malrani's address. Mrs. Peiris had said she felt faintish and was alone at the Vicarage and that she was trying to contact her brother Eardley. Rev. Mendis telephoned Eardley and asked him to go to the Vicarage. He (Edison) then set out from Dehiwela with his wife Myrtle and while sending her earlier to the Vicarage, dropped in to see the Bishop with whom he had an appointment. When Eardley Mendis rushed to the Vicarage by taxi he found Mrs. Peiris in bed, sweating. While they were there, Rev. Peiris had also come there and had said that he had gone to the Customs to clear Mrs. Peiris's unaccompanied baggage. He had said that while he was at the Customs, Dalrene had informed that Mrs. Peiris was ill and therefore he had rushed back.

Mr. Marapana continuing his submissions told the Court that Eardley Mendis had not told Dalrene that Mrs. Peiris was ill on 30th January. The only inference one could have from Dalrene coming to know about it was that she was eavesdropping when Rev. Edison Mendis telephoned his brother.

Mr. Wickramasekara asked, "There is no evidence that she was eavesdropping?"

"As telephone operator at Colonial Motors her business was to route the calls and not listen to the contents of the calls. The inference can be drawn that she had listened to this call," Mr. Marapana said.

Mr. Cecil Goonewardena commented, "When I was in the Attorney General's Department, the telephonist there knew all our movements. People who telephoned used to ask whether they were on a direct line."

"That only goes to prove my point," said Mr. Marapana.

Dealing with Dr. Weerasena's visit to the Vicarage on the night of 30th January, Mr. Marapana said that according to the doctor Mrs. Peiris had complained of drowsiness. He found that apart from the drowsiness there was nothing alarming in her condition. Because of this drowsiness he had asked Rev. Peiris not to give the drugs which had been prescribed by Dr. Sathanandan.

Mr. Bandaranayake asked, "On that night was there any question of her being hospitalized on the following morning?"

"No. Dr. Weerasena said that there was nothing alarming in her condition and no medical need to hospitalize her," said Mr. Marapana.

At this stage Mr. Marapana referred to the letter dated 30th January written by Rev. Peiris to his three children in triplicate and said that Rev. Peiris in that letter had not spoken of Mrs. Peiris being hospitalized the following day.

The letter, Mr. Marapana said, is a self serving document that had been concocted by Rev. Peiris to impress upon the children that Mrs. Peiris was actually not well that there was some organic disease in her.

Mr. Marapana said, "When Rev. Peiris gave a telephone call to Dr. Weerasena it was to get a letter of admission from Dr. Weerasena to admit Mrs. Peiris to hospital. The impression given to Rev. Mendis was that she was to be admitted for some further tests. When they wanted Mrs. Peiris to come and stay with them in Dehiwela, Rev. Peiris refused to send her on the ground that she had to undergo some tests. And when Rev. Peiris wants Rev. Mendis to pick up the admission letter from Dr. Weerasena's he takes his own time and goes by bus as he had been given the impression that there was nothing alarming in his sister's condition."

Mr. Marapana said that when Eardley Mendis went to his office around 8.15 a.m. on 31st January, he got a call from Rev. Peiris who asked for Dalrene. "He also told Eardley Mendis that Mrs. Peiris was groaning and sleeping. Just then Dalrene came in and Eardley gave the receiver to her. The question is why should Rev. Peiris ask for Dalrene? It is my submission that they were in contact with each other and knew each other's movements."

Mr. Bandaranayake asked, "On that night was there any question of her being hospitalized on the following morning?"

Replied Mr. Marapana, "No. Dr. Weerasena said that there was nothing alarming in her condition and no medical need to hospitalize her. He also points out that the drugs she was taking were absolutely necessary and that they should refrain from advising her to not take those drugs. As at 11.55 a.m. on 30th January 1979, there was no discussion about Mrs. Peiris being taken to hospital. Her condition had improved. But if one were to take as proved Rev. Peiris's admission to the House Officer, Mrs. Peiris had been in a state of fluctuating unconsciousness on 31st January."

Dealing with the medical evidence relating to Russel, Mr. Marapana said there was no doubt that his symptoms including his state of unconsciousness was due to hypoglycaemia caused by an anti-diabetic drug. The circumstances in Russel's case were suggestive of an absence of an insulinoma. In considering this question the Court had to take into account Dr. Sheriffdeen carrying out a post-mortem on his own initiative and searching for insulinoma. He said he had searched for it as humanly as possible.

Mr. Marapana said, "Russel's wife, Dalrene, had to take a greater share of the blame for neglect and inactivity. She was a willing participant in the murder of her husband. In regard to Russel's death, it would be relevant at the very commencement of my submissions to draw the Court's attention to the fact that, on the evidence available in regard to Russel's health, he was a perfectly healthy person and was not in the habit of taking any medicine until this mysterious illness sets in somewhere in June 1978."

Continuing, Mr. Marapana said that it would be his submission that except for the isolated instance when Russel was warded at Durdans for four days in July 1977 and the sores he had, Russel was a person who was in a very good physical condition. Referring to the evidence of Russel's father, Alex Ingram in regard to Russel's health, Mr. Marapana said that when he asked Mr. Ingram whether he considered his son a healthy boy his reply was, 'Why not?'

"Mr. Ingram had also told this Court that Russel took part in all sports at Wesley College where he studied and that even after he left he played for Borah Sports Club. He was married at the time he played club cricket. Mr. Ingram also testified that his son was a person who used to enjoy a drink in company, that he did not drink excessively, was a boy of a happy disposition, used to sing, playing his guitar and that even at Wesley College, he was in addition a chorister.

Even during the period Rev. Peiris was in the UK, Russel was quite normal according to Alex Ingram. Up to 9th June 1978, when he had the first intimation that Russel was ill, Alex Ingram found his son was in perfect health. He had not seen him taking any medicines. He did not show any of the symptoms he was supposed to have developed later," Mr. Marapana said.

"According to Alex Ingram even after his son left Durdans he returned to his normal condition. He was in good condition until Alex Ingram was informed that Russel was sick on 9th June 1978. There was the evidence of Miss Chandrakanthi Dharmadasa, who was a boarder at the Vicarage that Russel was in perfect health and had no sickness as at the end of May 1978. Piyal Weeraman of the Independent Newspapers Ltd. has testified that Russel was physically and mentally fit when he interviewed him for a job on 2nd November 1977. Russel started working there from 3rd November and even played cricket for the Independent Newspapers Ltd. It was on 9th June 1978 that Alex Ingram found for the first time that his son was ill."

"On 10th August, he is dead. Sixty days?" commented Mr. Bandaranayake.

"Yes."

"Out of which he was unconscious for twenty two days," Mr. Bandaranayake said.

Mr. Marapana said that Russel was not an alcoholic and Mr. Weeraman had never seen him drunk in office.

Mr. Bandaranayake asked, "What was his last working day?"

"Mr. Weeraman could not say when, but he says there was an application dated 14th June asking for leave on the 9th, 12th and 13th. It was on the 9th that Russel fell ill."

Mr. Marapana further said that while Russel was in a fit condition in Sri Lanka they had from Munilal's evidence that in the UK, Rev.

Peiris had got into a trance and later said that he had got a message from the angel that Russel was ill and that when he (Rev. Peiris) got back to Colombo he must look after him.

Mr. Marapana next referred to the evidence of Dr. Dayasiri Fernando who had stated that some time before 17th May 1978, Rev. Peiris came and met him at the Accident Ward of the General Hospital where he was working at the time and spoke to him about 'an interesting case'. Rev. Peiris had told Dr. Fernando that Dr. P.A.P. Joseph had wanted him to speak to him.

Mr. Marapana said, "The evidence would show that Russel was removed to hospital on 26th June and lapsed into a state of unconsciousness on 18th July, from which he never recovered. I would demonstrate to Court how Russel, who was during the good part of that relevant period, sick and confined to bed, unconscious at times, was permitted to wither away until permanent brain damage had set in on the first occasion itself by neglecting this man if not by inactivity."

Mr. Bandaranayake asked, "You say this was wilful neglect?"

"Yes. Wilful neglect by the first and second accused, not merely by their inactivity but also by uttering falsehoods which brought about a situation of immobilizing the others present at the time. They were made to believe that Russel had already been seen by Dr. Lakshman Weerasena, that pills had been prescribed by Dr. Weerasena, that sufficient medical attention was being given and that there was nothing more to be done."

Mr. Marapana said that Alex Ingram has said that he asked both Rev. Peiris and Dalrene "Why don't you get him into hospital?" and the reply was, "There is nothing that could be done. They might mess it up further." Rev. Peiris had also said that Russel was suffering from a pancreatic disorder and an operation was the only solution. All these things were said in Dalrene's hearing.

"This would be sufficient to demonstrate that the case against Dalrene on the basis of common intention was no different to that against Rev. Peiris, although there might be certain additional bits of evidence against Rev. Peiris, which was not available against Dalrene."

Mr. Marapana argued that in regard to the inactivity and deceit practised by them, Dalrene had to share a greater part of the blame as Russel was her husband.

"But the statements were made by Rev. Peiris?" asked Mr. Wickramasekara.

"But in Dalrene's hearing," Mr. Marapana said.

"Dalrene's defence was the same as that of Rev. Peiris. It was not even suggested that she too was deceived by Rev. Peiris in the way Alex Ingram claimed he was deceived. So in deciding whether there was a case in which the defence application not be called to answer the charges should be allowed, the Court has to see whether a real defence has surfaced and not a speculative defence such as 'What can I do? I don't know anything about it. I also believed him. I was also taken for a ride'. Dalrene's conduct in remaining silent when Rev. Peiris said those things in her hearing suggested that she was not deceived but that she was a willing participant in the murder of Russel," Mr. Marapana said.

Mr. Marapana, continuing his submissions said the totality of the circumstances in the case showed that Dalrene was a partner in the conspiracy to murder her husband Russel.

"Dalrene never did anything to treat her husband. She did not even change his bed linen. She had been silent when Rev. Peiris was discussing funeral arrangements for Russel when he (Russel) was very much alive. Is it the conduct of a normal wife?" he asked.

Mr. Marapana said sex was the least important thing in this relationship.

"There was something more than that. There was a strong emotion between the two. She was so attracted to Rev. Peiris as to kill her husband. When her husband died, there were many allegations, but she did not tell the police. After three months, when Mrs. Peiris dies under similar circumstances, she did not suspect anything. How could she? It was not surprising to her. She was in the conspiracy," Mr. Marapana said.

"The reason why Dr. Sheriffdeen did a pathological post-mortem was because he was not given the medical history of Russel. Due to medical curiosity he performed this," he said.

"On 18th July, Russel was taken to the hospital and dumped there. Later the two accused were busy getting the ration books transferred to the Vicarage. Just before Russel was taken to the hospital last rites were performed on him. Why this should be done on a man who was discharged from the hospital a few days earlier?" he asked.

Describing Russel's condition, Mr. Marapana said, "On the 14th he was on the bank of the pond, on the 15th in the pond and on the 16th they were discussing funeral arrangements while he was still alive."

Referring to the sleeping arrangements at the Vicarage, he said, when Russel became unconscious he was taken to Rev. Peiris's room where Dalrene also slept.

After Russel was admitted to the hospital, Mr. Alex Ingram (Russel's father) was asked to go home since his condition was not that serious. But Mr. Ingram had stayed at the hospital for three days.

"When Russel was taken to a psychiatrist, the doctor had wanted to know the case history. Then Dalrene was summoned there. But later Rev. Peiris came rushing in and wanted to speak to the doctor. He had even said, 'Don't know what she will say?' It shows that Rev. Peiris was concerned about what should be told and what should be concealed. Rev. Peiris had the opportunity of saying to the doctors without running the risk of being contradicted by Dalrene," Mr. Marapana said.

"Mrs. Cora Ingram had said she stopped talking to the accused as she found the two cracking jokes by the bedside of Russel. In regard to the food given to Russel, Dalrene never brought food for her husband but always used to say 'it will be brought by father (Rev. Peiris)'. When doctors prescribed a normal diet for Russel, why did she not bring him meals? Why was Rev. Peiris keen that the 'feeds' he brought for Russel be given to him in hospital," Mr. Marapana asked.

Continuing his submissions challenging the defence position that they should not be called upon for a defence, Mr. Marapana said that Russel got hypoglycaemic attacks after he took that food. One could not say a particular attack followed a particular meal but these attacks were the result of an anti-diabetic drug being introduced into the food, he said.

Mr. Marapana dealt with the evidence of Mrs. Therese Jackson and said that according to her, Russel was fully conscious at lunch time on 16th July. He had his lunch. Thereafter, at the lunch table she finds a discussion regarding funeral arrangements for Russel who was very much alive and at a time they could not think that he would die. Mrs. Jackson says she was surprised and questioned Dalrene but she remained silent.

Mr. Bandaranayake asked, "You say this is a man who just had a solid meal?"

"Yes, and he was fully conscious. This was two days after he was discharged from hospital on the 14th."

"It was a meal of solids?"

"There was rice with *mellum* and *wattakka* and the meal was topped with an ice cream," Mr. Marapana said.

Then there is also evidence that Rev. Peiris asked for the pills. Dalrene replied "Why father, they are with you." This indicated that pills were being administered to Russel. When Therese questioned Dalrene what these pills were she replied that was the treatment being given to Russel.

"So the question arises: Who prescribed that treatment? The doctors at the hospital say that when Russel was discharged on the

14th no medication was prescribed. Dr. Weerasena and Dr. Joseph have denied prescribing them. So if those pills described by Dalrene as the treatment being given to Russel, it was a vital bit of evidence against her as no doctor had prescribed those pills. Russel started sweating soon after these pills were given, used to breath with difficulty, and lapsed into a state of unconsciousness from which he never recovered. The last time he was stated to have taken these pills was at tea time on the 16th. He was in that state of unconsciousness right up to 18th July when he was admitted to hospital. Mrs. Jackson says that whenever she suggested that a doctor be brought, Dalrene used to say 'Father will do it.' No doctor was brought to the Vicarage to see him during that period," Mr. Marapana said.

Mr. Bandaranayake asked, "What you say is that they may have been unhappy about certain activities at the Vicarage but did not suspect any criminal activity?"

"Yes."

"Even though they suspected the clandestine affair they never suspected any criminal activity?"

"There was no reason to suspect it. They did not think the pills were being given without the authority of a doctor," Mr. Marapana replied.

Continuing Mr. Marapana asked, "Why Dalrene should have been a party to all these falsehoods being uttered about Russel's illness and the nature of the treatment given to him, if she was being taken for a ride? That was not some passive conduct on Dalrene's part. She was, by uttering those falsehoods, lulling Alex Ingram and the Jacksons to a false sense of security and inaction."

Dealing with evidence by Mrs. Jackson, Mr. Marapana said her testimony had not been discredited.

"How could it ever be alleged that she was concocting the evidence to blacken the case against Dalrene? The fact that she had failed to mention certain matters in her statement to the police did not mean that she was lying. The evidence of the Jacksons and Alex Ingram was attacked on the ground that they were belated witnesses. But there was an explanation for such delay. They had no reason to suspect the circumstances of Russel's death because they were made to believe that he was getting sufficient treatment and that it was only a question of merely keeping Russel until the much needed operation was performed. It was much later, after the investigations commenced and Mrs. Peiris was taken ill in similar circumstances that they got alert," he said.

Dealing with the evidence of the nurses, Mr. Marapana said through them the prosecution wanted to prove that Russel was seen to be getting hypoglycaemic attacks from 18th July till he died on 10th August and that Rev. Peiris used to bring food to Russel during that period and that he used to insist that the food brought by him should be given.

"He used to wait till the food was put to the container. Why was he so keen that the food he brought was given to Russel? It is the prosecution case that Russel got those hypoglycaemic attacks after taking those feeds because an anti-diabetic drug had been introduced into the food," he said.

"Dalrene left the Vicarage only because she was compelled to leave due to threats by Munilal in the UK to come down and throw her out if she does not leave within twenty four hours. Munilal had got agitated on hearing that his mother had got unconscious and was taken to hospital. He had got that information from his wife who phoned him on their wedding anniversary.

When Munilal telephoned the Vicarage and asked Rev. Peiris "How are you managing and who is looking after mummy?" he had replied "We are looking after her." Munilal asked Rev. Peiris whom he meant by "we", Rev. Peiris kept silent. It was when Munilal asked him whether it was Dalrene that Munilal had said angrily "I don't want her to look after my mother. She should leave within 24 hours otherwise I will have to come down and throw her out."

Mr. Marapana said that she went on 25th January because she was compelled to go. "They had taken an annexe in December but she continued to remain in the Vicarage while the annexe was kept closed. Mr. Marapana said that although Mrs. Peiris was admitted to Durdans on 15th January, none of the children were informed about it until Munilal's wife happened to mention it in their telephone call on their wedding anniversary on 2nd January. That was the date on which Mrs. Peiris was discharged from the hospital. Munilal says that he travelled three hundred miles from London to Cardiff to inform Mihiri. It was thereafter, that he gave three telephone calls to Rev. Edison Mendis and one to the Vicarage. Mrs. Peiris had spoken first and given the call to Rev. Peiris. There was resentment by this time among the children about Dalrene as they had come to hear various stories about Dalrene and their father. Munilal had in fact asked Rev. Edison Mendis to speak to the Bishop."

Mr. Marapana said that it was as a result of Munilal insisting that his mother be shown to Dr. E.V. Peiris that Rev. Peiris had taken Mrs. Peiris and not on his own initiative. Rev. Peiris had no choice in the matter, just as Dalrene was compelled to leave the Vicarage. Rev. Peiris was forced to take his wife to Dr. E.V. Peiris. Dr. E.V. Peiris's evidence became important in considering the information, which was supplied to him by Rev. Peiris with regard to his wife's illness.

"He had at various times made contradictory statements. He had given a history of Mrs. Peiris having had a pain in the knees, belching etc. which was never given earlier to Dr. Weerasena or the General Hospital. It was important that what puzzled Dr. E.V. Peiris was that Mrs. Peiris's blood sugar reading was as high as 190.

Mr. Marapana also referred to the fact that, having two request forms from Dr. Peiris, Rev. Peiris had gone to Dr. Weerasena and obtained a letter for an extended GTT for Mrs. Peiris. But at Glass House he withheld all three documents and asked for a two and a half hour GTT. "It would be my submission that Rev. Peiris's conduct in having got this test done at Glass House showed complete lack of bona fides on his part. All he did was to get some evidence in his favour – to get such a result that could be interpreted to suit his purposes," said Mr. Marapana.

Referring to Arumugam's evidence, Mr. Marapana said that when Arumugam was asked whether he noticed a change in Mrs. Peiris, his reply was that he asked Dalrene where Mrs. Peiris was and Dalrene had said "She is not well and is in the house". If Dalrene knew that Mrs. Peiris was not well she would have known the nature of Mrs. Peiris ailment. When Edison and Myrtle went to Durdans at 6.55 p.m. both accused were there and Mrs. Peiris was conscious. That was the occasion when Dalrene made the remark "Why Mrs. Peiris you had high fever and were delirious."

Mrs. Peiris was at Durdans from 15th December to 2nd January. It was during that period that Arumugam had to leave the Vicarage and Dalrene continued to stay in the Vicarage during that entire period. Arumugam says that when he asked Dalrene why Mrs. Peiris was in hospital she replied, "*Okige dane kanne thamai asa*" (the desire to eat at her alms giving!).

Mr. Marapana said that there was inactivity on Rev. Peiris's part. Showing to specialists was arranged by Dr. Weerasena and not by Rev. Peiris.

Mr. Wickramasekara said, "This shows that this time he had depended on Dr. Weerasena. There was nothing wrong in that?"

"But Mrs. Peiris had been ill from December. But no specialists were summoned till 15th January when Dr. Weerasena initiated it," Mr. Marapana answered.

Dealing with medical evidence about Mrs. Peiris, Mr. Marapana said she was admitted to the General Hospital at 12.15 p.m. on 31st January 1979. At the time of admission the Rev. Peiris told the House Officer, Dr. Terrence de Silva that the patient had suffered from body pains and loss of appetite since she returned from England.

"He also told him she felt giddy, had slurring of speech when she got up from bed in the morning and felt sleepy. When she took some sugar she felt worse. He also told Dr. de Silva that the patient suffered from a fluctuating level of consciousness varying from drowsy to deep coma. These symptoms were not mentioned to Dr. Weerasena who treated her since her arrival or to Dr. E.V. Peiris. Rev. Peiris had also given some medical reports about his wife to the house officer, which were kept with the bed head ticket. But the original letter of recommending hospitalization was not given. It was later recovered by the police from the Vicarage. The original was kept by him to prepare his defence. His comment to Rev. Edison Mendis that he had his defence was significant in this connection."

Dealing with the cause of death, Mr. Marapana submitted that hypoglycaemic coma, the result of the lowering of the blood sugar, was the cause given in the medical evidence.

"Dr. de Silva and Dr. Nagaratnam had ruled out the other alternative causes like diabetic coma, brain infection and overdose of anti-depressant drugs. Having eliminated the alternatives the doctors have concluded that Mrs. Peiris suffered from 'hypoglycaemic coma'. The medical evidence has also ruled out the other possibility suggested by the defence, a sudden fall in the blood pressure with attendant results. Taking the overall picture and the fact that Mrs. Peiris was admitted with blood sugar count of 30 mg% pointed to anti-diabetic drugs being administered on 30th January after Dr. Weerasena left."

"I also rule out the possibility of a suicide attempt by Mrs. Peiris. If that is the position she would have attempted suicide throughout the month. In respect of the second accused Darlene, there was evidence against her. She was speaking of giving alms while Mrs. Peiris was still alive. When Mrs. Peiris' relations wanted to take her to Moratuwa, Dalrene informed Rev. Peiris and got that stopped because that would interfere with their plan."

Dealing with the close relationship between Rev. Peiris and Dalrene, Mr. Marapana submitted that there was an emotional one as well as intimacy between them. Even after the matter had been raised and the police started investigations, the fact that she was going about with Rev. Peiris amply showed that she had been party to the conspiracy. Mr. Marapana said the totality of the circumstances in the case showed that Dalrene was a partner in the conspiracy to murder her husband Russel Ingram.

After Mr. Marapana's submissions, on 15th November, Mr. Bandaranayake called for the defence in respect of all the charges. The Court made this ruling on the defence application that they should not be called upon to answer the charge.

Mr. Obeysekera, in reply to a question by Mr. Bandaranayake said, his client would not testify in his defence, but he would be calling two witnesses, Dr. S.C. Abeysuriya and Mr. K.D.D. Henry, the Assistant Government Analyst.

Mr. Cecil Goonewardena, senior counsel for Dalrene said his client was not calling any evidence on her behalf. She was neither getting into the witness box nor would she make a dock statement. She stood by her original plea of not guilty.

Mr. Bandaranayake gave the Defence time to bring the witnesses before pronouncing a verdict.

Mr. K.D.D. Henry, Assistant Government Analyst was the first defence witness in the trial.

Examined by Mr. R. I. Obeysekera, he said that he had been serving as an Assistant Government Analyst from 1967. In 1975, he said he qualified further and obtained a Masters degree with special reference to Toxicology. He went on a scholarship sponsored by the British Council and also underwent further training in toxicology at several institutions including the London Hospital Medical School and the Department of Forensic Medicine of the Glasgow University.

"On 19th April 1979, certain productions were forwarded to me for examination and report. This included a bottle of milk. It was sealed with a seal of the JMO. He did not find glibenclamide or trace of any other anti-diabetic drug in the milk. Samples of the anti-diabetic drugs were also sent to him," Mr. Henry said. He further said that milk was sent in a hospital bottle.

Mr. Obeysekera queried whether he forwarded his report on 20th July 1979.

"Yes, it took a long time to do the tests and examine the drugs."

"If an anti-diabetic drug is given to a non-diabetic person will you find it in the system of that person?"

"It depended on the time. One would expect to find traces of an anti-diabetic drug in urine up to two days, in the case or faeces for 5 days, and in the system of a non diabetic person for three days. It also depended on the dosage of the drug. If a dosage of Euglucon administered to a person was more, then one would find more traces of it in a specimen," said Mr. Henry.

He said he also examined certain productions sent to him after the examination of Russel Ingram's body. They were a sealed bottle and three parcels. The parcels contained some saw dust around the body cavity and soil samples from above the coffin. He examined them on directions of the JMO for traces of any anti-diabetic drug but did not find any. There were no traces of Euglucon either.

Mr. Bandaranayake asked, "Is it your position that it does not accumulate in protein?"

"Yes."

Cross-examined by Mr. Tilak Marapana, Mr. Henry said that apart from the milk samples on which he was questioned by the defence there were other items which were sent to him by the JMO for examination and report. These included tranquilizers and sedatives, which he described to Court in detail.

Mr. Henry also said that some Euglucon tablets were round while others were oblong.

Dr. Sarath Abeysuriya, FRCS (Edinburgh and London), Senior Consultant Neurosurgeon, General Hospital, Colombo was the second witness for the defence. He gave evidence for four days.

Examined by Mr. Obeysekera, Dr. Abeysuriya said, "I had eighteen years service in Neurosurgery. I deal mainly with coma patients. I have a good knowledge of diabetes."

He said that on 3rd February 1979 he examined Mrs. Eunice Peiris in ward 47B, as requested by Dr. Nanayakkara, Consultant Physician. He examined the BHT and found that she was treated at the Durdans Hospital and that she had been treated for mental depression and was taking drugs. She had been treated by Dr. Sathanandan who was a specialist Psychiatrist.

"From the history I also came to know that there was a derangement in her sugar metabolism. I came to know that she had low blood sugar of 30mg% for some time, her pressure was low and she had been unconscious," he said.

Mr. Bandaranayake asked, "What did you do?"

"I applied firm pressure on the eye brows. She responded by slightly moving her limbs. That showed she was in a semi-coma. After ruling out the alternate possible causes, I came to the conclusion that her condition was the result of low supply of oxygen to her brain combined with low blood sugar. I saw Mrs. Peiris again on 14th February. The special investigations carried out on that day indicated a swelling on the left side of the brain," he said.

Commenting on the blood sugar reports of 20th and 29th January he said, "They were a little below the accepted level and that could have been her normal blood sugar level. The low blood sugar may indicate insulin activity in the body. The cause of the insulin activity may be due to insufficiency of compensatory hormones. My position was that Mrs. Peiris was suffering from reactive hypoglycaemia. The GTT done on 29th January indicated that she had reactive hypoglycaemia."

He mentioned that when hypoglycaemia sets in, the blood pressure increased slightly. Hypoglycaemia did not cause low pressure and low pressure was not a symptom of hypoglycaemia, he said.

"Have you come across a 'Nil' blood sugar report?" queried Mr. Bandaranayake.

"I have not. Now I know."

"By reading the newspapers?"

"Yes."

Dr. Abeysuriya said that Mrs. Peiris suffered from depression and she was treated. She was also examined by a psychiatrist between 15th December and 2nd January at Durdans hospital. She was prescribed Mogadon and Tofranil whilst at Durdans and had been instructed to take them even after she was discharged.

Dr. Abeysuriya agreed that the GTT done on 29th January had revealed that she had reactive hypoglycaemia.

Shown the book on hypoglycaemia he said there was a table, which showed depression as one of the causes for reactive hypoglycaemia. A depressed mental state in addition could cause a reactive hypoglycaemia and could give cause for other ailments as well. He further said that the respiratory centre of the brain controls the rate, rhythm and depth of respiration. Low blood pressure by itself is not a symptom of hypoglycaemia. In the case of Mrs. Peiris's low blood pressure he thought it was due to a shock like state owing to the collapse of the peripheral vascular mechanism brought about by a reactive stress, which in turn brought about hypoglycaemia.

"If this is continued for long periods the brain would get affected. This was noticeable in Mrs. Peiris's sugar levels. Sugar and oxygen are essential for the healthy condition of the brain. Low sugar and low blood pressure prevented the brain from getting the required quantities of sugar and oxygen," he said.

Continuing he said "Mrs. Peiris's low pressure was due to the diminished amount of cortisone in the body. The diminishing of cortisone was the result of Mrs. Peiris's depressive mental state. Mrs. Peiris was admitted to the Durdans Hospital on 15th January in an unconscious state. She was given glucose and she was better. The cause for the unconsciousness could not be pinpointed but could be associated with low blood pressure."

Mr. Bandaranayake asked, "Do you know what caused the mental depression?"

"Family problems."

"Can there be other reasons?"

"For instance?"

"Hypoglycaemia?"

"It can only cause temporary symptoms of mental depression."

"You cannot give a definite opinion?"

"Yes."

Dr. Abeysuriya said taking all the circumstances into consideration it is possible to come to the conclusion that Mrs. Peiris died of natural causes. The depressive state she was in caused the low sugar and the low pressure which resulted in other complications that caused her death.

Dr. Abeysuriya said that he was present at the initial part of the post-mortem of Mrs. Peiris. He was summoned to be present. He was only a spectator but was of the opinion that the examination was carried out well.

Examined by Mr. Cecil Goonewardena, Dr. Abeysuriya said he was summoned as a prosecution witness and he attended Court on the first day of the trial but was not called.

When Mr. Tilak Marapana cross examined Dr. Abeysuriya, he said that depression could be the cause that led to the diminishing of cortisone. He said that Mrs. Peiris suffered from depression and had taken anti-depressant drugs. Dr. Abeysuriya said that an Australian study confirmed a link between mental depression and low blood sugar. "But the mental depression should be severe and the link was not firm in all cases."

Continuing he said, "From the post-mortem examination report it was evident that the glands that secrete insulin were in normal condition. But others were not examined in microscopic detail. If all the glands were functioning normally there was no reason for excessive insulin in Mrs. Peiris's blood. In such a case it had to be taken from outside. But her depressive state had caused the malfunctioning of the glands resulting in excessive insulin. If blood sugar level was not corrected for a long time the brain will get damaged. Lowering of the blood sugar was caused during certain phases of the depression and not always. In an unconscious state the lowering of the blood sugar would not be the result of mental depression. But the unconscious state would be the result of the lowering of blood pressure due to mental depression. After being unconscious, mental depression will not have any effect on the patient. But the low blood sugar caused earlier by the depression would continue to be there for some time."

Mr. Marapana asked "Are you in a position to speak about the severity of depression in Mrs. Peiris?"

"No. A study in Australia had proved that mental depression had caused the lowering of blood sugar level."

"Have you read or come across a patient whose mental depression had caused the lowering of blood sugar?"

"No. The blood pressure of Mrs. Peiris dropped on 15th January. That led to the insufficient supply of oxygen to the brain and that made her unconscious," said Dr. Abeysuriya. He said he had not examined Mrs. Peiris when she had been conscious. To explain the clinical findings Dr. Abeysuriya said that he came to the opinion that Mrs. Peiris was moderately depressed.

Dr. Abeysuriya said that before he came to give evidence he came to know the nature of the findings of Dr. Sathanandan. He heard that Mrs. Peiris had some family problems. He said he gathered that some of her children were abroad and about a marriage, which did not work out, and also that there was a person staying at the Vicarage, which Mrs. Peiris did not like.

Mr. Marapana asked, "It is mere speculation on your part that Mrs. Peiris was severely depressed?"

"To express all the clinical findings as observed by me on 3rd and 31st, I assumed therefore that she may have relapsed into a state of at least moderate depression."

"You have to express that as it is the only way you can reconcile your opinion?"

"Yes."

Mr. Marapana then asked the key question.

"If Mrs. Peiris was given a sufficiently large dose of anti-diabetic pills on 31st January, would it not cause all the features of the disease you saw?"

"That is another possibility. The explanation I gave is another," Dr. Abeysuriya replied. He admitted that all features seen on Mrs. Peiris on admission to Durdans and the General Hospital could be the result of an anti-diabetic drug being administered on her.

Mr. Marapana asked, "Were the patients in a depressed state in a better position to withstand hypoglycaemia than in the recovered state?"

"No. They were concerned about the drop in the hydrocortisone level."

"You are looking for a red herring through a blue glass and in the process you have lost a shark and found a sprat!"

"That is wrong. It is the other way about. I am looking for a shark and the counsel has just found a little sprat," said Dr. Abeysuriya.

Mr. Cecil Goonewardena interjected, "The whole thing has become fishy!"

At this stage the defence counsel informed Court that they would not be leading any more evidence. The prosecution also informed the Court that they had closed their case.

Mr. Bandaranayake told the prosecution to sum up their evidence in the final address next day.

On 21st November, the Court ruled that the evidence given by Rev. Mathew Peiris and Mrs. Mihiri Wickramasinghe at the Inquest of Mrs. Eunice Peiris was inadmissible as it appeared to have been extracted under implied compulsion. The Court also held with the defence that the notes recovered from the Vicarage could also not be admitted in evidence as the prosecution had failed to satisfy the Court about its admissibility. Mr. Bandaranayake delivered the order with other two Judges agreeing.

On 28th November 1983, Mr. Tilak Marapana began summing up the evidence in his address to the Trial-at-Bar.

"The motive in this case is not just a casual sex incident, but had a high degree of affection," he said.

"Mrs. Eunice Peiris was a lady who came back from the United Kingdom quite hale and hearty and not taking any medication. But this same lady developed some sort of mysterious illness due to which she began to feel drowsy, sleepy, dizzy, giddy, weak and sort of lethargic in all her activities. This was during the period December 1978 to January 1979. The culmination of all this was her admission to hospital on 31st January 1978 in an unconscious state. Dr. Terrence de Silva has told us how he made a tentative diagnosis of hypoglycaemia and how he excluded the other causes, which may have accounted for Mrs. Peiris's condition."

"There can be no doubt that the coma was the hypoglycaemic coma which had caused irreversible brain damage prior to her being admitted to the hospital. At the post-mortem Dr. Subramaniam said he could not find any demonstrable cause which could have led to this hypoglycaemic coma. It is my submission that however eminent Dr. Abeysuriya may be, to say the least, he is mistaken, both in the assumption he made and on the assumption he made on the degree the hypothalamus would be affected in severe depression."

"My point is that if, in the depressed state the cortisone level is high, then there is no need for cortisone to be added to that. Dr.

Abeysuriya's evidence does not add anything at all to the medical evidence except that he himself, being a neurosurgeon, has agreed that Mrs. Peiris's illness was not due to a CVA. Regarding Russel and the unconscious state in which he was first hospitalized, the prosecution has proved beyond any doubt that it is a hypoglycaemic condition. On the occasion of the second hospitalization, on the evidence of Dr. Wijesiriwardena, Dr. Sheriffdeen and Dr. Nagaratnam, their having ruled out other causes, it finally narrows down to a hypoglycaemic condition. Just like in Mrs. Peiris's case, medical treatment was also given to Russel but eventually on 10th August 1979 he died."

"Russel was not having any natural condition which would have lead to his death, or to his blood sugar level being lowered. If it was accidental, then it had to be a series of accidents from December 1978 to January 1979. So also was suicide which would have had to be a series of unsuccessful attempts. And we have a Psychiatrist's evidence that she was not suicidal. I can conclude Mrs. Peiris's case by saying that this is definitely a case of induced hypoglycaemia."

Mr. Marapana said that when Dalrene conspired to kill her husband with the intention of getting together with Rev. Peiris there was also the intention to do away with Mrs. Eunice Peiris. Otherwise they could not have achieved their objective. There was the evidence of Dr. Dayasiri Fernando as to how the first accused had approached him prior to 23rd May and asked for medical opinion after informing the doctor of certain symptoms that Russel had.

He said on the morning of 18th July 1978, when Russel who was unconscious for three days was to be taken to hospital, the first accused administered extreme unction to Russel. (*Extreme Unction is another term, very common in past centuries but rarely used today, for one of the seven sacraments, the Sacrament of the Anointing of the Sick, which is administered both to the dying and to those who are gravely ill or are about to undergo a serious operation, for the recovery of their health and for spiritual strength.*) They were aware that when Russel who was unconscious on 24th June was admitted to hospital he got well and returned home. He submitted that it was his case that on this occasion they thought Russel would not come back. There was no reason for them to treat Russel like a terminal patient as on an earlier date he had recovered. He pointed out that between 24th and 26th June too Russel was unconscious. He submitted that this was not the way a wife would act and allow the father of her children to wither away.

Mr. Bandaranayake commented, "Without taking the matter into her own hands."

Continuing Mr. Marapana said, "On the very day that Mrs. Peiris arrived in Sri Lanka, Rev. Peiris went into a trance and said his wife had a stomach problem. It was known that Mrs. Peiris returned home quite hale and hearty. He told his wife that the angels wanted her shown to Dr. Weerasena. It is my submission that the Rev. Peiris having shown his wife to Dr. Weerasena introduced an anti-diabetic agent on the pretext of giving tablets prescribed by Dr. Weerasena."

Mr. Marapana said that when the second accused conspired to kill her husband with the intention of getting together with Rev. Peiris, there was also the intention to do away with Mrs. Eunice Peiris. Otherwise they could not have achieved their objective.

Commencing his submissions, Mr. Obeysekera told the Court that the prosecution had failed to exclude the possibility of a natural cause as there was no evidence of any ectopic area of the pancreas being sent for the testing after an insulinoma. He said as far as the evidence of Dr. Nagaratnam was concerned if Russel in the condition in which he was on 16th July has been given four tablets of Euglucon he would not have survived more than ten to twelve hours. Russel could not have possibly survived up to 18th July.

Continuing Mr. Obeysekera said, "There was evidence of Dr. E.V. Peiris that there were instances of persons with zero blood sugar level surviving a few hours. If it was an accurate reading of the blood sugar level at 9.30 a.m. he would not have survived more than three hours. The significant thing was that Russel's pressure had not dropped. If Dr. Nagaratnam's evidence was accepted the reason for pressure dropping was because the vasomotor centre was functioning."

Mr. Obeysekera asked whether the reading of zero blood sugar in Russel was correct, particularly in view of the fact that there was no drop in the blood pressure.

"According to Dr. Abeysuriya the reason for the no pressure drop was because the stage of suppression of the hypothalamus activity had not taken place. He would submit that Russel's condition could not be compared with that of Mrs. Peiris as she had a blood sugar reading of 30 mg and a drop in pressure. According to the FBC of Russel, the very first entry was at 2 p.m. It was not started in the morning. Dextrose was given only at 2 p.m.," Mr. Obeysekera said.

Mr. Obeysekera agreed with Mr. Bandaranayake that, if the Court was to accept Mrs. Jackson's evidence then it would have to be of opinion that Russel was in deep slumber prior to 18th July. Dealing with the entries in the BHT, Mr. Obeysekera said that the entry made by Dr. Karunakaran showed that a blood sugar level was taken at 1.30 p.m.

Mr. Bandaranayake commented, "You are unable to draw any distinction between the condition in which Russel was at 9.30 a.m. and the condition after dextrose was given?"

Mr. Obeysekera said, "There was no recovery."

Mr. Obeysekera submitted that this evidence created a grave doubt on the evidence of the Jacksons.

"Both Russel and Mrs. Peiris were non-diabetics, and if they had any traces of diabetic drugs in their system, then this was a matter that would have had to be explained. But, as there were no traces of any anti-diabetic drug it had become a problem for the prosecution. There was a wide area of doubt in this case and the conduct and utterances of the accused could not fill that void. The conduct of taking annexes, drawing Wills and the opening of bank accounts could not take the place of scientific proof that a drug was administered."

"In the case of Russel there was the question of an insulinoma. The Government Analyst proved beyond doubt that there were tests available here to establish anti-diabetic drugs in the system. Russel was transferred to a surgical ward in order to probe an insulinoma. According to the Deputy Solicitor General, Dr. Sheriffdeen had one experience of an insulinoma but he had not made use of it to write a paper. Further when they found hypoglycaemic attacks taking place in spite of dextrose infusion, none of them thought it necessary to test the blood sugar," said Mr. Obeysekera.

Dealing with Dr. Sheriffdeen's evidence, Mr. Obeysekera said that in spite of being aware that an allegation of poisoning has been made at the inquest, he filed the histological report on the pancreas and did not probe further. The histological report showed that there was no defect in the pancreas. Dr Sheriffdeen had not probed the ectopic area of the pancreas for an insulinoma.

Mr. Obeysekera said that this leaves a large area of doubt. According to Dr. Dayasiri Fernando, examination of the ectopic area was a serious business. There was no evidence of any ectopic area being sent to the pathologist for examination. Therefore, Mr. Obeysekera said that the prosecution had failed to exclude the possibility of natural causes.

Dealing with the evidence of the nurses he said the prosecution relied on their evidence on the maintenance of the FBCs. There was evidence that Russel continued to get hypoglycaemic attacks after the second hospitalization. The prosecution case was that these attacks were due to the administration of an anti-diabetic drug by the accused or by an agent through the food brought from outside. According to the FBC, a large quantity of glucose was given at least for the thirty hour period when no food was being given to Russel.

Continuing Mr. Obeysekera said, "The most important witness was Miss Ranaweera who testified that she brought to the notice of the doctor that the patient got attacks after meals. The house officer did nothing about it and their position in Court was that they knew nothing."

He said that at every turn the nurses were trying to blacken the case for the defence. The evidence of Russel getting attacks in hospital was due to hypoglycaemia caused by an insulinoma. This evidence benefited the prosecution no more than it benefitted the defence. Therefore, the benefit of the doubt should be given to the defence.

Mr. Obeysekera said that according to Professor Jayasena, if this drug was introduced into the food, the traces would have remained for a long time but the meals were not subjected to an analysis.

"The advertisement for a house did not mean that it was for a widow. There was evidence that Rev. Peiris was a very helpful person, and it could always be that the Vicarage address was given by someone who wanted a forwarding address. As far as the annexe was concerned there was no significance. Everyone knew that Mrs. Ranasinghe, wife of the owner of the annexe, was known to Rev. Peiris's daughter," said Mr. Obeysekera.

Mr. Bandaranayake commented, "But she was in England and it was with great difficulty she was brought here. It was obvious by this time Mrs. Ingram could not remain at the Vicarage and alternate accommodation had to be found."

Mr. Obeysekera asked, if deception and secrecy was part of the conspiracy, then why have a joint bank account?

"There was evidence that the Thursday services were started before 1977. The prosecution could not say that the trances that the first accused got into were part of the conspiracy. All that was part of a picture, which was started before the conspiracy period. Even then stigmata and the exorcisms were there long before the conspiracy period," said Mr.Obeysekera.

Dealing with the charges, he said that there was evidence that Rev. Peiris and his wife had been abroad earlier too.

"It could not be said that Rev. Peiris got his wife to go to England in order to have a free hand to conspire. That would be an artificial inference. Mrs. Peiris's continued stay in England was quite natural as her children were there. The fact that the Vicarage had been given to the Ingram family for looking after showed that both Rev. and Mrs. Peiris had confidence in them. Mrs. Peiris was quite happy to stay on in England. Even the anonymous cable stating that her husband was involved in a scandal did not make her return home," said   Mr. Obeysekera.

Mr. Bandaranayake commented, "Anonymous cables don't make people rush back home from abroad!"

But on the other hand, Mr. Obeysekera said, there was evidence that letters written by Malrani showed   Mrs. Peiris was being ill-treated by her daughter Mihiri and her husband. Those letters shed light on Mrs. Peiris's condition. He submitted that the condition of anxiety and depression that Dr. Weerasena found in Mrs. Peiris on 9th December 1978 was referable to her mental state during her stay in England.

"According to Dr. Sathanandan, Mrs. Peiris had reactive factors. The Durdans Hospital BHT showed Mrs. Peiris was treated for depression. His position was that Mrs. Peiris's condition could have deteriorated when she was in England. What Dr. Weerasena found was the turbulent effects of what Mrs. Peiris had gone through during her stay in England. It would be wrong to say that Rev. Peiris induced that condition in order to administer the drug. The Court should take into consideration the fact that she was conscious of the fact that she was depressed. There was evidence that Mrs. Peiris looked sad. Dr. Sathanandan's position was that she could have relapsed into that condition. The depression was relevant in the first place because of Dr. Abeysuriya's evidence. Her state and condition of drowsiness could equally be the result of depression and not because small doses of Euglucon was being given," said Mr. Obeysekera.

Mr. Cecil Goonewardena in his submissions stated that the evidence led in the case when considered would show that the relationship between Dalrene and Mrs. Eunice Peiris had been cordial. He said the motive now relied upon by the prosecution was that, the second accused wanted to get married to the first accused after killing her husband and the first accused's wife.

Mr. Bandaranayake commented, "Prosecution did not say she wanted to get married. What it said was that must have been the reason."

Dealing with the evidence of Eardley Mendis, Mr. Goonewardena said his evidence was that the first accused used to come to Colonial

Motors and speak to the second accused and bring lunch on a bicycle. He said referring to the witness's evidence that he tried to impute that there was a love affair between the two accused, which he had not mentioned in his statement or to any of his brothers and sisters.

"According to Arumugam the second accused hated her husband. Arumugam said that she used epithets such as '*Oka*' when referring to Russel ('*Oka*' is a disparaging word for a man). He said Arumugam tried to show that the first accused pretended to the congregation on a Sunday morning that he was leaving for Batticaloa, and then packed his wife and daughter to Moratuwa. Thereafter, the second accused came to the Vicarage and doors and windows were closed. The second accused left only in the evening. This evidence was led to prove deception."

He said this part of Arumugam's evidence was completely discredited by Malrani's evidence, who told Court that they left on a Friday and for one day. Mr. Goonewardena also pointed out that Arumugam had failed to mention in his first statement to the Police anything the second accused had said against her husband or Mrs. Peiris. He submitted that if what Arumugam testified to was true then he would never have forgotten to mention this in his statement.

He said the Court should reject this evidence as it was very unsafe to act upon such evidence.

Mr. Goonewardena said even with regard to the incident when the children were found on the Vicarage roof, Arumugam's evidence was that the first accused came out of the Vicarage buttoning his khaki shorts and Dalrene followed him in a nighty. In the statement Arumugam had specifically stated that the first accused did not come out.

Mr. Goonewardena said he was grateful to Mr. Wickramasekera for commenting that if the first accused did not come out how then did Arumugam know what he was wearing. He submitted that the evidence of Arumugam was totally unworthy of credit.

The prosecution placed piles and piles of evidence to prove motive but when they were considered the Court would find weaknesses in every bit of evidence. He asked what the second accused would have gained in marrying the first accused. If at all, the second accused would have been concerned about the welfare of her children and thus made the Will.

"In 1978 when Russel fell ill, it was the second accused who informed her father-in-law Alex Ingram. It was Alex Ingram's evidence that even during this period Russel and the second accused had sexual intimacy. It was also his evidence that the second accused showed alarm and concern about Russel's illness. The evidence was that Alex Ingram went to collect the letter from Dr. Joseph. There was an opportunity for him to inquire about Russel's condition but he did not do so."

"What was the wife doing? The prosecution case was that the wife should have found an opportunity and spoken to Dr. Joseph," said Mr. Bandaranayake.

With regard to the false statements made by the second accused during the time Russel was ill, he said the prosecution relied mainly on Alex Ingram's evidence. The prosecution's case was that the second accused would have known pills were being given to Russel. According to Alex Ingram's evidence he saw the first accused giving Russel some pills once and at that time the second accused was not present.

He asked whether there was any evidence to show that the second accused was aware that pills were being given to Russel or saw any pills being given to Russel by the first accused. The administration of pills was seen by Mrs. Jackson. But the Court would see that important matters on which the prosecution wanted the Court to draw inferences, she had failed to mention in her statement.

He submitted what was really diabolical was Mrs. Jackson's evidence that before pills were given, the first accused said it was now time to give the pills and asked second accused for the pills. The second accused then replied 'Why, father it is with you', and the first accused then takes pills from his pocket and requests Mrs. Jackson to give them to Russel. He submitted that this was the artificial evidence that the prosecution introduced to tie up the second accused with the conspiracy.

Apart from Mrs. Jackson's evidence being unreliable, that part of the evidence was unbelievable. It was also Mrs. Jackson's evidence that she felt that it was after pills were given to Russel that his condition changed. She had told her husband about this but they had waited for nine months before informing the police. He asked whether the Court could rest with confidence on the evidence of the Jacksons' taking into account their own conduct. He said the evidence was that the second accused did not prepare any food for Russel when he was ill.

Mr. Bandaranayake asked, "If that is so, why?"

Mr. Goonewardena said, "The evidence was that the first accused prepared things like mince meat. There was nothing special. It is still believed that men are the best cooks in the world!"

"Women cook for the family, while men cook for money!" said Mr. Bandaranayake.

Mr. Goonewardena said further that there was no evidence to show that the second accused took food for Russel. He submitted that the death of Mrs. Peiris and the changes relating to it was the weakest part of the prosecution case against the second accused. He said when the evidence was considered the Court could safely come to the conclusion that relations between the second accused and Mrs. Peiris were cordial.

"When the improbabilities, the omissions on important items of evidence, contradictions, the belatedness of witnesses, the artificial nature of the evidence and the conduct of principal witnesses were taken into account, there was nothing left in the prosecution worth considering against the accused," Mr. Goonewardena said, concluding his submissions.

Eight days of legal submissions by the prosecution and defence ended with the conclusion of Mr. Goonewardena's address to the

Court on 6th December. The lengthy trial which commenced on 14th March 1983 lasted 163 days. The Court reserved its judgment.

Mr. Bandaranayake said the prison authorities would be informed as to when the accused should be produced in Court for the purpose of hearing the judgment. The prosecution listed 149 witnesses but called 68 of them including several doctors and nurses. It also brought down at State expense three witnesses from England. They were Mr. Munilal Peiris and Mrs. Malrani Dodangoda, son and daughter respectively of Rev. Peiris and the family physician, Dr. J.G.C. Peiris.

CHAPTER 10

JUDGEMENT

On 15th February 1984, the Court delivered its judgement of the case. Mr. Bandaranayake took nearly nine and a half hours to read the 612 page judgement, which ended at 6.30 p.m. Mr. Bandaranayake kept on wiping his face and glasses while he read on. He was assisted by Judge D. C. W. Wickramasekera.

Mr. Bandaranayake made a kind gesture to a press cameraman, who was standing inside the Court. He requested the cameraman to take a seat.

While reading the judgment at times he paused when he noticed some mistakes. He said that he would convict the person who typed the copy!

I document here almost entire judgement for the benefit of readers.

Commencing reading the judgement Mr. Bandaranayake said, "Before we set about the task of examining the evidence placed before us it is appropriate that we mention here in general terms the evidence before us descriptive of this case."

"The first accused is a priest of the church of Sri Lanka, which is of the Anglican Christian Fellowship. His early education had been at Prince of Wales College, Moratuwa. He was ordained a priest in England in the 1950s, and upon his return to Sri Lanka he had been a curate and thereafter vicar of Saint Paul's Church, Kynsey Road, Colombo 10, and was the vicar of this church at all times material to this case. He was also known as an exorcist and he visited homes and conducted exorcism ceremonies at this church on Thursday evenings, which ceremonies were fairly well attended since about 1973."

"He had his wife and his three children, who are presently living abroad in the United Kingdom. The second accused was the wife of the deceased Russel Ingram. The second accused's father had been in the public service and her mother had been a nurse at the General Hospital. Sometime in 1976 Russel had lost his job and the Ingrams returned to Colombo from Kandy. The second accused who had been a typist was also unemployed at this time and they had three small children. It was in these circumstances that the Ingrams came to attend the first accused's Thursday exorcism services and came to be introduced to the first accused and began associating with him."

WRITING A BOOK

"It was thereafter that the first accused employed Mrs. Ingram, the second accused as his secretary and typist as he was at that time writing a book titled 'Damn the Bloody Exorcist'. The first accused was at that time also involved in the organization of the ceremonies concerning the approaching consecration of the Anglican Bishop of Colombo which took place in January 1978. According to the prosecution it was an association that developed from these beginnings and culminated in the deaths of the wife of the first accused and the husband of the second accused."

"The charges that have been preferred against the accused on Counts one and two of the indictment consist of conspiracy to murder Russel Ingram during the period 7th July 1977 to 10th August 1978, and committing his murder in August 1978 and on Counts three, four and five of conspiracy to murder Eunice Peiris in the period 7th July 1978 to 20th March 1979 and the murder of Mrs. Peiris against the first accused with a charge of abetment of that offence against the second accused."

Mr. Bandaranayake said that the prosecution case as presented rests largely on circumstantial evidence to support these allegations.

"The charges have been strenuously denied by both accused, and the defence has joined issue on every ingredient in them. In these circumstances a question basic to this whole case seems apparent and may be articulated thus. 'Is there a *corpus delicti* in regard to the death of each of the deceased persons?' Taking the case of Russel Ingram, 'Was his death due to natural causes, accident, misadventure, suicide, or homicide?' 'Was there a breach of law resulting in his death for which someone is responsible and answerable?'"

(*Corpus delicti* refers to the principle that a crime must have been proven to have occurred before a person can be convicted of committing that crime)

"An inquiry even by a Court into this evidence regarding an allegation of this nature must of necessity commence with the death of the person and the circumstances surrounding his death. So if the answer is that there was 'no *corpus delicti*', there would be no purpose in considering counts one and two any further, and both accused should be treated as innocent on these counts and acquitted. But if the answer is 'yes' we will have to go on to consider other issues that arise upon the charges. We take up the case concerning Russel Ingram's death first as his death was anterior in point of time and is so arranged in the indictment. We will address our minds in similar fashion to the question of the death of Mrs. Eunice Peiris in the course of this order. So for the time being we will concentrate our attention in answering the question we have formulated in respect of the death of Mr. Russel Ingram."

Mr. Bandaranayake said that the prosecution has set out to prove *corpus delicti* in regard to the cause of death as an essential element in the case by circumstantial evidence. "Our views on circumstantial evidence and the manner that such evidence ought to be used in a criminal case will be set down in another part of this order. For the present we say that the prosecution relied on a series of circumstances which it asks the Court to believe and accept as proved. These circumstances include medical opinion as to the cause of death. In order to establish this element of *corpus delicti* on the murder charge, opinion evidence therefore assumes vital significance and an importance facet of the prosecution case."

"A number of medical witnesses have testified in this case and spoke to facts observed, conclusions reached, medication and nursing care given and their opinion on important questions relevant to the charge. So it is proper that we at this stage give our minds to the applicable law in regard to expert opinion. When the Court has to form an opinion on any scientific matter, the opinion expressed in the course of testimony by a person with special knowledge, the benefit of which is not ordinarily available to a Court, so that an inference drawn by the expert maybe particularly reliable, and therefore of special value to the Court, maybe taken. But the opinion expressed should be found on a discipline, which has been adequately developed."

HYPOGLYCAEMIA

"In the present case a condition known as hypoglycaemia, which is a fall in blood sugar level and which affects brain cells has loomed large and the possible causes of its presence in the two deceased persons goes to the root of this case. It has been variously suggested, amongst other things, that it could either be spontaneous hypoglycaemia resulting from an increased secretion of insulin caused by a tumour or several tumours of the pancreas, or tumours in ectopic sites or have caused by islet cell hyperplasia also known as micro-adenomatosis, which is a proliferate type of cell generalized in pancreatic tissues, or yet another type called reactive hypoglycaemia, the cause of which is now known and the prosecution sets out to prove that none of these natural causes existed in the deceased person."

"So, the question arises whether enough is known to medical science about these conditions through research study, publications, teaching and treating, and whether the witnesses by their qualifications, training, knowledge and experience have been accessible to such special skills to make their opinion valuable."

"The prosecution has set out to prove that what has been observed and medically diagnosed is correct, that this condition of hypoglycaemia was caused by the agency of the accused. The question also arises whether the scientific men are truthful and reliable witnesses or whether they have some reason to slant their evidence. Has a proper scientific search been done? Further the opinion expressed by an expert witness is a relevant fact in the chain of evidence. A trial judge should consider it," Mr. Bandaranayake said.

"A critical appraisal of the experts' reasons for his opinion should be done by the Court. An expert must detail what influenced him and set out the basis for his opinion and the Court must form its own opinion as it is the function of the Court with the assistance of the expert to decide the matter. The judge must decide that the grounds upon which an opinion is based are satisfactory."

"We are here on the primary question of *corpus delicti*, i.e. the cause of death to the exclusion of natural causes, accident, misadventure or suicide. But in some cases according to their nature of complexity the proof of *corpus delicti* cannot be fragmented and compartmentalized without involving oneself with evidence suggesting the identity of the particular person or with the person of persons charged with having caused the death. There could well be cases where the evidence is interwoven and inseparable and interlinked. In such cases proof of identity need not wait upon proof of *corpus delicti*. Actually, any evidence that a person caused the death of someone would be at once evidence that a crime has been committed as well as an indication of who it was who committed the crime. Evidence can generally speaking be used for all purposes in a case. But, we might say at this stage that we are not taking into account for our present purpose any evidence suggestive of a motive."

DEATH OF RUSSEL INGRAM

"Bearing in mind these observations we will now proceed to set down the salient features of the evidence and critically examine it with a view to deciding the question as to whether a crime has been committed in respect of the death of Russel Ingram. Russel Ingram died at the General Hospital, Colombo, in ward 18 on the 10th August 1978."

Mr. Bandaranayake said that the immediate cause of the death of Russel Ingram has been given by Doctors Sheriffdeen and

Wijesiriwardena as bronchopneumonia caused by a prolonged state of unconsciousness.

"BHT P19 supports the evidence of Dr. Wijesiriwardena that the patient was admitted deeply unconscious on the morning of the 18th of July. Dr. Sheriffdeen confirms this condition by his visit to the patient at about 3.30 or 4 p.m. and has also diagnosed irreversible brain damage. It is also the evidence of the doctors and the nurses and is supported by entries in the Bed Head Ticket (BHT) and in the Fluid Balance Chart (FBC) that was maintained, that the patient was deeply unconscious, that this patient was indeed unconscious during the entire period of his hospitalization on this occasion, which ended in his death."

"Dr. Nagaratnam examined this patient on the 20th of July and on the 3rd of August. He too confirms that the patient was unconscious throughout and that on the 3rd of August he found that the condition of pneumonia had set in and also that the patient had suffered brain stem damage. The evidence of these doctors relative to this question has been summarized by us elsewhere. Suffice it to say that Dr. Nagaratnam's testimony is to the effect that, in regard to the period of hospitalization of Russel Ingram between the 18th of July and the 10th August 1978, it was just the management of a hopeless case. All that could be done for him was to maintain nutrition, to give adequate nursing care and turning the patient from side to side to avoid bed sores, remove any secretion from the lungs and meet infection with drugs. Largely, infections were to the chest he said from a continued state of unconsciousness and a patient was prone to pneumonia, i.e. inflammation of the lung brought about by infection."

Mr. Bandaranayake said that there were different types of pneumonia:

- Primary pneumonia, where an organism affects primarily the lung

- Secondary pneumonia, complicating in the lungs

- Aspirated pneumonia, which is the result of aspiration of infected material

Mr. Bandaranayake said that Dr. Nagaratnam's opinion was that Russel's condition would in all probability aspirated pneumonia developed in the ordinary course of nature.

BRAIN STEM DAMAGE

"Dr. Nagaratnam has endorsed the management of the patient as evidenced in the BHT and the FBC. He observed brain stem damage on the 3rd of August and he says that the initial hypoglycaemic condition could have initiated it. He also says that the post-mortem finding of pneumonia is consistent with his findings. We have it that Dr. Sheriffdeen did a pathological post-mortem on Russel Ingram on the 10th of August 1978 and he says that he found congestion of the lungs and no other immediate cause of death, which confirms his clinical finding that the immediate cause of death was the onset of pneumonia in the ordinary course of nature, which they could not combat."

"Besides the medical evidence referred to above, the evidence before us from other sources show that Russel Ingram had no external injuries upon admission to the hospital, only some bed sores. According to the documents available the bed sores were attended to while he was warded. There is no evidence of any infectious disease upon admission and it is a proved fact apparent from the documents and the oral testimony that the patient was in a continued state of unconsciousness for at least twenty two days, and that he received in the meantime proper and adequate medical and nursing care with a diagnosis of lung infection towards latter stages of his illness in August 1978. Antibiotics had been administered too."

"The consensus of medical opinion is that prolonged unconsciousness in the ordinary course of nature would result in lung infection and pneumonia, which could result in death. The doctors have testified by their own observations and in the background of the treatment they gave and in this case, death has occurred despite treatment, that is to say that it was unavoidable in a patient whose condition was so low. This is apparent upon a perusal of the BHT and

FBC and these are entries made contemporaneously by trained staff in the ordinary course of duty and we accept these entries as truthful."

"We hold that the medical opinion as to the immediate cause of death is correct and reliable and we hold this fact proved beyond all reasonable doubt, i.e. that the immediate cause of death of Russel Ingram was due to pneumonia arising in the ordinary course of nature from irreversible brain damage and a prolonged period of unconsciousness."

"We next come to consider this question of the fact of prolonged unconsciousness and permanent irreversible brain damage. There are really two episodes of unconsciousness connected with hospitalization between the period 26th June 1978 and 10th August 1979. It is convenient to deal with these two episodes on unconsciousness, which needed hospitalization in the order in which they occurred. So that first episode concerns Russel Ingram's admission to ward No. 44 of the General Hospital, Colombo, on the 26th June 1978 at about 2.30 p.m."

UNCONSCIOUS AT THE VICARAGE

"The circumstances in which the patient was taken to hospital that day were deposed before us by Mr. Alex Ingram, the father of the deceased. It is his evidence that Russel Ingram was unconscious at the Vicarage, which was the residence of the first accused who at the time was the Vicar of St. Paul's Church, Kynsey Road. It is the evidence in this case that Russel and his wife, the second accused, were living at the Vicarage during this period. It is from the Vicarage, which is about half a mile away from Ward 44 that Russel Ingram is removed unconscious to hospital. It is Alex Ingram's evidence that Russel had been unconscious at the Vicarage from about the 24th of June."

"This was contested by the defence and we will deal with that later. At the request of the first accused, Alex Ingram obtained the letter P14 which is a letter seeking admission given by Dr. P.A.P. Joseph, retired Senior Surgeon of the General Hospital. Armed with this letter

Alex Ingram and the first accused had taken Russel to hospital. We believe Alex Ingram when he says that his son was unconscious at the Vicarage that day, the 26th."

Mr. Bandaranayake said that this is corroborated independently by Dr. (Mrs.) Ruwanpathirana who made entries on the BHT, (produced as P18). "She saw the patient at 2.30 p.m. upon his being brought to the ward. She has made an entry that the patient was deeply unconscious and that the first accused gave a history to the effect that the patient had been in stupor and unconscious for 20 hours. This was sought to be proved by the prosecution as an admission against the first accused. We have no reason whatever to doubt the correctness of this entry and it must be remembered that entries in the BHT produced in the case as P18 and P19 had been contemporaneous entries made by trained medical and nursing staff in the ordinary course of duty in respect of each patient who is warded in the hospital."

"We have no reason to doubt the accuracy of these entries and we are of the view that all entries that have been lawfully referred to in the course of the evidence have been satisfactorily proved and that the condition or the stage of things that they represent in fact existed at that time. There has been no cross examination on the footing that entries were false or mistaken. We hold that the admission referred to has been proved beyond reasonable doubt and that the first accused did indeed give this history that the patient had been unconscious at his residence for twenty hours before 2.30 p.m. of the 26th of June."

"Dr. (Mrs.) Ruwanpathirana got blood and urine samples taken for testing, as it was her diagnosis that Russel was in a hypoglycaemic coma, i.e. unconsciousness caused by a severe fall in the blood sugar (glucose) which was an essential and vital nutrient of brain cells and the deprivation of which occasioned stupor and unconsciousness. For this diagnosis, she says, she had the history of the patient, the letter p14 and her own clinical findings. She thereafter had administered to the patient the normal saline drip together with 50% dextrose infusion."

Mr. Bandaranayake then said that the patient has next been seen, according to the oral evidence and according to entries in the BHT, by Dr. (Mrs.) Anula Wijesundera, who was the Senior House Officer of that ward at that time.

"This doctor confirmed that the patient Russel whom she saw at 2.45 p.m. on the 26th of June was unconscious. It may be noted here that she does so from a medical stand point and this will not be the case of a layman saying that a person was seen lying unconscious. Dr. (Mrs.) Wijesundera approved of the treatment that had already been administered by Dr. (Mrs.) Ruwanpathirana namely, normal saline and dextrose and thereafter Dr. (Mrs.) Wijesundera entered her notes at page three of P18 including the finding of Dr. (Mrs.) Ruwanpathirana."

"It may be noted here that when a medical officer decides upon the diagnosis he would do so in the ordinary way of assessing material before him and eliminating other disease or the other probable causes for a disease and sets down only his final opinion and other consequent steps that he took. The entries of Dr. (Mrs.) Wijesundera have to be looked at from this stand point. We have also the evidence of Dr. Nagaratnam who saw the patient at 3.30 p.m. in ward 44 and he too says that the patient was unconscious. The evidence of these doctors is in the record. We are completely satisfied from this evidence that Russel Ingram was indeed unconscious upon admission to hospital on the 26th June 1978."

DEXTROSE INFUSION

"But the evidence of these doctors goes further, for they say that the patient had recovered consciousness by 8 p.m. that same night, and this recovery could be attributed purely as a consequence of the infusion of dextrose. This is another aspect of the case which we will consider later. The doctors have also given us their opinion as to the cause of the coma, and that too will be considered and discussed by us at a later stage. For the present we hold upon the medical opinion and entries in the BHT and the evidence of Alex Ingram that we are satisfied beyond all reasonable doubt that Russel was indeed admitted unconscious to ward 44 of the General Hospital on the 26th of June

1978 at about 2.30 p.m., having been brought there unconscious by the first accused and his father Alex Ingram from the Vicarage, which was the residence of the first accused."

"It is to be noted here that Russel Ingram spent a few days in ward 44 and was then transferred to ward 18, which was the surgical ward for investigation into the possibilities that a natural cause was responsible for the coma he had been in. So, Russel Ingram continued to be in the ward 18 until the 14th of July 1978 at which time he was discharged from hospital fully recovered – the entry on P18 at RIGH 11(a) shows that the first accused took charge of him upon Russel's discharge from hospital. It may further be noted upon his discharge, he was not asked to continue with any medicine or drug, and he was not prescribed or given any pills or drugs. He was sent home with a discharge ticket produce by the defence (as 1D21), which contained an instruction that Russel be re-admitted to ward 18 on the 26th of July for an extended GTT and later a barium meal test in order to ascertain whether there was any natural cause such as an insulinoma for the hypoglycaemic condition reducing him to a state of unconsciousness."

"We accept this evidence as truthful. P18 shows and it also supports the oral testimony that throughout this first period of hospitalization in wards 44 and 18 from the 26th of June to the 14th of July 1978, Russel had been ordered normal diet. It is in evidence that in the early days of his hospitalization in ward 44 even after recovery of consciousness he was unwilling to take food orally. So that they continued to give him nourishment and sugar through nasal feed and drip but after the transfer to ward 18 he used to sit up and walk about and take normal food orally. There are no entries in P18 to show that after he recovered consciousness at 8 p.m. on the 26th of June, he ever again thereafter became unconscious."

FLUID BALANCE CHART

"If there had been another episode of unconsciousness it surely must get reflected in P18. Furthermore, there is the evidence that there was no FBC maintained for Russel during the period of the first hospitalization. No FBC is referred to in the BHT. This shows that there was no necessity for the maintenance of a FBC because that becomes necessary only if patient is unconscious and is unable to consume food himself when his body fluids are monitored and a chart maintained for that purpose. In these circumstances we accept the testimony placed before us that since Russel become conscious at 8 p.m. on the 26th of June he remained conscious throughout his hospitalization and he left ward 18 walking and healthy in the company of the first accused on the 14th with a direction that he return to the hospital for the purpose of taking more tests."

"A request for an extended GTT had been made to the laboratory on the 11th of July and had fixed the date of 26th July for this purpose. The GTT taken about the 3rd of July upon requisition RIGH13 showed a normal curve as far as blood sugar was concerned and that is in evidence."

"Dr. Wijesiriwardena was cross examined about references to blood sugar reports contained in ID21. Dr. Wijesiriwardena stated that these reports are now not available with him and these reports must have been taken outside the General Hospital. It is not necessary for us to consider this matter at this stage as it is not relevant to the question before us at the present time."

"There is also evidence that whilst Russel was in ward 18 during early July he was seen to behave in a rather peculiar manner, hiding once when the accused visited him and also disappearing from the ward for some time and returning later. This evidence suggests that Russel had some sort of mental affliction during that time. We accept the evidence of Russel's father, who accompanied him on the 26th of June, and who later visited him in the ward with his wife. We believe nurses Malini Wanigaratna and Lasantha Fernando and the doctors who speak to the fact that Russel was admitted unconscious to the hospital on the 26th. This is supported by the entries in the BHT. So upon a consideration of all the material before us on this subject we hold proved beyond all reasonable doubt that Russel Ingram had been admitted unconscious to ward 44 and had already been unconscious on the 26th of June 1978 before 2.30 p.m. and that he left hospital recovered on 14.7.1978."

SECOND EPISODE OF UNCONSCIOUSNESS

Mr. Bandaranayake then dealt with the second episode of unconsciousness and hospitalization with permanent irreversible brain damage from the 18th of July until his death on the 10th August 1978.

"The evidence before us regarding the circumstances in which Russel was brought unconscious to hospital and admitted to ward 18 comes from the Jacksons who are relatives of the second accused and who had been at the Vicarage on 16th night, 17th night and 18th morning, with the accused. Mrs. Jackson, a sister of the second accused, has testified before us that Russel became unconscious at tea time on the 18th afternoon upon taking some pills given to him by the first accused. Russel was in bed at that time and that a few minutes after consuming the pills he started sweating and became unconscious and he remained so till about 8 a.m. on the 18th morning, which was a Tuesday and a clinic day when he was removed to hospital by the first accused."

"The evidence of the Jacksons will be summarized in another part of this judgment and this aspect of the credibility of these witnesses will be dealt with by us in another part of this order. For the present we say that Russel was indeed unconscious at the Vicarage on the 18th and the first accused brought him to hospital and had him admitted to ward 18. This is supported by Dr. Sheriffdeen's evidence that the first accused saw him at the clinic that morning around 8 a.m. and told him that Russel was unconscious for one day and the first accused wanted a letter of admission. This admission of Russel is relied upon by the prosecution to corroborate the evidence of the Jacksons."

"Dr. Sheriffdeen acting on the statement of the first accused and without examining the patient, ordered admission of patient to ward 18. It must be remembered that this was a patient who had been under his care a few days previously and who was under investigation for possible surgery by Dr. Sheriffdeen."

"Russel had in fact been admitted to ward 18 and the relevant BHT had been produced and marked P19. Dr. Wijesiriwardena who had attended on Russel in early July once again had to deal with this patient and he says he did so at about 9 or 9.30 a.m. and he made entries in P19 at RIGH 31(b) to the effect that 'patient was fully unconscious, blood pressure normal, pulse 86 etc.' His findings are in that entry. He says that at that time there were no by-standers there to give him any history and therefore, he has not recorded any history in this entry. At this point it become necessary for us to consider what happened at the ward after Russel was seen by Dr. Wijesiriwardena at about 9 or 9.30 a.m.," Mr. Bandaranayake said.

'NIL' SUGAR VALUE

"Dr. Wijesiriwardena says he ordered blood and urine samples to be taken for testing for blood sugar and urine sugar and that he also ordered the administration to Russel of the normal saline drip and dextrose infusion as he made a diagnosis of hypoglycaemia as the cause of state of unconsciousness. The prosecution has produced in this case the blood sugar report dated 18th July 1978 and marked RIGH 54(a). This report bears the legend that it is on a sample of Russel's blood sent to the laboratory from ward 18 on 18th July 1978. This report showed a 'Nil' blood sugar value in the sample, i.e. no sugar recordable in the blood sample delivered."

"It is the prosecution case that this was the condition in which Russel was brought from the Vicarage that morning and admitted to hospital by the first accused. This is an important aspect regarding the question of irreversible brain damage of the state of prolonged unconsciousness between the 18th July and 10th August and relevant to the consideration of *corpus delicti*."

"Was this unconsciousness during this period of the second hospitalization brought along with him from the Vicarage for some illness that he had at the Vicarage or something that had happened to Russel after hospitalization due to the neglect or negligence of the medical and nursing staff of ward 18?" asked Mr. Bandaranayake.

"The defence joined issue with the prosecution on this question and have pointed to certain facts upon which they say the Court should entertain reasonable doubt as to the real cause of his prolonged unconsciousness and inability to recover during this period. The defence on the one had contested the 'Nil' sugar value. It does so in two ways. Firstly, that the sample taken in the ward has to be fixed by the nurse in a test tube with certain chemicals and that these chemicals may have in a busy ward become polluted in some way. The defence does not contest this zero blood sugar value on the basis that the laboratory technician had made some mistake or that his tests were not properly done."

"We may say here that even though the defence did not by cross examination suggest such a thing it is still incumbent on the prosecution to establish that these tests were properly done and that the technician was qualified and experienced and had the wherewithal to do them properly."

Secondly, the defence points out that Dr. Wijesiriwardena had not made entries in the BHT at about 9 or 9.30 a.m. directing that a blood sample be taken or directing normal saline drip with dextrose infusion. Furthermore, the defence says there is nothing to show that saline and dextrose were in fact administered to the patient at that time in the morning at 9 a.m. or thereabouts. In the absence of these entries the defence suggests that it would well be that Russel was left unattended until 1.30 p.m."

"When Dr. Karunakaran had made entries directing the administration of saline and dextrose and the taking of a blood sample for sugar test, it was suggested that the second accused had been requesting nurses in the ward to attend to Russel. There was no evidence placed before the Court in support of this suggestion. Russel Jackson said that both accused left the hospital soon after Russel was admitted. The defence says there could have been an interval of nearly five hours after admission that Russel was left unattended which lapse could easily have aggravated and worsened his condition. With immediate attention he might have recovered consciousness and all that followed may not then have happened."

"The defence also says that because of the absence of entries, the prosecution cannot establish beyond all reasonable doubt that a blood sample was taken in fact from the patient at about 9 a.m. so that the blood sugar report, RIGH 54(a), reflects the blood sugar position at 9 a.m. and that it may be a sample that was taken at about 1.30 p.m. upon a direction of Dr. Karunakaran so that this 'Nil' blood sugar report cannot be reliably taken by the Court as representing Russel's actual blood sugar position at the time of his admission that morning at 8.30 a.m."

"It is necessary that we consider this submission in some detail. The lab technician of the General Hospital, Mr. Oliver Fernando, testified before us. He gave us his qualifications and experience and described in fair detail the tests he performed on the blood sample sent to him during the lunch interval between 1 and 2 p.m. on the 18th July 1978 with the requisition marked RIGH 54."

"The sample he received bore the legend that it was the blood of one Russel Ingram a patient in ward 18. The witness inserted the serial number 54 and working alone tested the sample for sugar as described by him. He did the normal recognized test for blood sugar, which was generally used in the lab. He received the 'Nil' value, i.e. the test showed there was no blood sugar in the sample. Being surprised with this result as he had never before had such a result, he repeated the test and again got a 'Nil' value. He then phoned Dr. Perera, the Head of the Lab and informed him of this result. Dr. Perera has since died and has not therefore testified before us. Upon his instructions, Fernando repeated the test the third time and yet again got the same 'Nil' result. He telephoned the result to the ward and later prepared report RIGH 54(a) which he signed, and countersigned by Dr. Perera later."

"Dr. Wijesiriwardena was the doctor on duty at ward 18 that morning when Russel as admitted around 8.30 a.m. He says he saw and examined Russel at about 9 a.m. and he made certain entries which are produced and marked in this case RIGH 31 (b). He found Russel deeply unconscious and these findings are borne out in this entry. The doctor says as his diagnosis was one of hypoglycaemia being the cause of the coma, he would have immediately ordered blood and urine samples to be taken for sugar testing and have also immediately ordered the patient to be put on saline and dextrose infusion. He has however not made any entries to this effect. He says he may have forgotten at that time to make these entries but he instructed the nurse to do these things. He knew this patient earlier as he had looked after him earlier, that same month."

"At this point we find on a perusal of the BHT that Dr. Karunakaran had seen Russel at 1.30 p.m. and made entries in RIGH 32. Dr. Karunakaran has not testified before us and is supposed to be abroad for some years. There is also in the page three in this BHT which is marked RIGH33, where Dr. Wijesiriwardena has given seven instructions and instruction four thereof is to maintain the FBC and instruction six is to continue IV fluids slowly and this Dr. Wijesiriwardena says was done before 1.30 p.m."

"So Dr. Wijesiriwardena offers the explanation, namely that his entry at RIGH 33 which was made on a loose continuation sheet shows that Russel was being given IV fluids before 1.30 p.m. and this sheet may have got unstuck from the BHT or may have got misplaced for some reason and therefore, was not available to Dr. Karunakaran when he came in the afternoon."

"Therefore, upon reading the entries in RIGH31 only Dr. Karunakaran would have proceeded to make entries ordering the saline and dextrose and also ordering blood and urine tests. Dr. Wijesiriwardena says in this context one could account for Dr. Karunakaran's entries at RIGH32 being numbered page one, which is a fact later on RIGH33 would have been found and appended. So, Dr. Wijesiriwardena's position is that his entries at RIGH33 were made before Dr. Karunakaran's entries at RIGH32."

Mr. Bandaranayake then referred to the evidence of nurse Manawadu, who was on duty at the time of Russel's admission.

"She has said that on the orders of Dr. Wijesiriwardena, she took blood and urine samples at 9 a.m. and then administered normal saline and dextrose infusion. She kept blood sample in the normal way in the fridge but she had forgotten to take the requisition from Dr. Wijesiriwardena at that time. When Dr. Karunakaran visited the ward later she got the requisition prepared and sent the sample she had taken in the morning at 9 a.m. with the requisition RIGH 54 for test. She herself has identified her hand writing and that of Dr. Karunakaran on RIGH 54."

"We have therefore, to consider whether the evidence of Dr. Wijesiriwardena and nurse Manawadu on this matter is reliable and whether the blood sugar 'Nil' value clearly represents the state of Russel's blood sugar upon admission. The defence suggests that the omission pointed out by them in the BHT entries is an important matter and that a reasonable doubt cast on the testimony of Dr. Wijesiriwardena and nurse Manawadu. The defence submits that in this background there is reasonable doubt that at the time of admission Russel got the necessary medical attention."

"The defence says that there is reasonable doubt as to whether 'Nil' blood sugar value in RIGH53(a) really represents the state of Russel's blood sugar upon admission that morning, because in the absence of contemporaneous entries one does not know at what time the sample was taken and one is merely left with the oral testimony of nurse Manawadu, who may now be interested in showing that there was no neglect on the part of the hospital staff that morning. The defence, however, submits that in any event the prosecution must satisfactorily prove that the sample that was sent to the lab was not polluted in any way so as to cause a 'Nil' reading."

Continuing Mr. Bandaranayake said, "We have considered the evidence and submission on this point of both the prosecution and the defence. The following factors appear important:

- Ward 18, a special surgical ward manned by skilled medical and nursing staff.

- Dr. Wijesiriwardena knew this patient before, and knew he had been treated for hypoglycaemia and knew that he had recovered upon the administration of dextrose and that he was supposed to come for further tests to ascertain whether there was an insulinoma, a symptom that could be cured by surgery and which could have been the source of hypoglycaemia; he had himself issued 1D21.

- The patient was deeply unconscious and that fact he has noted in RIGH31; the fact that he examined the patient at 9 a.m., we accept.

- Patient admitted to the ward on a letter from Dr. Sheriffdeen, the Consultant Surgeon, from his clinic that morning.

- The patient according to the BHT entries has shown a faint sign of recovery at 10 p.m.

In the background of all these factors it is too much and improbable that in all these circumstances this deeply unconscious patient was left quite unattended by known staff for nearly five hours since his admission."

Mr. Bandaranayake said that nurse Manawadu had attended on this patient during his first admission to ward 18 and throughout the second admission. She was staff nurse at the time, the senior head. The explanation offered by Dr. Wijesiriwardena that he forgot to attend to part of the paper work could conceivably happen in a busy ward.

"Then there is another aspect which appears to be relevant to this question presently under consideration. It is also the evidence of Dr. Nagaratnam that glucose and oxygen are the two nutrients of brain cells, but if a patient is left for 2 to 3 hours with no glucose supply in the blood, other body mechanisms come into operation in an emergency situation in times of need; glycogen, which is stored in the organs such as the liver, muscles and heart, is reconverted to glucose and metabolized. Ketone bodies found in certain parts of the body also store glycogen which could be re-converted to glucose and used in an emergency for two to three hours. We have no reasons to doubt the correctness of this opinion and no other doctor has expressed any contrary view."

CAUSE OF DEATH 'PNEUMONIA'

Mr. Bandaranayake said that the immediate cause of death 'pneumonia', was confirmed at his pathological post-mortem by Dr. Sheriffdeen.

"He examined the deceased's brain, the chest and the abdominal regions. He found the lungs congested which confirmed his clinical opinion that there was pneumonia and so he says the immediate cause of death by pneumonia was confirmed. He also examined macroscopically the liver. There was no tumour or cirrhosis. He also examined the kidneys, the adrenal glands, the hypothalamus and pituitary glands. They were all normal with no tumours. He next cut the skull and examined the brain carefully with the assistance of Dr. H.R. Wickramasinghe, the neuropathologist, who was occupying the adjoining room. Dr. Sheriffdeen says that one reason for the examination of the brain was to see whether there was any cerebral cause for the state of unconsciousness. He examined the brain macroscopically on the surface and also by slicing it into thin slices with the assistance for Dr. Wickramasinghe. He found it to be a perfectly normal brain, the contours normal, coverings normal and no tumours. The sliced sections showed no abnormality or tumours."

"He says if there had been a blood clot or stroke there could have been evidence of localized haemorrhage or areas of softening in the brain where the blood supply had been cut off. If there had been any infection to the brain, such as meningitis or encephalitis, it would have been visible to the naked eye at the post-mortem examination of that part of the brain. There was no such inflammation or signs of meningitis or encephalitis. So he found no cerebral cause for the state of coma at this post-mortem which he says confirmed his clinical diagnosis that it was hypoglycaemia, a fall in blood sugar level that had caused this prolonged unconsciousness."

"Dr. Sheriffdeen thereafter began looking for any natural cause for the hypoglycaemia, i.e. a fall in the blood sugar level which had been a strange and unaccounted phenomenon during the second period of hospitalization and so he examined all the organs and glands that increase and decrease and regulate the blood sugar level in the human system in order to ascertain if there was any disease or natural cause, which would account for this condition. This aspect of the case will be considered by us at a later stage. For the present, we set down that it was the considered opinion of Dr. Sheriffdeen from his knowledge of Russel's state of unconsciousness on the 26th of June and his startling recovery in ward 44 by 8 p.m. upon administration of glucose and his knowledge of all that evidence about the responses he got of his examination of Russel."

"His finding of irreversible brain damage, the pneumonia and continuing blood sugar falls in hospital whilst being unconscious while the patient was under his care and his pathological post-mortem findings, which confirmed his clinical findings that the cause of the coma, which Russel had suffered before his death was due to unaccounted falls of blood sugar depriving the brain of this essential nutrient."

INTEGRITY AND EXPERIENCE OF

DR. SHERIFFDEEN

Mr. Bandaranayake said that the Court had no reasonable doubt as to the integrity and experience of Dr. Sheriffdeen as a Senior Consultant Surgeon of the General Hospital and a teacher in surgery at the University.

"We have no reasonable doubt that his pathological diagnosis as to the cause of the coma can be accepted by us and acted upon by us with confidence. The cross examination of this witness has not raised any reasonable doubt in our minds as to this opinion and there is nothing before us to suggest that the treatment of mainly dextrose given to Russel in July, August 1978 or in June was incorrect or improper or insufficient or that there was any misdiagnosis or bungling."

"The opinion of Dr. Sheriffdeen that hypoglycaemia was the cause of the coma in July and August 1978 is in favour with the opinion of Dr. (Mrs.) Anula Wijesundera, each confirming the other. We accept that both clinically and at the post-mortem Dr. Sheriffdeen satisfactorily eliminated for good reasons given other ordinarily possible causes to a condition of unconsciousness in a person and so we accept his conclusion as to the cause of coma as reasonable as convincing and as correct. No insulin injection whatsoever or anti-diabetic drugs whatever was given during this period of hospitalization by the hospital authorities as part of his treatment."

"But this is not all. In regard to the second period of hospitalization and the question of the cause of coma we also have the opinion evidence of Dr. Nagaratnam before us. His qualifications were MBBS, MRCP, FRCP, and Senior Physician, General Hospital, Colombo. He is apparently one of the leading physicians of the General Hospital, Colombo. He has explained to the Court what hypoglycaemia is, i.e. that the blood sugar is maintained in the body at certain normal levels and is measurable and is usually within the scale of 60 to 100 mg% but this figure is slightly variable depending on the scale used for the measurement. Sometimes it could be 70% to 110% or 80% to 120 mg%. These differing figures have been given to us by various witnesses. This is because the graduation varies with the lab."

"The witness says that the blood sugar in the form of glucose is an essential nutrient feeding the brain cells and excess glucose not needed for the body is stored in the body up to a point having first been converted into glycogen. This glycogen is generally stored in the liver but is also found in the muscles, heart and ketone bodies and could be reconverted into glucose when needed. When the blood glucose level falls below about 40 mg% unconsciousness can occur. In some people it may have to fall below 30 mg% for unconsciousness to occur."

"Now in maintaining the blood sugar level a number of factors are involved, i.e. glucose production on the one hand and glucose utilization on the other. A number of normal factors regulate it. Hormones, whose action increases blood sugar and other hormones, whose action reduces the blood sugar. A balance of both maintains the normal blood sugar level. The hormone insulin reduces the blood sugar level while hormones produced from the adrenal glands like adrenaline and glucocorticoids and secretions from the pituitary glands increase the level of glucose."

"Now when there is a fall in blood sugar level certain signs and symptoms may appear. This fall of the blood sugar level would affect a person's alertness or consciousness which happens in stages and which are observable depending on the rate of reduction of blood sugar. According to Dr. Nagaratnam, the first symptoms could be dizziness, giddiness and lethargy, which could be followed by sweating, palpitation, slurring of speech, tremors, agitation and anxiety, aggressiveness or violent behaviour. All symptoms may not be present depending on the rate of fall of the blood sugar level. If the drop is very gradual the signs may not be there. If the drop is rapid they appear. Then when hypoglycaemia is prolonged, brain cells deprived of glucose begin to get damaged. The other signs and symptoms appear. They broadly lie side by side. They are 'Neuropsychiatric', and 'Neurological'."

Neuropsychiatric signs are: 'Behavioural disturbances', 'Depression', 'Hallucinations' and 'Manic schizophrenia'.

The neurological signs are weakness or paralysis of one side of the body like a stroke or of all four limbs, and also when tickled the big toe moves up (plantar responses).

Thereafter the signs are: 'Drowsiness', 'Semi-consciousness', 'Unconsciousness' and 'Deep unconsciousness'."

"Finally brain stem damage occurs when vital cells get into a state of decerebrate rigidity where it increases the tone of the upper limbs or where the upper limbs get flexed and the lower limits get rigid and extended and that indicates brain stem damage. The doctor told us what he would do with the leg to ascertain this; that is the evidence."

CEREBROVASCULAR ACCIDENT

Mr. Bandaranayake said that Dr. Nagaratnam has also enumerated other possible causes of coma, which he says he has ruled out in this instance.

"He gave his reasons. He definitely rules out unconsciousness caused by cerebrovascular accident which is the interruption of the flow of blood to the upper part of the brain resulting from thrombosis or embolism. He has ruled out meningitis, which is an infection to the covering of the brain. He has ruled out coma caused by liver or kidney failure. He has ruled out alcoholic coma or corrosive poisoning or other poisons. Upon a consideration upon all information available to him from both hospitalizations, information from the point of history and physical examinations done by him, laboratory data and the patient's response to a certain line of treatment, he is of the opinion that the patient's coma was due to hypoglycaemia."

"The description given here by Dr. Nagaratnam of the different stages of the fall of blood sugar level and the resulting observable signs and symptoms has not been contested either by direct cross examination of him or through the evidence of other medical witnesses."

"Two specialists testified before us after Dr. Nagaratnam concluded his evidence, and they were Doctors Dayasiri Fernando, a specialist surgeon, summoned by the prosecution, and Dr. Abeysuriya also a specialist surgeon summoned by the defence and neither of them were questioned regarding the accuracy of what Dr. Nagaratnam said on the matter just discussed. Dr. Nagaratnam's opinion has been expressed in the background of his knowledge, skill and experience and he has given us satisfactory scientific reasons for his conclusion. He was consulted by Dr. Sheriffdeen in regard to Russel Ingram. Dr. Nagaratnam had approved the treatment that was being afforded to Russel. This diagnosis of hypoglycaemia being the cause of the coma has not been contested at this trial in any meaningful way. No reasonable doubts have been raised in our minds. As to the reliability of his opinion, we accept Dr. Nagaratnam's testimony and his evidence that it was hypoglycaemia that had caused the episodes of unconsciousness, which resulted in Russel's hospitalizations as referred to. We are confident that his opinion is reliable," Mr. Bandaranayake said.

"So we have here a preponderance of medical opinion by the prosecution coming from medical and surgical specialists, doctors

(Mrs.) Anula Wijesundera, Sheriffdeen and Nagaratnam, and opinions that the incidents of unconsciousness of Russel Ingram brought to their notice, stemmed from a blood sugar problem. A prolonged lowered blood sugar level results in unconsciousness, which in the ordinary course of nature leads to infection of the lungs and resulting pneumonia and death. We hold that the cause of the episodes of unconsciousness discussed have been proved beyond all reasonable doubt to be due to the condition known in medical parlance as hypoglycaemia."

Mr. Bandaranayake said, "Besides these two episodes of unconsciousness and hospitalizations and the medical opinions available to the Court and our findings thereon, there has been placed before the Court by the prosecution, evidence that between the 9th and 13th of June 1978, and again intermittently thereafter until the 26th of June and then again between the 16th and 18th of July, Russel was observed at the Vicarage where he was then living with his wife to be ill in bed and having to keep away from work looking lethargic, sweating, behaving irrationally, feeling drowsy, his state of consciousness fluctuating sometimes stuporose or even unconscious."

"It was Mr. Russel Jackson who told us in most expressive language that he found Russel Ingram sometimes in the pond sometimes on the bank. The prosecution says that the behaviour and condition of Russel Ingram observed by the witnesses in this period at the Vicarage is also relevant to the question presently before Court, namely the question of *corpus delicti* in regard to his death. The witnesses we have in mind on this point are the Ingrams and the Jacksons who say they visited Russel at the Vicarage during this period, whose evidence is summarized elsewhere and the Court will separately assess their evidence on the question of credibility. Suffice it to say at this point that any evidence we can believe from these witnesses relating to this aspect of the case we are presently discussing, i.e. *corpus delicti* could be properly considered by us. We have examined their evidence relevant to this matter with great care that is, evidence suggestive of any signs or symptoms of hypoglycaemia as presented to us by Dr. Nagaratnam whose evidence on the matter we have accepted," Mr. Bandaranayake said.

"We find that there is such evidence coming from the Ingrams and the Jacksons that is to say their observations of Russel, his behaviour, his appearance, the fact that he was in bed, his movements, the manner of his speech, all such observations are there in the evidence. We have considered the evidence carefully and coming to the conclusion that we can rely on that evidence with confidence. As we have said earlier a critical analysis of these witnesses and the evidence that they gave would be done by us elsewhere."

BEYOND ALL REASONABLE DOUBT

"At this point we will mention our findings, that is, we can believe and act on their evidence relevant to the topic being presently considered and so we say that we are satisfied beyond all reasonable doubt that at the Vicarage, which was the home of the first accused and where Russel lived during this period 9th June to 26th June and again from 16th to 18th July, and that Russel showed symptoms and signs of hypoglycaemia and that before that period he was a man who had been in ordinary good health thorough out his life, except for one period of hospitalization at the Durdans Hospital in July 1977, and that just prior to his getting bouts of unconsciousness in June and July 1978 he had no infectious disease. He had no external injuries but that hypoglycaemia signs and symptoms were observed at the Vicarage from where he was admitted on both occasions unconscious to hospital."

Mr. Bandaranayake said that the Court in the previous paragraphs held that upon the preponderance of medical testimony presented by the prosecution, Court came to a finding that the cause of the coma was hypoglycaemia.

"The proved evidence of the findings at the Vicarage in June and July 1978 strongly showing the presence of hypoglycaemic signs and symptoms in Russel when viewed in the background of the medical testimony and the proximity of the time of the hospitalizations satisfies us beyond all reasonable doubt that his condition at the Vicarage which caused all these observed signs and symptoms was indeed hypoglycaemia and that this hypoglycaemia was not confined to this period of hospitalization but also afflicted Russel intermittently at the Vicarage."

"This we hold as being established beyond all reasonable doubt. We say this when looking at the overall picture of Russel's illness in 1978 in the background of all the proved medical evidence before us and other proved facts and circumstances that it would be quite irrational, improbable and inconsistent and in the teeth of the evidence for this Court to conclude that in June and July 1978 at the Vicarage he suffered from some other unknown, unidentified, unconnected and independent cause other than hypoglycaemia for witnesses to observe lethargy, slurring of speech, sweating, irrational behaviour, drowsiness, stupor and unconsciousness. This fact of unconsciousness at the Vicarage before the admissions have been established beyond all reasonable doubt and expressed so by as in previous paragraphs. We are convinced beyond all reasonable doubt that Russel Ingram had hypoglycaemic attacks whilst at the Vicarage during this period."

Continuing Mr. Bandaranayake said, "Having come this far and having concluded beyond all reasonable doubt that the cause of the coma was hypoglycaemia, the next very important and vital question which we must address our minds to is the question of the cause of the hypoglycaemia. If it was caused by accident or misadventure or suicide then there cannot be *corpus delicti*. So in order to establish *corpus delicti* the prosecution must now establish that the hypoglycaemia was intentionally induced and it is to consider these questions that we now turn out minds."

GLUCOSE IS NECESSARY

Mr. Bandaranayake said that it is the medical opinion in this case that hypoglycaemic conditions even leading to death can be present in a person by natural causes.

"For the metabolism of cells glucose is necessary. It provides energy. Insulin in the blood also helps glucose to enter the cells. A hypoglycaemic condition is one in which there is a reduction of blood glucose from the normal level maintained by the human system. This condition has been explained to us by several medical and surgical specialists, Doctors Sheriffdeen, Nagaratnam, Joseph and Dayasiri Fernando. Their qualifications, knowledge and experience have been enumerated in the summaries of their evidence set down elsewhere. Apart from explaining what it means they have also explained the causes, which could bring about this condition."

"There seems to be no variance or disagreement or contradiction amongst them on this question. In other words the causes of hypoglycaemia as placed before us by the preponderance of medical opinion makes it safe for us to accept that testimony and proceed accordingly. Dr. Nagaratnam has been treating diabetics both with insulin and with anti-diabetic drugs over a number of years as a Senior Physician of the General Hospital."

"We mentioned here diabetes because it is a condition opposite to hypoglycaemia. Dr. Sheriffdeen has also treated a number of diabetic patients over the years and has in fact surgically successfully treated a patient for the condition of hypoglycaemia, which is opposite to diabetes. Doctors Joseph and Fernando are highly qualified surgeons who are held or have held senior appointments of the University and in the Public Health Services. They can, therefore, speak with authority on the subject. So we say again that we accept what has been explained to us by them as to the various causes of the condition known as hypoglycaemia and we hold that the evidence placed before us proves beyond all reasonable doubt that the cause of Russel's state of unconsciousness in June, July and August 1978 was the effects of hypoglycaemia."

Referring to the defence witness called, Dr. Abeysuriya, Mr. Bandaranayake said he supported the evidence of the opinions of prosecution medical witnesses as to the possible causes of hypoglycaemia.

"So we will now set out the various possible causes of this condition as providing the background to a critical analysis of their evidence, which the prosecution has placed before us in regard to the specific cause which occasion this hypoglycaemic condition in Russel Ingram and which the prosecution wants us to believe and to hold as the reason which caused his death. According to the medical evidence we have accepted hypoglycaemia, i.e. a falling of the blood sugar level, can be caused by several factors."

INSULINOMAS OR ISLET CELL TUMOURS

Mr. Bandaranayake said that it would be convenient to divide hypoglycaemia into (a) Natural causes or endogenous hypoglycaemia, and, (b) Un-natural causes or exogenous hypoglycaemia.

"We now find that there are several categories of endogenous or natural causes of hypoglycaemia. This natural hypoglycaemia can be caused by:

- Endocrine organ disorders. These are disorders of the ductless endocrine glands in the body.

- Advanced stage disorder of the liver and the kidneys.

- Non pancreatic large hungry tumours

- Reactive hypoglycaemia

- Spontaneous hypoglycaemia which is divided into: (a) Hyperplasia or also known as micro adenomatosis of the islet cells of the pancreas or its ectopic tissues, and (b) Insulinomas or islet cell tumours in the beta cells of the pancreas or its ectopic tissues.

The unnatural causes or exogenous hypoglycaemia are divided into two situations:-

- Medical hypoglycaemia where a diabetic patient taking insulin or an anti-diabetic drug to control his diabetes accidentally takes an overdose of insulin or an anti-diabetic drug.

- Factitious hypoglycaemia where a non-diabetic normal healthy person either intentionally, accidently or unknowingly takes insulin or an anti-diabetic drug given to him intentionally."

This last condition, Mr. Bandaranayake said was what the prosecution said happened in this case.

"The evidence has been led to support this proposition which the prosecution wishes the Court to believe as proved beyond all reasonable doubt."

Mr. Bandaranayake then went on to explain further what each of these causes is about.

"So take the first of the natural causes.

(a) Malfunction of the endocrine or ductless glands secretions: These glands secrete through their walls directly into the blood stream. Two such glands relevant to our discussion are the pituitary glands and adrenal glands. The pituitaries are in the brain and the adrenals are by the kidneys. Their secretions besides other functions maintain a balance between sugar and insulin, which balance maintains a normal level of blood sugar. Similarly the malfunction of the thyroid glands too could interfere with the blood sugar level. The malfunction could be clinically diagnosed by symptoms and signs.

Insulin is also a form of hormone, which is secreted by the endocrine portions of the pancreas but we will deal with this later in this order.

(b) The second natural cause could be the effects of advanced liver or kidney disease. These conditions could be diagnosed clinically. There is also another possible cause of hypoglycaemia namely the toxic effects of acute alcoholism.

(c) The third natural cause elicited above can be the result of large non-pancreatic 'hungry tumours', which are being in the sense that they are not cancerous but which secrete large amounts of a substance like insulin or they have the capability of utilizing large amount of glucose which can also produce the lowering of blood sugar. These tumours can be located in the liver and some are called retroperitoneal tumours. They could sometimes be located in the region of the chest and the lungs or abdomen. These tumours can be one to twenty pounds weight and could be palpated from outside.

(d) The fourth natural cause is the condition known as reactive or rebound hypoglycaemia, which is essentially a reaction to blood sugar. When the blood sugar is high this condition can occur. The cause of it is not known but it has been known to exist with other conditions. It is usually seen more while after meals and could be controlled by diet alone by taking small frequent meals. It could very very rarely result in unconsciousness. But even so, not for long.

(e) The fifth natural cause is 'tumours' of the pancreas or its ectopic tissues, i.e. pancreatic tissues found on other sites outside the pancreas proper. Now this type of hypoglycaemia is called spontaneous hypoglycaemia. One such condition of pancreatic disorder is called hyperplasia or microadenomatosis. These are conditions which are not seen to the naked eye, but that can be seen upon microscopic examination. It is also a generalized condition diffused all over the tissue areas and could be easily found if present at histology."

"The islet cell tumours of the islets of Langerhans of the pancreas are known as insulinomas, i.e. tumours occurring in the beta cells of the pancreas, which cells secrete insulin. In passing it may be noted that there are also cells called alpha cells which secrete another hormone but we are not concerned with those alpha cell secretions. We are concerned here with the beta cell secretions, which secretion is the hormone insulin. These insulinomas are a very very rare condition. This is the accepted evidence of all medical witnesses. They could be visible to the naked eye and could also be felt if on the surface areas or just underlying when they could be successfully surgically removed at an operation. Dr. Sheriffdeen says he was looking for an insulinoma of 1 mm diameter. Dr. Nagaratnam says that they could be as small as

1 or 2 mm in diameter. Dr. Dayasiri Fernando has however placed a publication from a medical journal before us, which says that it could be as small as 0.5 mm."

MEDICAL JOURNAL

"These insulinomas could be found not only in the pancreas proper but in the beta cells of any pancreatic tissues at some other ectopic sites. Dr. Nagaratnam has told as that other ectopic tissues generally maybe found in the vicinity of the pancreas. The pancreatic bed where the pancreas lies is the spleen, part of the duodenum, ileum etc. Dr. Dayasiri Fernando has elucidated the area of possible ectopic sites with reference to the medical journal. The prosecution would have to eliminate all of these natural causes described above and the medical causes and all of the factitious causes except one beyond all reasonable doubt if it expects to prove the *corpus delicti* in respect of the death of Russel Ingram."

"We now turn to say a brief word about unnatural causes of hypoglycaemia. Medical hypoglycaemia is, as we have said, a state of lowered blood sugar caused in a diabetic patient who has been prescribed either insulin or an anti-diabetic drug to control his diabetes by taking an overdose of such anti-diabetic agent. We are left with what is called factitious hypoglycaemia, i.e., an induced state of hypoglycaemia found in a non-diabetic normal person induced either by himself, intentionally, as in a case of a suicide with his knowledge and acquiescence; accidentally, by one who himself experimenting with a blood sugar agent; or accidentally, as in the case of a person consuming it unknowingly; deliberately i.e., willfully, knowingly, wrongly and intentionally and usually secretly, administered to a victim to cause his death - homicidal."

Mr. Bandaranayake said that the last one is what the prosecution must establish beyond all reasonable doubt to the point of certainty as the only inference, which the Court can draw from all the facts and circumstances placed before it in order to succeed in proving that there was *corpus delicti* in respect of Russel's death.

"So we now come to consider whether the prosecution has placed sufficiently cogent and convincing evidence upon which they can say that there were no natural causes, which resulted in the hypoglycaemic condition which in the ordinary course of nature caused his death."

"We now come to consider whether there was any malfunctioning of the pituitary gland or malfunctioning of the adrenal glands or thyroid glands, which is the first possible natural cause which we have described above. The medical evidence before us is that when food is ingested it is digested in the small intestines and glucose enters the liver. The liver processes it and releases that much of glucose as is needed by the body into the blood stream and stores any remainder as glycogen both in the liver and in other areas such as the muscles. When the released glucose in the blood reaches the pancreas the beta cells of the pancreas immediately respond to this increased blood sugar and secrete insulin thereby maintaining a normal sugar/insulin level. Then, when there is such increased insulin activity in the blood, the pituitary gland responds by releasing pituitary hormones."

"The growth hormones and the ACTH hormones activate the adrenal glands, which in turn secretes the adrenal hormone. These pituitary and adrenal hormones tend to increase the blood sugar and this is a continuous cycle taking place and the balance of insulin/sugar is maintained naturally. For a day it has been estimated that there is 25 to 40 units of insulin produced by the beta cells of the pancreas."

PITUITARY DISORDER

Considering the opinions of doctors Nagaratnam and Sheriffdeen, who were the two specialists who attended on Russel on this question, Mr. Bandaranayake said that Dr. Nagaratnam's opinions were based on his clinical observations of this patient for nearly a month and the information he has received from the history, lab reports, response to the course of treatment, all viewed in the background of his knowledge, skill and experience. Dr. Nagaratnam's evidence was that features of pituitary disorder can be clinically observed, e.g. pigmentation, headache, vomiting, and disturbance in vision. There were no such signs in Russel or any history thereof during other periods of hospitalization in June, July and August 1978.

"Dr. Nagaratnam says that evidence of adrenal malfunction is also clinically observed, with signs of hyperpigmentation. There was no such sign in Russel. Dr. Nagaratnam says that he looked for tumours of the pituitary and adrenal glands and found no signs. Dr. Sheriffdeen when he did the pathological post-mortem on the body on the 10th of August 1978, has said that he examined the brain by slicing it into thin slices. He examined the pituitary gland and found it macroscopically quite normal."

"We bear in mind Dr. Nagaratnam's evidence that having regard to the large quantities of 5% and 50% dextrose that Russel had been receiving normally daily during this second hospitalization there must have been, if it was the cause, something to produce a large quantity of insulin, which not only combated the large infusions of dextrose but overcome them and despite the dextrose lowered the blood sugar to hypoglycaemia levels even during unconsciousness."

"So Dr. Nagaratnam says that there must be something, which produced all this. Insulinoma should have been a large virulent secreting tumour or several of them. It is Dr. Nagaratnam's evidence that he found nothing wrong clinically with the functioning of the pituitary or the adrenal glands and that these glands continued to function normally even in the state of unconsciousness and we have before us proof from the entries in the FBC and the BHT and the evidence of the doctors and nurses that Russel indeed showed recurrent signs of hypoglycaemia while lying unconscious with the drip of saline and dextrose."

"This is a fact we can observe for ourselves through recorded contemporaneous entries. The defence complains that the pituitary glands were not subject to microscopic examination. There is evidence before us if there had been some reversible disorder of the pituitary gland, it would not be seen in histology. Only an irreversible disorder will show in histology."

"We have in evidence before us that the cause of Russel's illness, the treatment he got during the two hospitalizations and the fact that he was on normal diet throughout. We have no reasonable doubt as to the reliability of the opinions of the Doctors Nagaratnam, Sheriffdeen and Dayasiri Fernando before us, that there was no disease or malfunctioning of the pituitary gland, which contributed or caused the state of hypoglycaemia in Russel in June and July 1978."

"The fact that the defence has pointed out to us that histology was not done does not in the background of all the reasons we have just set out, cast any reasonable suspicion or lurking doubt that histology might possibly have shown up and adequate reason to cause the lowered blood sugar level. We are of the opinion that we have sufficient reliable data, sufficient evidence before us to confidently eliminate any possibility that an natural malfunctioning of the pituitary gland could have caused this hypoglycaemia state and we accordingly hold that it has been proved beyond all reasonable doubt that the functioning of the pituitary gland had nothing to do with this state of hypoglycaemia."

Mr. Bandaranayake then dealt with the adrenal gland, which is also an endocrine ductless gland, and the kidney.

He said, "Its secretion affects circulation, maintaining blood sugar levels and muscle action. Dr. Sheriffdeen found the adrenal glands, both left and right, normal at the autopsy. He examined the kidney along with it and both the kidneys and adrenals were normal. He was looking for a tumour or any other disease. Dr. Nagaratnam says that adrenal gland malfunction is clinically detectable. Sign of such malfunctioning is hyperpigmentation and there was no such sign. The defence has pointed out to us that no historical examination was done. We have considered that position."

"Here again the evidence before us is that clinically that such a disease condition has been eliminated and the pathological post-mortem done by the surgeon where he specifically microscopically examined the gland, which he says showed no signs of disease. We believe Dr. Sheriffdeen has honestly given this evidence to us and that he did in fact examine the adrenal glands along with the kidney. We accept his skill and his ability to macroscopically recognize a diseased condition in this gland, which could be so seen."

"We also bear in mind the cause of Russel's illness and the treatment given and the medical opinions expressed, so when we examined all the evidence before us we are satisfied that beyond all reasonable doubt that we could confidently eliminate a disease of the adrenal gland as causing the hypoglycaemia. In the face of all the evidence before us we do not think histology of the adrenal could have made any difference to this case."

"We consistently bear in mind the amount of insulin that must have necessarily been circulating in Russel's blood stream during this period of unconsciousness for battling and overcoming large doses of dextrose that was being administered. When we consider all these we do not have any reasonable doubt that a malfunction of the adrenal gland causing Russel's state of hypoglycaemia could be eliminated. We accordingly hold that such malfunctioning or tumour of the adrenal gland was not there."

THYROID GLAND

Mr. Bandaranayake then dealt with the thyroid gland. He said, "Dr. Sheriffdeen says that he did not examine the thyroid gland, but clinically eliminated hyperthyroidism as a cause of Russel's hypoglycaemia. He said there are unmistakable clinical signs of such defect such as continuous excessive sweating - not intermittent sweating - as observed in this case, weight loss in spite of normal diet, bulging of the eyes. So he had been clinically satisfied that there was no deficiency of the functioning of the thyroid gland. We are satisfied that Dr. Sheriffdeen is a frank honest witness, a competent doctor and we accept his evidence on this matter. Dr. Nagaratnam too says that there were no clinical signs of hyperthyroidism during Russel's illness. We are satisfied that these doctors have sufficient data upon which they have expressed their opinions. We accept their evidence on this matter. We have to repeat that we believe this evidence in the background of Russel's illness and his treatment. We hold that the prosecution has proved beyond all reasonable doubt that hyperthyroidism or any thyroid malfunctioning was not the cause of Russel's hypoglycaemia."

In eliminating malfunctions of the pituitary, the adrenal or thyroid glands, Mr. Bandaranayake said that the Court has taken into account that on the 26th of June 1978, on the first hospitalization Russel regained consciousness the same day upon administration of dextrose and never got unconscious again during that hospitalization and left hospital recovered and well on the 14th of July.

"Furthermore, it is the evidence before us that prior to his getting unconscious on the 9th of June 1978, as observed by Alex Ingram at the Vicarage, that Russel (except for three or four days in July 1977) was a healthy person, healthy youth, and active sportsman. Taking all these factors into consideration and the facts which we ourselves have observed such as continuing symptoms of hypoglycaemia in ward 18, it is extremely improbable that during the healthy periods of his life he had any disease of the endocrine glands or the thyroid gland. So taking into account what we have set in the earlier paragraphs about the pituitary and the adrenal we confidently rule out the possibility that any malfunction or insulin secreting tumours of the pituitary, adrenal or thyroid caused his hypoglycaemic condition in June, July and August, 1978."

LIVER DISORDERS

Mr. Bandaranayake then dealt with the liver.

"Dr. Nagaratnam has said that a diseased liver is enlarged and palpable, can be felt - this we might say is something generally known even by a layman. Dr. Nagaratnam says that liver disorders are clinically observable - pain, puffiness, swelling, jaundice etc. None of such signs or symptoms was present in Russel. There were no signs of cirrhosis or hepatitis, no vomiting. Dr. Nagaratnam has treated innumerable such patients and so has Dr. Sheriffdeen. At the pathological post-mortem Dr. Sheriffdeen says he examined the liver macroscopically and it was a normal liver – no disease or enlargement. No cirrhosis or hepatitis. This confirmed his earlier clinical diagnosis that Russel had not been in a hepatic coma at any time. Dr. Sheriffdeen's post-mortem findings support Dr. Nagaratnam's findings."

Mr. Bandaranayake said the evidence of Dr. Joseph was that in advanced cases of liver or kidney disease, hypoglycaemic conditions could occur. This opinion has not been even contradicted by any other specialist.

"Here both clinically and at autopsy according to the evidence we have, the liver was found to be normal. We accept the testimony of these doctors. Having regard to the history given on the 26th of June as evidenced in P18 and the fact that no treatment was given for any liver condition throughout his two hospitalisations and no evidence of any signs of such disease from any of the witnesses who were close to Russel at the Vicarage in June and July 1978 we confidently rule out liver disease as being the cause of his hypoglycaemia in June, July and August 1978."

"We now turn to the possibility of kidney disease causing hypoglycaemia. It is already proved in evidence that Russel's unconscious state during the two hospitalisations and at the Vicarage was not caused by any renal failure or kidney disease. We have given our reasons for the finding earlier and Dr. Nagaratnam says that there was no clinical evidence that Russel suffered from hypoglycaemia caused by any kidney disease. We know that he was not treated for any kidney disease."

"Dr. Sheriffdeen says that at the pathological post-mortem he examined the kidneys and the adrenal gland and that they were both normal, both right and left. This confirmed his earlier clinical diagnosis that uraemic coma was not involved in Russel's state of unconsciousness in July and August 1978."

"The evidence of Dr. (Mrs.) Anula Wijesundera who was the Senior House Officer in ward 44 has also said that uraemic coma or kidney disease was not the cause of Russel's state of unconsciousness on the 26th of June 1978. This has been confirmed by Dr. Nagaratnam. Nor have any of the other doctors Ruwanpathirana, Wijesiriwardena or Banagala have ever treated Russel for any kidney ailment. Nor is there any history of it."

"The evidence which we accept is that he was a healthy young man never known to complain of any kidney pain or urine trouble. In the background of all of this evidence we unhesitatingly accept the evidence of Doctors Nagaratnam and Sheriffdeen as reliable and that the cause of Russel's hypoglycaemia was not occasioned by any kidney disease. Dr. Joseph says it is possible for hypoglycaemia to occur in cases of advanced kidney disease. It is our view that if there was such advanced kidney disease it should have been both clinically and at post-mortem observable by skilled specialists. The evidence is that he had no kidney disease at all. Accepting this evidence, we are satisfied beyond all reasonable doubt that Russel's condition of hypoglycaemia was not caused by any kidney disease and we eliminate such possible natural cause confidently."

ALCOHOLISM

"It would be convenient at this point to consider whether Russel could have suffered from hypoglycaemia caused by acute alcoholism. It is the evidence of Dr. Joseph that acute alcoholism, i.e. compulsive addiction to large quantities of alcohol, could if such large quantity of alcohol is consumed after two or three days of dietary neglect or fasting cause a lowered blood sugar level. In considering this we have the evidence of Alex Ingram as to his son's drinking habits that he was a social drinker."

"We have the evidence of Mr. Weeraman, Director of Independent Newspapers Limited, who employed Russel at the request of the first accused on the 3rd of November 1977 in the firm's advertising department and confirmed Russel in his job on the first of January 1978. These matters we hold proved beyond reasonable doubt. Mr. Weeraman says that Russel was mentally fit and that he participated in the activities of the firm's sports club and played in the firm's cricket team, which participated at club cricket level. He says Russel was generally regular in his attendance. He has told us about the leave that Russel has taken between the 1st of January up to the 9th of June 1978, when he fell unconscious. He has told us that Russel was a well-dressed person and that he met the public on behalf of his firm. He also said that Russel was not alcoholic and that he never found him drunk in office."

"We have also the evidence of Mr. Wanigasekera, Munilal Peiris and Chandrakanthi Dharmadasa that except for a brief illness in July 1977 that Russel was in good health and doing a job. Russel along with the second accused looked after the Vicarage, says Munilal, during the absence of his parents who left the country on the 5th of February 1978, until the first accused returned on the 25th of April 1978. Munilal had been to the Vicarage several times and the Ingrams had visited him. Russel came to his going away party when he left the country on the 29th of March 1978 and Russel was healthy. None of these witnesses have said that Russel was an inveterate drunk or confirmed alcoholic."

CREDIBILITY

Mr. Bandaranayake said that it was a proved fact that Russel was doing a job and going to an office from November 1977 to June 1978 and the Court believed these witnesses on this matter.

"We have employed ordinary tests of credibility in coming to this conclusion; observation and demeanour of the witnesses and tests of probability, consistency and contradiction. The defence pointed to the evidence of Arumugam, the church *Appu*, who has said that Russel used to drink. We have considered his evidence as well. Our views on the credibility of Arumugam are set down elsewhere in this order. We hold that there is no reliable evidence before us from all who had contact with Russel at the Vicarage or at his work place or elsewhere between September 1977 and 9th June 1978 that he was a compulsive drinker or a confirmed alcoholic suffering from acute alcoholism."

"The medical opinions already discussed in this part of our order where we have accepted the position that Russel had no liver diseases is also a relevant fact. Dr. Joseph says that this condition of hypoglycaemia caused by acute alcoholism would not last long and that it is the toxic effect of alcohol that decreases blood sugar. So that the time taken for a large amount of alcohol to remain in the blood stream would be the limiting factor in regard to the period of lowered blood sugar level."

"However, it will be seen that this cannot possibly account for Russel being unconscious for the periods referred to in the evidence. Such a toxic effect of alcohol cannot account under any circumstances for the continued hypoglycaemic attacks, which Russel had during unconsciousness in July and August 1978 in ward 18 when no alcohol was given to him but only dextrose. No history of acute alcoholism has been given to the hospital at admission. The fact of these hypoglycaemic attacks in ward 18 flatly contradicts any possibility of acute alcoholism causing the lowered hypoglycaemic blood sugar level. So, considering all of this we rule out without any hesitation that Russel's hypoglycaemic condition as caused by alcoholism. It was not so caused."

HUNGRY TUMOURS

"We now turn to consider whether a tumour or tumours, medically known as 'Hungry Tumours' for convenience, could have been the cause of Russel's hypoglycaemic condition. It has been explained to us by the medical specialists that there are certain known non-pancreatic tumours, i.e. tumours growing in body tissues other than pancreatic tissues which are very large, weighing anything between one to thirty pounds which by their behaviour and nature could cause a fall in blood sugar causing hypoglycaemia. They are not malignant tumours either. These tumours secrete insulin like substance. They also have the capability of consuming large amounts of blood glucose for their requirement. This dual effect could cause a lowering of blood sugar. They are located in the abdominal cavity and in the chest cavity in the liver or in the lungs or anywhere in the abdomen etc."

"Dr. Joseph has told us that they are large and massive and usually unlikely to be missed. Dr. Nagaratnam has told us that they are clinically identifiable and could be palpated. This evidence as to the nature, behaviour, presence, size and location stands uncontradicted. We have no reason to doubt the veracity of the evidence in this regard or doubt its reliability and we accept the medical evidence as to the probability of the existence of such tumours in human beings and in the result they could result in hypoglycaemia. Dr. Nagaratnam has expressed the opinion that clinically there were no signs that Russel had such a tumour."

"At the pathological post-mortem done by Dr. Sheriffdeen, it is in evidence that he examined organs in the abdominal cavity including the liver, kidneys and intestines, and also organs of the chest cavity including the lungs and there were no such 'hungry tumours'. Dr. Sheriffdeen was looking for a tumour of the size of one mm. He found none. We believe these two specialists and we are quite satisfied that sufficient examination has been done to eliminate the presence of a 'hungry tumour' and that it has been eliminated with certainty. We accordingly hold that the prosecution has proved beyond reasonable doubt that a 'Hungry Tumour' did not cause the hypoglycaemic condition found in Russel, which occasioned deep unconsciousness and irreversible brain damage and ultimately caused his death."

REACTIVE HYPOGLYCAEMIA OR REBOUND HYPOGLYCAEMIA

Mr. Bandaranayake then discussed the condition known as 'Reactive or Rebound Hypoglycaemia', which has been explained to as something which could bring down blood sugar levels to hypoglycaemic levels, i.e. levels below 50 mg% or 40 mg% and below, occasioned by a reaction to glucose.

"We have already said that the normal blood sugar level is between the values of 60 mg% – 100 mg%. But that this value is variable according to the scale used. The evidence is that the cause of this reaction is not known but it is observable and quite common. It is called 'post-prandial' in that after food, there is increase in blood sugar and there is heightened insulin activity resulting in a lowering of blood sugar below normal levels two to three hours after meals."

"There are certain features about this group that should be noted, namely, that they never produce a true coma. Dr. Joseph says that a person can occasionally go unconscious but he will not remain long unconscious. It is the evidence of Dr. Nagaratnam that reactive hypoglycaemia does not result in unconsciousness and that the only treatment necessary is the giving of small amount of food at regular intervals. It is also the evidence of Dr. Joseph which he stressed that neuropsychiatric symptoms do not occur in this group. Dr. Joseph says he observed brain damage in Russel on the 15th of July 1978 at the Vicarage. He says he set Russel a simple arithmetic test and found that Russel could not work it - to subtract 7 from 100 - and Russel said it could not be done."

"The prosecution summoned Dr. Joseph mainly as a witness to facts: but being a retired highly qualified specialist and senior surgeon and teacher, we permitted him to express certain opinions, which we felt valuable. The explanation and description of this condition of 'Reactive Hypoglycaemia' expressed by doctors Nagaratnam and Joseph are mostly in accord with one another. We accept that testimony and by its very terminology what is meant is a lowered blood sugar condition resulting from a reaction to sugar."

NEUROPSYCHIATRIC SYMPTOMS

"We have no reason to doubt this and none is apparent in the evidence in this case. We accept the evidence of these two doctors that unconsciousness resulting from this reaction is very rare and if it does, is only for a very short time. We accept Dr. Joseph's testimony that neuropsychiatric symptoms do not occur from this condition. It should be so. Indeed long periods of unconsciousness do not occur by its very nature. We accept the position that once the cause of the reaction is removed - increased blood sugar combated by the activity of insulin and the blood sugar level is brought down thereby - there will be no criteria for continued reaction and the blood sugar will rise again in due course by the action of compensatory mechanisms or food. So thus we confidently accept the evidence that unconsciousness is very rare or almost never."

"Now we look at the picture of Russel's illness upon the evidence before us – the evidence of Alex Ingram that Russel was unconscious for about two days prior to the 26th of June; the admission by the first accused contained in the BHTP18 and proved against him where he has said at 2.30 p.m. of the 26th that Russel had been unconscious for twenty hours previously and at times stuporose. When discharged, he was well and allowed to go home with no continuing medicine prescribed to him. He was continuously conscious and on normal diet, which was that his body was not reactive to sugar."

"He never went unconscious during that first period of hospitalization after the recovery on the 26th. Then we have the evidence of Dr. Joseph that Russel had suffered brain damage when he examined him on the 15th of July night which again is not a condition associated with reactive hypoglycaemia. We have the further fact of deep unconsciousness on the 18th of July with a zero blood sugar reading and irreversible brain damage which again are quite uncharacteristic of reactive hypoglycaemia. Upon the medical evidence which we have accepted and the factual evidence of witnesses Dr. Joseph, Mr. Alex Ingram and Dr. Wijesundera as seen in P18, the picture is clearly not one of reactive hypoglycaemia."

"Dr. Nagaratnam has specifically expressed the opinion on his clinical findings that Russel was not suffering from reactive hypoglycaemia at any time while he was in hospital for the reasons already set down. Dr. Nagaratnam's opinion is that taking the medical picture as a whole if there was some natural cause, which could explain Russel's condition it must have been a large intensively secreting tumour such as an insulinoma, which would cause this condition."

Mr. Bandaranayake said that there has been evidence placed before the Court that reactive hypoglycaemia would exist along with a situation of severe or even moderate depression arising out of a mental disorder.

CAUSE OF DEATH OF MRS. PEIRIS

"This evidence was led by the defence specifically in relation to the cause of death of Mrs. Peiris, which charge is also contained in the indictment but with which we are not presently concerned. In fact upon being directly asked by the Court whether that evidence had any relevance to the case of Russel, counsel for the first accused was hard-pressed to say that it may have some connection. But this matter of mental depression was not presented or pointed out by the defence specifically in connection with the death of Russel and the witness who testified to it was a witness called by the defence, and his testimony was confined to his examination of Mrs. Peiris."

"Nevertheless, we feel it our duty to address our minds to this evidence at this point also. It was the evidence of Dr. Abeysuriya, called by the defence, that in cases of severe to moderate depression arising out of a mental disorder there could also be reactive hypoglycaemia and that the depression could cause a break down in the hypothalamus-pituitary gland complex resulting in the fall of blood pressure, which would then interfere with the supply of oxygen to the brain cells, and that condition of anoxia coupled with low blood sugar because of reactive hypoglycaemia could cause irredeemable brain damage and prolonged unconsciousness."

"When considering that opinion in relation to the case of Russel Ingram, even if we are to hold (and we are not deciding this at the moment) that the opinion is accurate, trustworthy and medically reliable, we find that in the case of Russel, there is no evidence that he suffered from any severe depression during the relevant period June-August 1978."

Mr. Bandaranayake said that there was no history that he was severely depressed, no external head injuries or other injuries or incurable diseases, no known family or children problems, nothing to indicate a cause of severe depression.

"He had been going to work up to the 9th of June. He had been the Social Secretary in his place of employment. Mr. Weeraman his employer has not said that Russel showed any signs of depression. In fact he said Russel was working well and he confirmed him in his job on the first of January and that his job entailed meeting the public. There is evidence that in ward 44 and thereafter in ward 18 during the period of his first hospitalization, after he regained consciousness he was aggressive and violent at times refusing food. But this according to the medical opinion is the result of brain damage resulting from prolonged hypoglycaemia. Then again between the 26th of June and the 14th of July he was on normal food and did not show any signs of hypoglycaemia."

"Then again on the 18th of July he has been admitted to the hospital with a zero blood sugar reading and from then onwards up to his death in August he was deeply unconscious. It was the evidence of Dr. Abeysuriya that in unconsciousness, the criteria of depression are removed so that the hypothalamus-pituitary-adrenal functions return to normal. If this is so, one cannot account for sudden signs and symptoms of hypoglycaemic attacks seen in the hospital from about the 26th of July onwards during unconsciousness. Between the 18th of July and the 26th of July in the state of this unconsciousness any criteria of severe depression would certainly have been removed."

"The BHT entries of 26th of July and 27th of July show that his pulse was regular, of good volume and tension and there was no fall in blood pressure. What Dr. Abeysuriya was seeking to say was that reactive hypoglycaemia can be caused and is caused by severe to moderate or even just moderate depression. Now once the depression which affects the mind is removed as a result of unconsciousness there cannot be reactive hypoglycaemia resulting from depression, but we do find from the BHT hypoglycaemic attacks from the 26th July onwards for about eight or ten days."

"So, according to these medical opinions these attacks from the 26th July onwards could certainly not have been caused by reactive hypoglycaemia. So even if one were to accept Dr. Abeysuriya's theory that reactive hypoglycaemia can result out of severe depression that evidence is irrelevant to the case concerning Russel. So taking this picture of factual evidence into account, we hold it to be proved beyond all reasonable doubt that the prosecution has completely eliminated any possibility of severe or even moderate mental depression causing reactive hypoglycaemia and causing Russel's illness."

"We have referred to the opinion of Dr. Nagaratnam that Russel was not suffering from reactive hypoglycaemia and that was not the cause of his unconsciousness. We have examined the evidence before us and our observations upon it as to the cause of Russel's illness. We eliminate with confidence that a depressed mental state had nothing to do with Russel's condition. Dr. Sheriffdeen too has expressed an opinion based on his clinical findings that Russel was not suffering from the condition known as reactive hypoglycaemia. Dr. Sheriffdeen supports the opinion of Dr. Nagaratnam that in cases of reactive hypoglycaemia the patient does not become unconscious."

"Taking into consideration medical opinions expressed above on this condition of reactive hypoglycaemia, its symptoms and behaviour, which we accept and which is the preponderance of medical opinion, and taking into account the course of his illness, we are confident that the medical opinions are reliable and that these specialists are skilled and competent to express them."

Mr. Bandaranayake said that Dr. Nagaratnam and Dr. Sheriffdeen had ample opportunity of clinically eliminating reactive hypoglycaemia as the cause of Russel's unconsciousness and permanent brain damage. Their opinions were confirmed by the evidence of Dr. Joseph and are not contradicted in any way by any other medical opinion.

"In the circumstances we hold that the prosecution has proved beyond all reasonable doubt that the condition known and explained to us as reactive hypoglycaemia did not cause this state of unconsciousness and was not responsible for the irreversible brain damage Russel had suffered by the 18th of July 1978 and which ultimately led to his death in the ordinary course of nature."

HISTOLOGICAL EXAMINATION OF THE PANCREAS AND NODULE

"So far we have discussed situations or conditions due to the malfunction of certain organs or due to serious diseases of certain organs other than the pancreas, or certain tumour conditions in known non-pancreatic tissue which could result in a lowering of blood sugar to hypoglycaemic levels. We have also referred to insulin reacting to increased blood sugar and we have held that the prosecution has proved beyond all reasonable doubt that none of these endogenous conditions caused the state of unconsciousness and the irreversible brain damage observed in Russel on the 18th of July" Mr. Bandaranayake said.

Then he dealt with other conditions in pancreas that can reduce blood sugar.

"We now get onto the specific disease conditions of the pancreas or pancreatic tissue which could bring about the same result, i.e. lowered blood sugar levels causing hypoglycaemia. These specific diseases of the pancreas or tissue are according to the specialists known as 'Hyperplasia', 'Adenomatosis', 'Nesidioblastosis' and 'Insulinoma'. At one end of pancreatic disease is hyperplasia and at the other end is insulinoma or tumour of the islet cells (the beta cells) of the pancreas or its ectopic tissue. Ectopic tissue is a tissue of one organ found in some other place where it should not be found."

"This question of insulinoma causing hypoglycaemia will be discussed separately in the course of this Judgement. So far at present we concern ourselves with the questions of 'Hyperplasia', 'Adenomatosis' and 'Nesidioblastosis'. This group of diseases is described as causing spontaneous hypoglycaemia, which means unpredictable spontaneous secretion of insulin. It should be remembered that according to the evidence these conditions are not visible to the naked eye and are also not palpable. Their presence can be discovered only by microscopic examinations of tissue. So in the context it can be easily understood that Dr. Sheriffdeen did not specifically look for these conditions as in any event they would not have been visible. But he says the possibility of their existence crossed his mind so that was one of the reasons why he sent the pancreas for histology," Mr. Bandaranayake said.

"So, before we can consider the medical evidence relating to hyperplasia, adenomatosis and nesidioblastosis as causing spontaneous hypoglycaemia in Russel we have to first consider the evidence relating to the voyage of Russel's pancreas from his abdomen to Prof. (Mrs.) Balasubramaniam's work table and under her microscope. We must first, therefore, be satisfied that the pancreas, she says she examined on 23.08.1978 at the medical college pathological laboratory, was Russel's pancreas."

"The evidence relating to this begins with Dr. Sheriffdeen who says he did a pathological post-mortem on 10.08.1978 at the general hospital post-mortem room. He says he took the pancreas out of its bed at the post-mortem and carefully examined it and felt it and then cut it into thin slices with his scalpel and further examined it and found nothing - no abnormality and no tumours. In the course of his post-mortem examination, he found a nodule in the duodenum and he took it out and examined it and found it to be normal. Then he wanted the pancreas to be microscopically examined for insulinoma. He also thought of hyperplasia, adenomatosis and nesidioblastosis. He then put the specimen pancreas and nodule in a tin and walked back to ward 18 and nearing the ward he met Dr. Wijesiriwardena and handed over the tin with the specimens for him with instructions to forward the specimens for histology to the lab."

"Dr. Wijesiriwardena takes up the narrative and has told us that he had a look into the tin and found a pancreas and he wrote out a requisition which has been produced in the case by the prosecution as exhibit P20. In that requisition dated 11.08.1978, the patient's name has been written as Russel Ingram with a request from ward 18, '? Insulinoma' – history of recurrent attacks of hypoglycaemia finally going into a coma, patient died of pneumonia. Post-mortem: macroscopically pancreas normal, nodule in duodenum'."

"Dr. Wijesiriwardena said that the nurses would have written the label on the container, which is not a production before us. Containers with specimens for histology are normally kept in the nurses' or the doctors' room in the ward and the medical orderly would take it over to the laboratory. The specimen is kept in saline solution on the 10th and 11th of August 1978. There were no other pancreas specimens in this ward 18 other than Russel's."

"One S.A.D. Weerasinghe Perera testified before us that he used to do duty during this period and that he took the specimen pancreas and nodule in the tin with the requisition P20 from ward 18 to the path lab. He cannot remember the exact date. He used to take specimens on Mondays, Wednesdays and Fridays. The 11th of August was a Friday so that Monday would be the 14th."

"Mrs. Kalubowila, a technician in the medical college path lab, has stated that she entered the particulars of this specimen in the path lab register having checked the specimen with P20 and the label. This register has been produced before us and the entry she made proved at the instance of this Court as X19. The entry is dated 15.08.1978 and has been entered against the serial number 1988/U78 and the particulars given in P20 have been entered at C19 thus – 'Russel Ingram – Pancreas and Nodule'. The specimen may have been brought on the 14th and accepted by another technician and the entry made by her on the 15th the serial number is entered on P20 and on the container label."

Mr. Bandaranayake said that the pathologist Dr. Balasubramaniam has told Court that specimens are kept in a fixative and not in the fridge.

"She has said that thereafter the technician would take the specimen and the request form and check them and keep them for the pathologist's examination. When the request forms are brought to her she goes through them and then goes to the lab and examines the specimens first macroscopically and thereafter microscopically. Post-mortem specimens are not urgent. But specimens sent during surgical operations for biopsy get immediate attention. According to the relevant entries Dr. Balasubramaniam says she has examined Russel's pancreas and nodule on 23.08.1978. She has also told us that this was the only pancreas received in this path lab in August 1978 and that after examination she issued her report produced as exhibit P36. The pancreas and nodule have not been produced for obvious reasons."

NO JUDICIAL POST-MORTEM

"Now we find that no judicial post-mortem has been done on the body of Russel Ingram because Dr. Sheriffdeen had already done a pathological post-mortem. Alex Ingram has told us that the parents were angry over this as the post-mortem examination had been done without their knowledge and in their absence. We believe the witnesses that a post-mortem was indeed done by Dr. Sheriffdeen on the 10th of August. The document P20 shows that the pancreas and a nodule were indeed sent from ward 18. The report P36 shows that histology was indeed done on the pancreas."

"Taking all these facts into consideration we are satisfied beyond all reasonable doubt that the specimens examined by Dr. (Mrs.) Balasubramaniam on 23.08.1978 at the path lab were indeed the same specimens taken out of Russel's abdomen by Dr. Sheriffdeen on 10.08.1978. The oral testimony supported by the documentary evidence leaves us completely satisfied that the specimens examined under the microscope were indeed Russel's pancreas and nodule."

"Now we have already adverted to the fact that the conditions known as hyperplasia, adenomatosis and nesidioblastosis are medically known to enhance insulin secretion, are observable only under a microscope."

Mr. Bandaranayake said that the prosecution has therefore presented the Court with the opinion evidence of Dr. (Mrs.) Balasubramaniam, the pathologist, who did the histology on the pancreas and nodules.

"Dr. (Mrs.) Balasubramaniam is the Associate Professor of Pathology in the Faculty of Medicine, Colombo University. She is a MBBS (Ceylon), 1960. Then after some study and experience in different hospitals she joined the Medical Faculty and was a demonstrator in Pathology until 1965. She then proceeded to England and did post graduate work and teaching in path departments at Royal London Hospital and St. Thomas Hospital. In 1970 she did a PhD degree in Pathology from London University. From 1971 to 1977 she was Senior Lecturer in Pathology in the Colombo University. Between 1977 and 1979 she was in the United Kingdom and worked in a National Health Hospital in England and at Dundee Medical School in Scotland."

"As a professor she teaches pathology to under graduate and post graduate students and is also a Consultant Pathologist to several hospitals in Sri Lanka. About her experience she has further told us that along with some others she does about eight thousand histologies per year. In the course of her work she has examined over 100 pancreases and tested its tissues for various disorders. She has also personally found an insulinoma of the pancreas and she has also seen another slide containing an insulinoma of the pancreas in an examination done by another pathologist. It is in this background of knowledge, skill, training and experience that the prosecution presents her opinion evidence on the results of the histology she did on Russel's pancreas and duodenum nodule."

"The Professor told us that she first examined the whole sliced pancreas and nodule macroscopically by palpation. She said she was familiar with normal pancreatic tissue and the structure of its various cells. Normal pancreatic tissue was yellowish white in colour. She said that normal insulin producing tissue consists of two parts the 'Exocrine' and the 'Endocrine'. The 'Exocrine' part consists of acini and ducts separated by connective tissue in which are blood vessels and nerve fibres. The 'Endocrine' part consists of islands or islets called the 'Islets of Langerhans' named after the German Scientist, who first discovered their existence."

"These islands consist of two main types of cells - the beta cells and the alpha cells, and delta cells. The alpha cells secrete the hormone glucagon and beta cells secrete the hormone insulin. Of these cells by far the commonest are the beta cells. These beta cells also act as the glucose sensor cells. So the normal function of the beta cells is to secrete insulin to keep a normal blood sugar level. The witness said that she was quite able to identify a beta cell under the microscope. The witness said that having examined the whole sliced pancreas and nodule for abnormalities that she found no abnormalities macroscopically, no colour change, which is usually seen in adenomatosis, and no tumours seen or felt."

"She proceeded to process parts of the pancreas and the whole of the nodule. She made four representative slides from the thicker slices of the pancreas. She expressed the opinion that the pancreatic sections showed no evidence of insulinoma. We shall go into this aspect of the evidence in greater detail in a forthcoming paragraph. For the present the witness said that she found no abnormality in the cells as seen in the slides."

NO HYPERPLASIA

"She explained what the condition called 'hyperplasia' was. She said hyperplasia occurs in the beta cells which could cause increased insulin activity. She however said that hyperplasia was a generalized condition occurring throughout the tissue and therefore easily observable and differentiated from the normal cell. She explained the difference. In hyperplasia, under the microscope, the islets are seen to be much bigger than normal and also each individual cell that goes to form the islets is larger than normal and also the number of such large cells is more than normal."

Mr. Bandaranayake said that there was therefore an increase in the size of each individual cell as well as an increase in the number of cells that go to constitute an island.

"There was no such condition in the specimen slides as seen under the microscope and the cells and their formations were normal. So the condition of hyperplasia in her opinion did not exist in the pancreas. She then went on to explain another abnormal condition, which could produce enhanced insulin secretion and very much like hyperplasia, only more pronounced and this condition too she was familiar with and could be identified. This condition is called 'adenomatosis'. Her position is that, in both hyperplasia and adenomatosis, there is diffuse proliferation of cells but in adenomatosis, the proliferation in more marked than in hyperplasia and is seen in a formation known as the 'Tumourlet formation'. Further, the colour of tissue changes in adenomatosis to pinkish or purplish from the normal yellowish white. She observed no such colour change. Again, in adenomatosis the tissue is usually firmer than the surrounding tissue. She did not feel such a presence. So her position is that this abnormality known as adenomatosis was not there in Russel's pancreas."

Mr. Bandaranayake said that yet a third abnormality of the cells producing increased insulin and observable under the microscope and with which the witness was familiar is called 'nesidioblastosis'.

"She earlier said that the exocrine part of the pancreatic tissue and acini and ducts separated by connective tissues containing blood vessels and nerve fibres. In nesidioblastosis, there is a proliferation of the lining of the ducts. This lining is known as epithelium. So this condition consists of proliferation of the epithelium tending to form a tumour. She says this condition was not present in Russel's pancreas. The nodule found by Dr. Sheriffdeen in the duodenum was also processed and examined and found to be merely a lymph node. It was just lymphoid tissue that you get all over the body and quite incapable of secreting insulin."

NO INSULINOMA

"The expert opinion was that there were no pathological abnormalities to be seen in the slides in Russel's pancreas that she examined under the microscope, no hyperplasia, no adenomatosis, no nesidioblastosis and no insulinoma of any sort. No cancerous tissues, no cysts. Tumours and insulinomas are coloured usually from pink to purple and they could be red depending on the amount of blood supplied. They are always darker than the surrounding tissues. But here there was nothing abnormal. There was no sign of diabetes in the pancreas or leucocyte infiltration usually seen in prolonged cases of diabetes for years and years. There were none of the changes usually seen in a diabetic patient."

"Under cross examinations the witness said that slides are normally prepared by a technician. The technician who prepared the relevant slides has not been a witness for the prosecution. Preparation of slides takes about twenty four hours and is handled by the technician under the supervision of the pathologist. The technicians are qualified and trained in the department and they used a process to make slides that have been used for more than hundred years all over the world. Only the machines are new and automatic. After her macroscopic examination, the evidence is that the pathologist further sliced the pancreatic tissue into pieces that could get into the machine i.e. 10 to 12 micro centimeter, the section being about 1.5 cm in length and width. She took the areas for preparation at random from the body and the tail of the pancreas, after her macroscopic examination and after she found no colour changes, no signs of abnormality, no tumours by sight or by feeling. This was the routine method adopted the world over for histological examinations."

Mr. Bandaranayake said that the entire pancreas would have thousands of sections and slides of every section are never made and a microscopic examination of every slide and every cell is never done anywhere in the world.

"The machine rotates the slices in various fluids and that part is done by the technician under the general supervision of the pathologist. Once the machine is switched on it takes ten to eighteen hours to complete the process. In this instance the witness said that the process was properly done. The slides itself would show the process was properly done. She was quite satisfied that the four slides represented a satisfactory sufficiently representative examination which would show up abnormalities of the descriptions already mentioned if they existed."

"Furthermore, in re-examination the witness said that she was aware that the specimen sent was of a dead man for research purposes and not for investigation and that the pathologists are very vigilant in examining for research purposes as they are there for that purpose and it could well be the subject matter of a paper or a publication if something rare and abnormal was found. So considering all of this the witness said that she found no abnormality in Russel's pancreas either microscopically or macroscopically. So she sent her report P36 dated 25.08.1978 where she has said that her macroscopic and microscopic examination revealed no abnormalities."

"The defence has criticized the prosecution opinion evidence regarding the absence of any conditions such as hyperplasia, adenomatosis and nesidioblastosis. The defence directed their cross examination of Dr. (Mrs.) Balasubramaniam to three main matters, viz:

- To examine whether there was satisfactory evidence that it was Russel's pancreas, which she took up for histology. We have already discussed this matter in detail and expressed our opinion that it has been proved that it was Russel's pancreas.

- To examine whether the technique of making the slides was satisfactory.

- To examine whether what was done and what was examined under a microscope was sufficient to express a reliable medical opinion eliminating various disease conditions under discussion in the specimens."

"Dr. (Mrs.) Balasubramaniam was not specifically cross examined on whether any of the disease conditions known as hyperplasia, adenomatosis and nesidioblastosis were capable of causing prolonged hypoglycaemia with deep unconsciousness and irreversible brain damage in an adult. The defence submitted that, the fact that her opinion is based on a microscopic examination of four slides makes it unreliable. The criteria or the data upon which her opinion is based is scanty, incomplete and insufficient that in these circumstances one should hesitate to act on such opinion with confidence. Except the pancreas and the nodule, none of the other organs or tissues where a pancreatic ectopic tissue is medically known to exist has been subjected to any kind of histological examination, so that there is a large area of unexplored possibilities of natural disease conditions and, Dr. Sheriffdeen's macroscopic examination was not enough and that Dr. Dayasiri Fernando says he would have done a very thorough examination microscopically in a laboratory."

"In these circumstances the defence says that there is a reasonable doubt or several such doubts arising upon the prosecution evidence as to the absence of these several endogenous pancreatic disease conditions under discussion and that the benefit of such doubt should accrue to the defence. It is the position of the defence that the high standard of proof required of the prosecution has not been reached by this opinion evidence; that the proved circumstances do not add up to exclude one or more of the endogenous pancreatic disease conditions to be present in Russel, either in his pancreas or in pancreatic tissue elsewhere to have naturally caused his illness."

"At this point we reiterate that it is for the prosecution to prove every fact or circumstance which it asks the Court to believe to exist beyond all reasonable doubt. We are conscious of the high degree of proof expected of the prosecution in a criminal case. The defence need not trouble to point out anything or show any alternative ways in which something might have happened. The defence need not show us any infirmities and doubts in the prosecution case. The defence need not prevail upon the Court that there are reasonable doubts arising upon the evidence and which the Court should take into account. So bearing in mind all these matters we proceed to examine the evidence before us relevant to what we are presently considering."

Mr. Bandaranayake said that the specialists who testified before the Court, doctors Dayasiri Fernando, Nagaratnam and Sheriffdeen have not considered hyperplasia, adenomatosis and nesidioblastosis to be important causes of spontaneous hypoglycaemia in adults.

"Their position appears to be that these diseases can and do cause a low blood sugar but not prolonged hypoglycaemic levels in adults or as seen in Russel Ingram. The trend of the medical opinion before us is that the prolonged hypoglycaemic condition observed in Russel is, if resulting from an endogenous disorder, to be more consistent and more probable of tumour or insulinoma secreting significant amounts of insulin (if the cause of hypoglycaemia was a natural endogenous cause) and not any of these other endogenous conditions of hyperplasia, adenomatosis and nesidioblastosis. This opinion has been reached considering that Russel was a young adult male, his picture of ill health, the numerous states of consciousness or semi consciousness with zero blood sugar reading, and the recurrent state of hypoglycaemic attacks during unconsciousness despite large and adequate infusions of dextrose whilst in hospital."

BRAIN DAMAGE

"The evidence of Dr. Dayasiri Fernando, who is a specialist in diseases of the digestive system, the liver and the pancreas, and a person who has received a specialized training in England as a scholarship student and a witness upon who the defence strongly relied, shows that the most practical and compelling reason for the blood sugar fluctuation and the recurrent hypoglycaemic attacks causing deep unconsciousness and irreversible brain damage as evident in this case, was either because of a pancreatic tumour or tumours, either in the pancreas or in its ectopic tissue secreting such large amounts of insulin as to overcome all these dextrose infusions. If there was no such insulinoma then it must be an outside induced factitious agency. He has also said that if he was told that no anti-diabetic drug or insulin was being given, then he would be compelled to think in terms of pancreatic tumour. This was indeed the opinion of Dr. Nagaratnam too that taking the entire picture of the illness and as a physician and under whose care Russel was, a large intensely secreting tumour or tumours should have been present and active to cause Russel's condition. If not that it must be an outside induced hypoglycaemia."

"It was even put to Dr. Sheriffdeen in cross examination that 'nesidioblastosis' is a condition causing persistent hypoglycaemia in new born babies up to the age six months. The defence was relying upon information contained in a medical journal on 'Hypoglycaemia' by Turner, Rubenstein and Foster, appearing in 'International Medicine', Volume 1 of September 1981. Dr. Sheriffdeen was not familiar with this publication and the terminology in this publication. Dr. Sheriffdeen was also questioned about the book produced by the defence on 'Hypoglycaemia' by Marks and Rose, the Second Edition."

"We also find that the whole pancreas has been sent for histology which never happens in a biopsy of a living person and that a skilled and experienced pathologist has adopted methods of histology employed worldwide and she has selected what in her opinion as a person constantly on this job were sufficiently representative areas of pancreatic tissue for microscopic examination. No other specialist has contradicted her evidence or expressed any view that what she has done was inadequate. She did not know the patient or any details of his illness and there was not any hint of a criminal case at the time. She says that she was examining the tissue from the point of view of research and she was not rushed. By her testimony she has shown great familiarity with normal healthy pancreatic tissue, with diseased tissue, and also of various disease conditions of the pancreas. She has explained to us in fair detail what conditions she was looking for," Mr. Bandaranayake said.

"We are satisfied upon the evidence that the technique used in preparing the slides was proper and that they were to her satisfaction for the purpose of submitting a pathologist's report and expressing a reliable opinion. We accept her position that four slides of tissue were sufficient in the circumstances of showing up a disease if present. She found nothing macroscopically. She was looking at thinly sliced portions of the whole pancreas and the evidence which we accept is that 'hyperplasia', 'adenomatosis' and 'nesidioblastosis' are generalized proliferate conditions in the tissue so that a representative section should show it up if present."

NORMAL PANCREAS

"Dr. Nagaratnam has told us that a pathologist would pick areas and cut up sections. Upon this evidence we hold that Russel's pancreas was a normal pancreas without disease, without diabetes, without tumours and without the disease conditions of 'hyperplasia', 'adenomatosis' or 'nesidioblastosis'. We also hold that the prosecution has proved beyond all reasonable doubt that the nodule was nothing but a harmless lymph node quite incapable of secreting insulin."

"As for the presence of these disease conditions in pancreatic ectopic sites, it was the evidence of Dr. Sheriffdeen that at the pathological post-mortem apart from examining the pancreas itself, he examined other organs and sites of the abdominal cavity where ectopic pancreatic tissue has been reported to be found in medical journals. He had read fairly widely on this subject before he had operated successfully on a female patient in 1973. He has described the site during this search he found the nodule in the duodenum. He said that there was no ectopic pancreatic tissue to be seen. All he found that was unusual was the nodule in the duodenum. He said that there was no ectopic tissue or anything suggestive of it. Where tissue of one organ is found in another organ there are differences in colour and so on that are discernible to a trained eye."

"We might remind ourselves that he examined the bed of the pancreas, the greater and lesser curvature of the stomach, the ileum, duodenum etc. His evidence is that in all the likely places there was no evidence of ectopic pancreatic tissue. Dr. Sheriffdeen is a general surgeon of great experience who is presently concentrating on vascular surgery. He had Russel in his care. He knew the clinical signs symptoms and history. He knew Russel's reactions to the medical care. He knew that no insulin or anti-diabetic drugs were ordered or administered to Russel by the medical authorities of the hospital as part of his treatment. He knew that Russel was not a diabetic and that clinical opinion has been confirmed by Dr. (Mrs.) Balasubramaniam's microscopic examination of his pancreas."

"So in this background we accept Dr. Sheriffdeen's testimony that he looked carefully for pancreatic tumour or insulinoma, which itself according to the evidence is a very very rare condition, but of which he had personal experience because he had successfully operated and removed an insulinoma. So he says he was looking for something as small as one millimeter in size both in the pancreas as well as in the other abdominal organs as insulinoma can be found in other abdominal organs only if there is ectopic pancreatic tissue is implanted in that organ."

"So when one is looking for a tumour as small as one millimeter, one is obviously at the same time having in mind this fact that such a one millimeter tumour can be sighted only at ectopic pancreatic tissue. We are quite satisfied that Dr. Sheriffdeen did a careful and knowledgeable search in the pancreas and around in other abdominal organs for an insulinoma as well as the tissues in which it may be found. We accept his evidence that there were no such ectopic sites macroscopically and we believe him when he says that such foreign tissue is distinguishable to the trained eye."

HUNGRY TUMOURS

Mr. Bandaranayake said that in the course of the judgement the Court held that the prosecution has proved that other endogenous causes of hypoglycaemia, such as diseases or malfunctions of other organs such as the pituitary or adrenal glands or the thyroid gland or the liver or the kidney or acute alcoholism or hungry tumours or reactive hypoglycaemia, did not cause Russel's state of hypoglycaemia and irreversible brain damage.

"We are presently dealing with the possibilities of hyperplasia, adenomatosis or nesidioblastosis, which are spontaneous causes and which are the result of diseases of the pancreas or its tissue causing this condition of hypoglycaemia and brain damage. The preponderance of medical opinion before us is that in Russel's case, endogenous causes of spontaneous hypoglycaemia such as hyperplasia, adenomatosis and nesidioblastosis could not have been a practical or a significant cause of his condition. We are confident that the medical opinions on this matter are fair and reliable and we accept the reasons given. We also accept Dr. (Mrs.) Balasubramaniam's evidence that the disease conditions hyperplasia, adenomatosis or nesidioblastosis were not present in Russel's pancreas or nodule. We are satisfied with the histology that she did."

"We are of opinion that the slides were sufficiently representative areas of the pancreas to show us a generalized proliferative condition if it existed. We are also satisfied with her histology and her evidence that there was no tumour or insulinoma condition either in Russel's pancreas and that the nodule was harmless. We accept Dr. Sheriffdeen's evidence that there was no ectopic pancreatic tissue macroscopically seen suggestive of pancreas disease. We accept the medical opinion that hyperplasia, adenomatosis or nesidioblastosis could not have made any significant contribution or caused Russel's illness."

Mr. Bandaranayake said that the Court has observed upon the documentary and oral testimony:

- That Russel got into deep coma caused by hypoglycaemia whilst he was at the Vicarage and was hospitalized on two occasions in June and July 1978.

- That after each hospitalization, the administration of 50% dextrose and normal saline stopped the hypoglycaemic attacks.

- That after the dextrose on the 26th of June he recovered consciousness and remained conscious and after a few days ate normal food and got well and was discharged from the hospital.

- That at the second hospitalization on the 18th of July with a zero blood sugar reading, with two infusion of 50% dextrose and normal saline and more infusions of 5% dextrose, Russel's blood sugar shot up to 243 mg% by night fall of the same day. This blood sugar reading is more than double a normal level and that for several days thereafter the blood sugar levels remained high at 162 mg% on the 19th, 165 mg% on the 20th, 67 mg% on the 2nd, 127 mg% on the 23rd and again 103 mg% on the 23rd.

"It is significant that these high blood sugar values between the 19th and 23rd have been reached with only 5% or 10% dextrose infusions on these days and not 50% dextrose infusion as is evident in the FBC, strongly suggesting therefore, that once the blood sugar was revived upon admission on the 18th, the insulin secretions within his body were normal. We observed this phenomenon during both admissions and especially during the second admission when a FBC was maintained, i.e. that after the initial help by the administration of 50% dextrose to recover the blood sugar, it remains high with a minimum of extra glucose infusion. So much so that this extra sugar infusion during those days immediately after recovery could account for the abnormal high blood sugar readings that are in evidence during those days."

"So now taking into account all the evidence that has been placed before us, after considering all the submissions made to us by the defence, we conclude beyond all reasonable doubt that there was no disease condition of hyperplasia, adenomatosis or nesidioblastosis responsible for Russel's illness. It is our judgement that the prosecution has proved and established that these diseases hyperplasia, adenomatosis or nesidioblastosis did not afflict Russel."

Continuing Mr. Bandaranayake said, "We now come to the last of the possible endogenous causes of hypoglycaemia, which the prosecution must eliminate if it were to ask the Court to decide as proved that there was no natural cause responsible for Russel's sickness and his death. In considering the question of *Corpus Delicti* this is perhaps the most important and significant part of the evidence, which the Court must consider with the utmost care and precaution with due regard to whatever the defence may point out by cross examination or by submissions. This is a matter upon which the defence has strenuously joined issue with the prosecution by their cross examination of the expert witnesses and by their submissions to the Court."

BEYOND REASONABLE DOUBT

"We bear in mind the presumption of innocence and the burden of proof. The prosecution must establish all the ingredients of the charges that have been framed against the accused beyond all reasonable doubt and that there is no burden on the defence whatsoever to show any fact or circumstance favourable to the accused but that they are free to do so if they so desire. The defence does not have to prove the innocence of the accused in a criminal trial. The burden of proof is always upon the prosecution and the standard of proof is the high standard of proof beyond reasonable doubt. Bearing in mind all these matters we proceed to examine the evidence. This possible endogenous cause of hypoglycaemia is an insulin secreting tumour of the pancreas or situated in its ectopic tissue. This tumour is medically known as an islet cell insulinoma causing spontaneous hypoglycaemia, i.e. a low fasting blood sugar level."

Mr. Bandaranayake said that one clinical method of tentatively diagnosing the existence of such tumour is by doing what is known as an extended GTT over a period of five hours or over sometimes extending even up to seven to nine hours.

"The details of how such a test is done have been placed in evidence before us. No such extended GTT was done for Russel because during the first admission what was ordered by the doctor was not done by some mistake and when Russel was discharged on the 14th of July 1978, he was asked to return to hospital on the 26th of July to enable such an extended GTT to be done and during the second admission he was found upon admission to have suffered irreversible brain damage and was on a constant dextrose drip, so that no purpose could have been served by such a test according to the medical evidence. It was just a question of indefinitely keeping his vital functions alive."

"So there is no evidence placed before us by the prosecution on any clinical diagnosis of insulinoma or its absence by these means. The prosecution has not placed such evidence to aid the Court. The prosecution has placed evidence of the fact and course of his sickness evidence of hospitalization supported by the BHT and the FBC and the oral testimony of witnesses. The prosecution has placed evidence of clinical diagnosis by other methods, such as treatment offered and rendered, the patient's responses to such treatment, the opinions of experts who have special skills and experience and who attended on him with the reasons for their opinions and other experts who have examined his organs and who are able to testify knowledgeably in the background of their learning, training and experience."

"It may become necessary for the Court in the course of this judgement to have to refer to evidence already cited as repetitions are almost impossible to avoid when dealing with a chain of circumstances. The elimination of the existence of insulinoma being is the main scientific fact. The prosecution has called in aid the expert opinions of four specialists, viz. doctors Dayasiri Fernando, Sheriffdeen, Balasubramaniam and Nagaratnam to assist the Court in coming to a finding of fact upon this matter. So we are proceeding to consider the evidence as to whether Russel was naturally afflicted by insulinoma or insulinomas which was responsible for his state of ill health."

"Dr. Dayasiri Fernando had never seen or examined or treated the patient Russel. His evidence before this Court falls into two parts – the first part is of a factual nature dealing mainly with conduct of the first accused upon which evidence the prosecution relies and which evidence will be dealt with in the course of this judgement. The second part of his evidence is evidence of opinion about pancreatic tumour and other diseases of the pancreas and which the prosecution as well as the defence have treated his opinion as valuable and this is the part of his evidence which the Court now proceeds to consider. Dr. Fernando was called by the prosecution as a witness to fact and cross examined by the defence as a witness to opinion. Counsel for the defence also put to him passages from the book 'Hypoglycaemia' by Marks and Rose, second edition, Chapter 7 – Pancreatic Hypoglycaemia."

"He said that he had personally seen Professor Marks and had met Dr. Rose. The witness agreed that this book was standard work on all aspects of hypoglycaemia. But, Dr. Fernando said he based his opinion about the testimony he was to give on Priestley's 'Moynihan Oration' 85 cases on insulinoma, and Prof. Berbosa's Master of Surgery degree thesis."

INSULINOMA

Accordingly, Mr. Bandaranayake said that Dr. Fernando stated the following:

(a) Insulinoma is a very very rare condition. Only a small number of cases have been found in the whole world since it was first described in 1902. He has personally never come across one. The smallest insulinoma recorded has been 0.5 mm in size.

(b) The characteristics of insulinoma are that it is round, dark blue or blue-black in colour depending on the amount of blood. In the tumour the colour will change. If it has a lot of blood it can be easily seen in the organ in which it is; also insulinomas are firm in consistency to the touch and palpable. It can be surgically removed.

(c) The pancreas is a soft organ, which can be palpated.

(d) If the tumour is in surface tissue it can be felt and seen, i.e. macroscopically identifiable. If however it is located in the body of the tissue and it is occult (hidden), it maybe difficult to palpate depending on its depth. It depends on the site, it is rare and growth differs in individuals.

(e) There are cancerous tumours and there are benign tumours. Tumours can grow very fast sometimes. Benign tumours can also be secreting ones whereas cancerous tumours are always usually secreting. Even those that are secreting can have periods of remissions. A higher level of insulin in the blood is called hyperinsulinism.

(f) A tumour must not only be present, it must also secrete and be functionally significant to cause hypoglycaemia, i.e. it must secrete enough insulin to be of significance to the blood sugar level.

(g) Insulinoma may not be found during surgery because it is occult or too small to be palpable.

(h) The amount of insulin secretion does not depend on the size itself. Even a small tumour can secrete a lot of insulin.

(i) There may be multiple secreting insulinomas situated in different places and secreting together to make cumulatively a significant volume or quantity of insulin. There could be several tumours as many as 13 or 14 secreting ones at the same time. Blood glucose monitoring is necessary during surgery in order to be sure that all secreting insulinomas are excised.

(j) The rate of secretion in insulinoma can be moody, i.e. periods of remissions and periods of secretion but with time as it progresses the rate increases. The insulinoma could be in remission for five years.

(k) Tumours are known to be extensively distributed so apart from the pancreas, other organs in the abdominal cavity will also have to be examined for the possibility of ectopic tissue and for the possibility of multiplicity of tumours and small size.

Mr. Bandaranayake said that according to Dr. Fernando, 70% of known ectopic sites are at the duodenum, stomach and small bowel, and of these, 27% in the duodenum, 25.5% in the stomach and 15.9% in the small bowel.

"And the commonest location in these organs is the submucosa. A cross section shown an inner membrane and other mucosa covering the common site is beneath the mucosa membrane, i.e. 10 mm deep from the surface. The other 30% is situated in the Meckel's diverticulum out-pushing, in the umbilical fistula, mesentery, omentum, spleen, hilum of spleen and capsules, gall bladder, bile duct, liver, pancreatic bed and transverse colon attached to the abdominal wall.

MEDICAL JOURNALS

Continuing Mr. Bandaranayake said, "This evidence was generally accepted by both sides. This evidence has not been contradicted by other evidence. Dr. Fernando mainly relied on medical journals and his readings to express this opinion and not from personal experience. We have no reason to doubt their accuracy. We adopt them as proved in this case. Dr. Fernando said that insulinoma was indeed a very very rare condition. That opinion is the consensus of the medical opinion in this case. Furthermore, he said that to be of significance a single insulinoma it should be at least 5 mm in size and this evidence stands uncontradicted and is relied upon by the defence and is not challenged or contradicted by the prosecution. It was the defence in the first place who elicited the opinion of this doctor on these conditions."

Mr. Bandaranayake then turned to the evidence of Dr. Sheriffdeen who did the pathological post-mortem as already stated.

"In dealing with the earlier question of the elimination of disease of the pancreas such as hyperplasia, adenomatosis and nesidioblastosis, we referred in detail to Dr. Sheriffdeen's examination of the pancreas and other possible sites. But it is nevertheless necessary here to remind ourselves of what he did. He said he opened up the abdominal and chest cavities first and he macroscopically examined the pancreas having taken it out of the body. He said he did a careful systematic search of the whole pancreas, its head, body and tail and then palpated it carefully both sides. He found nothing. He then cut it into thin slices as thin as a scalpel (knife) could hold and he examined each slice macroscopically. He saw no insulinoma, he felt no insulinoma and he saw no colour changes or any other signs. He said he was looking for an insulinoma as small as one millimeter."

"We have just set down that the medical journal says that the smallest insulinoma has been 0.5 millimeter, i.e. half a millimeter. But that in any event an insulinoma should be at least 5 mm in size and secreting to be functionally significant. Dr. Sheriffdeen had 5 years earlier, in 1973, successfully operated and removed an insulinoma from the pancreas of a female patient who was 27 years old and who recovered and is still alive. That insulinoma he said was 2.3 centimeter or 23 millimeter in size. The doctor said that in that case too the symptoms and signs were excessive sweating, slurring of speech, thirst and hunger. Her fasting blood sugar, 27 mg% at a 5 hour extended GTT, suggested insulinoma. He told us that the pancreas lies in its bed. Dr. Joseph has told us that it is in the shape of a comma with a head, neck, body and tail and that it is attached to the abdominal wall. Dr. Sheriffdeen has told us that it is attached to the posterior abdominal wall by tissue known as the mesentery and that it is also attached to the duodenum (small intestine) by two ducts. By cutting around these you can remove the pancreas."

"The normal weight of a pancreas is 30 to 40 grams and it is about 12 cm by 4 cm in size. So this pancreas which he removed appeared quite normal. Both in regard to size, dimensions and weight although not weighed in a scale. He then examined the greater and lesser curvatures of the stomach and the duodenum. He extracted the nodule in the ileum for signs of any insulinoma. There was none except the nodule. It is well to remind ourselves that according to the evidence of Dr. Fernando, 70% of ectopic sites are found in the stomach, duodenum and small bowel."

"Dr. Sheriffdeen also examined the mesentery, the bed of pancreas, the jejunum, the omentum, the hilum of the spleen close to the tail of the pancreas, the liver and adrenal glands on both sides, the kidneys on both sides. He was looking for an insulinoma as small as 1 mm by sight and palpation and found nothing. It will be seen that according to Dr. Fernando's evidence that the other 30% of the ectopic sites would be in these areas just mentioned. It would therefore be correct to say that Dr. Sheriffdeen has in fact looked carefully macroscopically at substantially all the areas mentioned by Dr. Fernando as possible ectopic site areas and found no signs of insulinoma, but in fact found a nodule in the duodenum, which has now been processed and microscopically examined and has been found to be nothing except a lymph node incapable of secreting insulin."

SECRETING TUMOUR

"Dr. Sheriffdeen has told us that to have surmounted all the dextrose this patient got and still show signs of hypoglycaemia meant that he expected to see a secreting tumour, i.e. that it should have been large enough to be visible to the naked eye. This witness went on to say that it was very unlikely that a single very small tumour could have produced this large amount of insulin. Under cross examination, he said that he cannot exclude the possibility of an insulinoma being seen under microscopic examination but in that case, one would have to microscopically examine every cell of the entire pancreas, the entire stomach and the bed of the pancreas, the entire hilum of the spleen, the entire spleen, the entire jejunum, the entire ileum, which is 22 feet long, the entirety of the mesentery, the omentum, the ducts, and the liver."

"If one were expected to do histology on every section of those parts it would be totally impracticable, it was not humanly possible. He said such a process would not be a reasonable process, medically speaking. It is not the practice to do such a thing. What is done is what is reasonable. One looks at the entire area macroscopically and takes out only the suspected portion or portions. So in this instance he did not send any of those other organs or areas of histology as macroscopically there were no suspicious areas. Again under cross examination Dr. Sheriffdeen was referred to a Chinese publication in 'Archives of Surgery', Volume 115, May 1980, entitled 'Insulinoma experience in surgical treatment' published by the Department of Surgery and Pathology, Capital Hospital, Chinese Academy of Medical Sciences, Peking, which reported a study of sixty cases in a personal series extending over a life time of one doctor."

"We know roughly that the population of China, which is estimated to be over 800 million people. This might suggest the rarity of this disease. On the evidence before us it would appear that so far in Sri Lanka three or four insulinomas have been found. One in Jaffna by the doctors Yoganathan and Vetpillai reported in the Jaffna Medical Journal, volume 17, and the others have been found at the Colombo General Hospital. One by Dr. Sheriffdeen himself. The defence by their cross examination in referring to the Chinese publication was to make the following points:

i.   That as insulinomas could be very small, during surgery may be found too small to see or palpated.

ii.   Insulinomas could be occult or hidden deep in tissue and therefore may go unobserved.

iii. There could be multiple secreting tumours so that the removal of one may not be enough.

The above references to the Chinese publication show that what is referred there is to what can be noticed in surgery."

"The defence points out that there could be all these possibilities even though the examination is being done on a dead body, so that the chances of missing very small insulinomas, which maybe hidden deep in tissue are present. The defence has also heavily relied upon material contained in chapter 7 of the book by Marks and Rose and pointed out to us. In regard to the evidence of Dr. Sheriffdeen, the defence points out that he could have missed very small deeply situated but significantly secreting multiple tumours, that his macroscopic examination was inadequate and that he should have sent these other organs also for histology. So the defence says that there is a gap in the prosecution case, that the macroscopic examination by Dr. Sheriffdeen does not provide sufficient cogent proof of the absence of ectopic tissue or of multiple small tumours situated therein capable of producing sufficient insulin to cause Russel's hypoglycaemia."

Mr. Bandaranayake then discussed the last of the possible endogenous causes of hypoglycaemia, which the prosecution must eliminate if it were to ask the Court to decide as proved that there was no natural cause responsible for Russel's sickness and his death.

BURDEN OF PROOF

"In considering the question of *Corpus Delicti*, this is perhaps the most important and significant part of the evidence which the Court must consider with the utmost care and precaution with due regard to whatever the defence may point out by cross examination or by submissions. This is a matter upon which the defence has strenuously joined issue with the prosecution by their cross examination of the expert witnesses and by their submissions to the Court. We bear in mind the presumption of innocence, the burden of proof that the prosecution must establish all the ingredients of the charges that have been formed against the accused beyond all reasonable doubt and that there is no burden on the defence whatsoever to show any fact or circumstance favourable to the accused but that they are free to do so if they so desire. The defence does not have to prove the innocence of the accused in a criminal trial. The burden of proof is always upon the prosecution and the standard of proof is the high standard of proof beyond reasonable doubt."

"Bearing in mind all these matters we proceed to examine the evidence. This possible endogenous cause of hypoglycaemia is an insulin secreting tumour of the pancreas or situated in its ectopic tissue. This tumour is medically known as an islet cell insulinoma causing spontaneous hypoglycaemia – i.e. low fasting blood sugar level."

"We have recounted in previous paragraphs the steps Dr. Sheriffdeen took in his search for an insulinoma. We have set down the areas of the abdominal organs that he says he examined. We have set down Dr. Fernando's evidence regarding such search, where to look etc. and we have already shown a comparison between what Dr. Fernando says, what ought to be done and what Sheriffdeen says he did. We have already held that Dr. Sheriffdeen has in fact substantially examined macroscopically all the areas mentioned by Dr. Fernando and saw no evidence of ectopic pancreatic tissue. That is tissue of the pancreas found in some other place where it should not be found. So Dr. Sheriffdeen says there was no pancreatic tissue to be found anywhere outside of the pancreas that he examined."

'Dr. Sheriffdeen has also told us that it is not possible to microscopically examine every bit of abdominal organ and tissue and that it is never done anywhere in the world. That evidence is supported and corroborated by Dr. Balasubramaniam. Indeed as laymen we can see the magnitude of such a task if such were undertaken and the reason for not expecting or insisting that such be done even in a scientific examination, such a venture would lead to millions of slides having to be prepared and examined. One has to view these matters in a pragmatic and practical human experience. It is the evidence in this case that in such matters there is discretion with the doctor scientifically permissible. Discretion to pick out from his experience and knowledge suspicious areas of tissue if there be any," Mr. Bandaranayake said.

REALISTIC PROFESSIONAL MEDICAL APPROACH

"Here, this task has not been done by an inexperienced young doctor. It has been done by a consultant surgeon, a man of high qualification and experience, a man who has had a personal experience with this very rare disease of insulinoma. In considering the adequacy and reliability of what has been done we have to approach the question from a human stand point from the manner in which human affairs are conducted and not from the stand point of the laws of mathematics. The proper question we should pose to ourselves is has he done what was reasonably sufficient in the circumstances to express a reliable professional medical opinion? Was it a proper and realistic professional medical approach? Has he used his discretion adequately, properly and sufficiently to express a reliable opinion?"

"In answering this question we once again turn to the evidence showing the relationship between this doctor and his patient. Dr.

Sheriffdeen had the opportunity to closely observe the course of the illness clinically. He has taken the view that if there was natural cause for hypoglycaemia it should be an insulinoma or several of them secreting necessary quantities of insulin to overcome the dextrose that had been administered to the patient in hospital. We know that was regularly done and large quantities administered towards the end of July. We have also the evidence of doctor that the only possible explanation, if a natural cause is insulinoma and a large one and that situated in the pancreas or close to it. Dr. Nagaratnam also had Russel under his care. So these two, Sheriffdeen and Nagaratnam are persons who were intimately involved with Russel's illness – but not so Dr. Fernando."

"Dr. Fernando's evidence under cross examination was mostly opinions, based on information from medical journals. He in fact said so. He had never seen this patient but had only briefly heard of signs and symptoms from the first accused. So, Dr. Fernando's evidence was of a general nature and not given in the context of personal observations. So Dr. Sheriffdeen looks for something as small as one millimeter - in all the organs in the abdominal cavity that he mentioned. He saw no insulinoma or any ectopic pancreatic tissue. As we said before on question involved in Dr. Sheriffdeen's opinion is one of sufficiency. In the background of evidence about insulinoma has he done a sufficient close inspection upon which the Court can draw a relevant inference safely? We have already stated that we are satisfied with his skill, experience and the care with which he set about his post-mortem examination. Now, is what he has done sufficient to permit of safe inference?"

"The Court must be able to draw a line somewhere. It is in evidence which we accept that looking microscopically at every part of abdominal tissue looking for tiny insulinoma is quite impracticable if not impossible. So in this type of case the doctor has first to choose suspicious tissue. Now even if he were to do so and histology could show a negative result, still it could be argued that too was not enough, that a further search and more examinations of more slides might have revealed a tumour. So the point at which a Court may draw a line would depend on the facts and circumstances of each case and what is thought to be reasonable and sufficient in order to draw an inference safely. Of course it could well be that what has been done in a particular case is per se insufficient."

"In this case we are of the view having seen and heard the witnesses having regard to the responsibilities that they discharge in the course of their everyday lives and the fact that the patient was under this care for some time that this is not a case where it is per se insufficient. It is our view Dr. Sheriffdeen's testimony can be used safely within its own compass. That is to say that it is acceptable to the Court for the purpose of saying that it is highly improbable that there was insulinoma or any pancreatic ectopic tissue in the abdominal organs besides the pancreas that he examined at this post-mortem examination."

"So we now have the fact that the presence of insulinoma in ectopic sites where such tumours may have existed is rendered highly improbable by reason for the macroscopic examination of the deceased abdominal and other organs done. We have the further fact, the further circumstance that judging from the known behaviour and pattern of his hypoglycaemic attacks it is manifestly and overwhelmingly improbable that those attacks were caused by any type of insulinoma, that it is totally inconsistent with the presence of insulinoma anywhere in Russel's system. We have the other proved fact that insulinoma of the pancreas itself has been ruled out by the microscopic examination done on it by Dr. (Mrs.) Balasubramaniam."

"Now taking all these circumstances into consideration we ask ourselves would all of these still be consistent with insulinoma? We find that to take such a view would place an incredible strain on human experience. So taking all these facts and circumstances together into consideration we find that their cumulative probative force dispels all reasonable doubts that these circumstances just mentioned are capable only of one construction, that there is only one inference that this Court can reach and that is that there was no insulinoma in Russel's system responsible for the hypoglycaemic attacks and that these facts and circumstances are incapable of drawing any inference consistent with the presence of tumour or tumours known as insulinoma causing this hypoglycaemia. In the protracted consideration and analysis of the testimony placed by the prosecution before us bearing on the question of *Corpus Delicti* in relation to the cause of Russel's death we have reached several findings of fact for all of which we have given our reasons."

Mr. Bandaranayake said that in the first place the Court came to a decision that the prosecution has proved beyond reasonable doubt that Russel Ingram died of pneumonia, which developed in the ordinary course of nature from the prolonged state of unconsciousness he was in. The Court next decided that the prosecution has proved beyond all reasonable doubt that the cause of his unconsciousness and the cause of irreversible brain damage were hypoglycaemia and not any other cause.

IRREVERSIBLE BRAIN DAMAGE

"We next considered the question as to the cause of hypoglycaemia and in doing so we have now decided that the prosecution has established beyond all reasonable doubt that it was not the result of any endogenous system disorder or natural disease whatsoever."

"So we are now left with the fact of hypoglycaemia and the fact of irreversible brain damage that had occurred by the 18th of July 1978. That fact is proved. What caused it? If it is not by a natural cause, is it reasonable to assume that it must have been then a factitious cause? Dr. Nagaratnam says that must be a factitious cause if it is not a natural cause, that it must be induced and that there are several ways in which it can happen, i.e. that it must have been induced and there are several possibilities. In view of the charge of the indictment against the accused it is incumbent on the prosecution to eliminate all other possible induced causes of hypoglycaemia and to prove beyond all reasonable doubt that it is induced hypoglycaemia amounting to murder."

"In considering an induced cause in relation to hypoglycaemia it is the evidence before us that blood sugar can be artificially lowered either by the injection of insulin or by the administration of anti-diabetic drugs. So we are told that there are methods known to medical science, normally used to assist diabetic patients and to reduce their blood sugar level, to wit: insulin injection or the administration of an anti-diabetic drug. So it becomes necessary for us at this stage to consider the evidence about drugs. Their nature and performance and effects in order to be able to consider other questions such as the different situations and circumstances under which a lowered blood sugar maybe induced."

Referring to the evidence of Professor Jayasena, Mr. Bandaranayake said, "Evidence about drugs has been placed before us by the prosecution, who has called Professor Jayasena, a Professor of Pharmacology of Peradeniya University, who is both a Medical Doctor as well as a Chemist and is presently with the World Health Organization. We are satisfied of his knowledge and experience and we hold that his opinions are valuable and reliable and can be acted upon confidently. His qualifications are set out in his evidence. We will here set down the opinion evidence which we accept and hold to be proved. It has not been contradicted by any other evidence and is substantially supported by Dr. Nagaratnam, a physician of thirty years standing, upon whose opinion also the prosecution rely with regard to the administration of drugs to the patient. Dr. Nagaratnam uses these drugs in the ordinary course of his practice and is therefore, familiar with their use on human beings."

"Professor Jayasena's evidence, which we hold to be proved, is as follows: The primary cause of diabetes is the lack of insulin usually produced by the beta cells of the pancreas. This lack of insulin causes a rise in blood sugar. If it goes beyond 180 mg per 100 ml of blood, the sugar goes beyond the renal threshold and spills over into the urine. This is known as 'Overt Diabetes'. But if the sugar is elevated but below 180 mg%, it is knows as latent diabetes. These conditions occur when glucose is not utilized fully due to the lack of insulin. Insulin helps glucose to enter into cells. So insulin can be administered directly into the blood stream by injection. If swallowed in injection form it gets digested and is of no effect."

Mr. Bandaranayake said that alternatively, two groups of anti-diabetic oral tablets have been developed and are available.

- Sulphonyl ureas such as tolbutamide, glibenclamide and chlorpropamide

- Biguanides such as phenformin and metformin.

"The first group of drugs, that is the sulphonyl ureas, is effective only if there are residual functioning beta cells still left in the pancreas. The drug increases the secretion of insulin in these functioning beta cells. In the second group, the drug can act even in the total absence of any functioning beta cells and helps the utilization of glucose by other body cells. They can act in the absence of insulin and help to bring the level of glucose down."

Mr. Bandaranayake said that anti-diabetic sulphonyl ureas are Diabenese and Euglucon, both glibenclamide, and they come in tablet form.

HALF LIFE OF EUGLUCON

"Glibenclamides such as Euglucon are administered once a day either in 2.5 mg or 5 mg tablets to diabetic patients. That is the normal dosage. Their effects last for twenty hours. A normal person should not take anti-diabetic drugs. A normal person has functioning beta cells in the pancreas, so Euglucon will increase the secretion of insulin. A normal pancreas produces twenty four to forty units of insulin a day. Euglucon will increase that volume. Euglucon is not soluble in water but if crushed will be suspended in water. If mixed with fruit juice or milk or soup, it will remain in suspension and settle down and the liquid will be thick. Euglucon however, is disintegrated in the stomach and goes into solution and is absorbed."

"When an anti-diabetic drug is absorbed the body starts metabolizing and it undergoes changes and as a result of this breakdown process the activity of the drug is gradually lost. If there is a total amount of activity, the time taken for half that activity to be lost is called the half-life. The half-life of Euglucon is 6 to 7 hours. For example, if 10 mg is given and all 10 mg is absorbed, in about six to seven hours the activity of 5 mg will be lost. Therefore, at the end of the next six to seven hours, 2.5 mg of activity will be found lost and so on."

"First signs such as sweating can be observed ten to fifteen minutes after administration of an anti-diabetic drug to a normal person. When blood sugar goes down, unconsciousness can set in. Euglucon goes to the liver and on to the pancreas and starts acting immediately. The reaction would depend on the dosage and the level of fasting blood sugar. If already weak, onset is sooner. If the original blood sugar was high, symptoms will take longer. If glucose is then administered symptoms would take longer or disappear. Activity of Euglucon persists for about twenty hours. It has been manufactured to last that long to help a diabetic patient who may then need to take only one tablet per day. A normal person can get several attacks of hypoglycaemia with a single dose of such an anti-diabetic drug as it is a long acting drug. Signs of hypoglycaemia can be seen even in an unconscious patient as the drug acts on the sympathetic nervous systems. That happens when blood sugar starts coming down."

Continuing Mr. Bandaranayake said, "Dr. Nagaratnam has told us that he has been prescribing Euglucon to diabetic patients for many years and is familiar with its properties. He added that the drug has a property known as the dribbling effect because apparently, a certain portion of the drug is stored in what has been described as a 'hidden compartment' and is gradually released. The accuracy of this theory of 'hidden compartment' and the dribbling effect was contested by the defence as something not yet definitely determined medically. If the theory is accepted, all this means is that a dose of the drug can act for a long time without the necessity of repeated administration of the drug. This really does not make a difference in this case."

EVIDENCE UNCONTRADICTED

"Dr. Nagaratnam has told us and which evidence we accept, that even though insulin has taken the upper hand and a patient is unconscious or stuporose without dextrose infusion, still there are compensatory mechanisms in the body, secretions of the pituitary and the adrenal glands, the breakdown of glycogen, which is stored in the liver and in the muscles and converted back into glucose, can keep a patient alive for some time. This evidence stands uncontradicted. He has also told us that when blood glucose is low and the patient still conscious but hypoglycaemic, the assimilation of sugar or the taking of a meal would bring immediate relief because food containing carbohydrate, which digest to glucose. So it will be seen that it is possible for someone administering an anti-diabetic drug to a person to also give him meals. The combined effect of both would result in the blood sugar level fluctuating, going up and down and producing what has been called in this case as 'Swinging Blood Sugar Levels'."

"It is the evidence that once the drug is given sugar levels in the blood begins to drop. Even a small dose of 2.5 mg of Euglucon could start this process in a normal person or a diabetic. A meal either liquid or solid tends to enhance or uplift blood sugar. So for instance, when blood sugar level drops after a dose of drug and one gets signs of hypoglycaemia, even ice cream taken by the victim would cause the blood sugar to elevate. When blood sugar starts dropping, Dr. Nagaratnam has explained to us the symptoms that will be felt by the patient and the signs that maybe observed by others depending on the rate of fall. A person is said to become hypoglycaemic when the blood sugar falls to about 50 mg or 40 mg. It would be pertinent at this point to remind ourselves of the signs and symptoms that could be seen when the blood sugar begins to fall to hypoglycaemic levels. We already have referred to this earlier in our order but we feel that it bears repetition now."

Mr. Bandaranayake then explained the clinical features of hypoglycaemia and said that the first symptoms are dizziness, giddiness and lethargy. "The first signs are sweating, slurring of speech, tremors, agitation and anxiety. If the fall is gradual signs will be seen depending on the rate of fall. When hypoglycaemia is prolonged (which maybe even for a few hours and need not be for days) other signs can appear. They are behavioural disturbances, depression, hallucinations and manic schizophrenia. Thereafter it leads to coma.

That is drowsiness, semi-consciousness (stuporose), unconsciousness and deep unconsciousness. Weakness or paralysis of one of the body like a stroke or paralysis of all four limbs can occur and also when tickled the big toe moves up (plantar reflexes)."

PICNIC IN WALES

Continuing Mr. Bandaranayake said, "We have also evidence in this case that the first accused was a diabetic patient. It was the evidence of his daughter Malrani, who left Sri Lanka for England in 1976 that her father, the first accused, was a diabetic but as far as she knew he controlled his diabetes through diet. It is however the evidence of Munilal Peiris who says that his father, the first accused, was a diabetic and that the first accused controlled his diabetes both through his diet as well as by drugs. Munilal Peiris has told the Court that somewhere in April 1978 when he and the first accused went on a picnic in Wales, UK, they stopped at a chemist shop and the witness and the first accused went to the shop and that while the witness bought a pair of sun glasses the first accused bought one hundred tablets of the anti-diabetic drug Euglucon and he paid ten pounds for it. The witness said that he saw the label on the foil of the tablet cover and that is how he identified what it was. We accept his testimony on this matter although the defence has suggested to us that it is unreliable."

"We also have the evidence of Mr. Leon Dias, Manager of Osusala, who says that from about 1977 the first accused used to regularly buy Euglucon and sodium bicarbonate once every three weeks. He said that Euglucon was freely available from about 1977 onwards and it was sold at Rupees sixteen per foil and that each foil had 10 tablets of 5 mg strength. He further said that this drug was in the first schedule of the Foods and Drugs Act and therefore could be sold over the counter without a prescription. He knew the first accused well and he usually served doctors and priests before he served the public."

"We have the further evidence of Mr. S. M. Sudusinghe, Managing Partner of New City Chemist, a Pharmacy and Grocery at 889, Maradana Road, Colombo 10, situated within walking distance of the Vicarage. He said that he knew the first accused for over ten years and that Mrs. Eunice Peiris had an account with him in his shop and both she and the first accused used to buy things on this account. He had sold anti-diabetic Euglucon tablets to the first accused."

"In particular he said he sold fifty tablets of Euglucon of 5 mg strength to the first accused on 12.07.1978. The prosecution has produced documentary evidence of this bill by the counterfoil of the bill book produced marked as X7 with the No. 7374 marked as X7A. This sale has also been entered in the credit ledger produced before as and marked as X8 and page 193 thereof bears the credit account of Mrs. Eunice Peiris, and this sale is reflected at page 194 at the entry marked X8A. The counterfoil shows that it has been sold to Rev. Mathew Peiris. These entries were made in the ordinary course of business by the sales clerk under the witness's supervision and control. At the end of the month these bills are sent to the Vicarage for settlement in Mrs. Peiris's name. These bills have been paid by the first accused up to the end of November 1978."

"We accept the evidence of this witness that the first accused did indeed buy fifty tablets of Euglucon of 5 mg strength on 12.07.1978 while Russel Ingram was in Ward 18 of the General Hospital, just two days before he was discharged and returned home to the Vicarage. In the background of the evidence regarding anti-diabetic drugs, which according to the medical evidence which we accept, could produce the result of inducing the lowering of blood sugar in a human being, we proceed to examine the evidence in regard to the possible different circumstances under which an exogenous or induced hypoglycaemic state could be achieved."

"If the taking of tablets, which is freely available in the market is possible, the prosecution must be able to eliminate beyond all reasonable doubt that the state of hypoglycaemia seen in Russel was not medically induced or that Russel did not take his own life or that Russel did not accidently take these tablets by his own act to cause his several states of hypoglycaemia. The prosecution if they are to prove *Corpus Delicti* in this case, must eliminate beyond all reasonable doubt these other factitious causes of induced hypoglycaemia and prove beyond all reasonable doubt that the hypoglycaemic attacks suffered by Russel Ingram were the result of induced hypoglycaemia by the act of someone else, and that it was done deliberately and intentionally, that it was induced in him intentionally and not accidentally in order to cause his death."

SUICIDE

"The first of such factitious causes as we have said just now could be medically induced hypoglycaemia, i.e. in a diabetic patient where insulin or an anti-diabetic drug could be taken as a remedy or an accidental overdose of such could cause hypoglycaemia. Here the evidence we have accepted beyond all reasonable doubt that Russel was not a diabetic. That is the evidence of his parents and that has been corroborated by the microscopic examination done on slides of his pancreas by Dr. (Mrs.) Balasubramaniam."

"Furthermore, no history of diabetes has been given to the hospital at his two hospitalizations by those who admitted him unconscious and who were persons who were well known to him. Again, diabetic coma has been medically eliminated as the cause of his unconsciousness. So we have it as a proved fact that he did not have any disease, which necessitated the taking of any anti-diabetic agent either drug or insulin injection. So we are able to eliminate with confidence the possibility that hypoglycaemia was induced by an overdose of something he was taking on medical advice to combat a disease either by insulin injection or by means of an anti-diabetic drug."

Considering the question of suicide next, Mr. Bandaranayake said, "Did Russel take his own life in an emotional crisis engendered by some strong stress factor? In considering suicide, we must bear in mind the cause of death already proved and that is a state of hypoglycaemia with unconsciousness and irreversible brain damage together with prolonged unconsciousness and intervening phenomenon of pneumonia arising in the ordinary course of nature. That was the immediate cause of his death. So we are here considering a self-induced hypoglycaemia. Upon the medical evidence, which we accept this is possible in two ways – either by insulin injection or by an anti-diabetic drug. Several varieties of it are known to exist. Now we must examine this question of suicide by this means, in the background of Russel's health, his education, his temperament such as is available to us upon the evidence."

"We must consider this question first intrinsically, whether this method of taking his own life is it all likely. We say this for the reason that to commit suicide by injecting oneself with insulin or taking an anti-diabetic drug is to use an uncommon, sophisticated method. There are commoner methods of suicide that we need hardly mention here. Jumping before a moving train or bus, hanging himself with a coir rope, or taking some easily available poison or sleeping pills just to mention a few. So in examining this question of suicide by this method it is necessary to first examine whether he had the knowledge to use such a drug or injection or whether he had the opportunity to do so. We have already referred to the fact that Russel was living in the Vicarage with the first accused and to the fact that the first accused was a diabetic and that he bought Euglucon tablets. So there is a possibility that this anti-diabetic drug was in the house in which Russel lived in which event Russel might have had access to it."

"Furthermore, the evidence of the chemist is that these drugs were available in the open market and could be bought over the counter without a prescription. On the question of knowledge there is also the evidence of Chandrakanthi Dharmadasa that a book entitled 'Body, Mind and Sugar' was on the first accused's bookshelf during the period that the first accused and his wife had left Sri Lanka on a world tour, that is to say February, March, April 1978, when Russel was living at the Vicarage with his wife, the second accused and acted as the care-taker of the Vicarage. The prosecution placed before us several excerpts from this book marked P40A to P40N. Those excerpts give considerable information about diabetes and its opposite condition hypoglycaemia and state of unconsciousness and so on. So this information was available to Russel if he wanted to read it. There is no evidence at all that Russel had access to any apparatus to inject himself with anything. Even that could be available if one looks for it.

Nor is there any evidence that any drugs or tablets or pills were in his possession at any time or that he was taking any medicine of his own. The evidence was that he was not a diabetic and that he was never known to use any anti-diabetic agents for any disease condition."

"Now, from the evidence that we have the background of Russel appears to be of a healthy young man, a sportsman type, educated up to the Senior School Certificate and doing a job as an Advertising Agent and not of a particular intellectual or learned type. There is no evidence that he was a voracious reader or was of a particular inquiring disposition. In these circumstances, we consider it hardly likely that such a man would interest himself with such sophistications. He has no personal health reason to read the book. His general good health has been testified to by several witnesses up to 9.6.1978. His father has told us that he was a healthy fellow and that they did not have a family doctor because all his children were healthy fellows."

STUBBS SHIELD BOXER

"His mother has told us that when he first started going to the Vicarage in about September 1976 he was in good health. Then we have the evidence from Munilal Peiris that Russel, towards the end of 1976 and early 1977, was helping his father along with the second accused in connection with the preparation for the consecration of Bishop of Colombo. We have the further evidence of the Independent Newspapers Limited who employed Russel in November 1977 and who said that Russel was in good health and that he was quite active and that he confirmed in his job on the first of January 1978 and that Russel was a member of their Club's Cricket Team. We have the evidence that as a school boy he had been a Stubbs Shield Boxer and playing football and cricket at Wesley College, Colombo."

Continuing, Mr. Bandaranayake said, "Munilal Peiris has told us that Russel and the second accused looked after the Vicarage in the absence of his parents from February 1978 until his father's return in April and that Russel had attended his farewell party on the 29th of March 1978, and that Russel was in good health at the time. We also have the evidence of his mother Cora Ingram that she went to Russel's wedding anniversary celebration to the Vicarage on the 18th of April 1978 and we also have the evidence of Chandrakanthi Dharmadasa that Russel was living in the Vicarage and he was in good health and going to work up to the day that she left for good on the 27th of May 1978. We finally have the evidence of Mr. Weeraman that Russel was coming to work regularly from November 1977 up to the 9th of June 1978 when he was absent and he has taken leave for the 9th, 12th and 13th June 1978. Mr. Weeraman corroborates Alex Ingram who says that he found his son ill and in bed in the Vicarage on 9.6.1979."

"In exactly two months, on 10th August 1978, Russel was dead. The evidence of these witnesses on the good health of Russel during the period up to the 9th June 1978, which we have referred to, we believe and we accept as proved by the prosecution in this case beyond reasonable doubt. Coming back to the question of suicide, we find that there is no evidence that Russel Ingram had read the book 'Body, Mind and Sugar'. There is no evidence that he was at all knowledgeable about diabetes, its opposite condition or any other disease condition for that matter. The evidence before us is that after the day's work he comes home and sometimes has a drink of arrack, so it is our considered view that it is highly unlikely that such a man as Russel would involve himself in an uncommon method such as use of an anti-diabetic drug to kill himself slowly."

"Next we consider the course of his illness, both at home and in hospital from the available evidence that we hold proved. The evidence of his father in regard to the circumstances leading to his first hospitalization and the evidence of Dr. Joseph on what happened at the Vicarage on 15.7.1978 and the evidence of the Jacksons of events in the Vicarage on the 16th, 17th and 18th morning of July 1978. It is our view that these proved events show that Russel was ill and that no doctor actually treated him and that he was under the care of the first accused."

"We have particularized their evidence elsewhere and given our reasons for believing them and so we do not wish to be repetitive. If in fact Russel had intentionally induced all the signs and symptoms observed by these witnesses themselves and they found such a person on their hands then surely the accused themselves, his own wife and the chief house holder, would have called for medical assistance instead of trying to deal with such an aggravated medical situation themselves. In fact the evidence, if believed, is that his parents and relatives were induced into thinking that Russel was being medically treated."

"Next, the medical evidence which we have accepted as proved is that Russel had repeated attacks of hypoglycaemia whilst lying deeply unconscious in hospital. It is the opinion of Dr. Nagaratnam that those attacks could not have occurred under any circumstances by reason of taking anti-diabetic drugs before admission to hospital on the 18th morning. The effect of anti-diabetic drugs do not last that long. So that drugs taken on or before the 18th cannot continue to affect the human body 8 days later."

"Therefore, any drug that Russel may have taken before the 18th could not have showed the effects on the 26th and thereafter. He was unconscious upon admission on the 18th and he remained unconscious until he died. Now, it is the opinion of Dr. Nagaratnam that the chemical effect of an anti-diabetic drug cannot remain in the human system and be effective for so long. His position is that such drugs are manufactured to be effective for diabetic patients if properly administered for twenty four hours. This is confirmed by Professor Jayasena. The process of their action has been explained to us. According to the evidence of Dr. Sheriffdeen, the first accused has told him that Russel was unconscious for one day before he was admitted to hospital on the 18th. So all of this evidence tends to eliminate any possibility that Russel's continued attacks of hypoglycaemia was as a result of drugs that he had taken before the 18th of July."

"The Government Analyst called by the defence has testified before us that traces of an anti-diabetic drug could be found by a laboratory in urine for up to two days, in faeces for up to five days and in blood for up to three days. So the medical and scientific evidence before us, which we accept, completely rules out the possibility of self-introduced hypoglycaemia in the context of the facts and circumstances of this case relating to Russel's hospitalization in July 1978. If he did not do it to cause the second hospitalization then it is unlikely that he did it to cause his first hospitalization."

Mr. Bandaranayake said, "That upon the facts that the Court has considered, namely:

(a) That neither he nor any other members of his family were diabetic. He had no reason ordinarily to be acquainted with the use of insulin or any anti-diabetic drug and that he was never known to treat himself with such sugar reducing agents;

(b) That looking at the evidence intrinsically he was not the kind of person to show any inclinations to get acquainted with a sophisticated uncommon method of taking his own life even though he may have had access to information of its use and access to the drug itself;

(c) That it is highly improbable that if he had in fact made himself so obviously badly ill whilst he was living as a lodger in the Vicarage in June-July 1978 with his wife and the house holder namely the second accused and the first accused respectively, that they would not have offered him medical help instead of caring for him themselves;

(d) By medical and scientific evidence that completely rules out self-induced hypoglycaemia on or before the 18th of July 1978 by imbibing an anti-diabetic drug or by insulin injection to be the cause of continued attacks of hypoglycaemia on 26.7.1978 and onwards for several days;

SUICIDE, ACCIDENT AND HOMICIDE

"Dr. Nagaratnam's evidence that such attacks as mentioned in (d) must have been induced at that time to have occurred during his unconsciousness and that the evidence in the case is that no anti-diabetic drug or insulin was prescribed and administered to the patient by the hospital authorities. Our judgment is that the prosecution has established beyond all reasonable doubt that Russel Ingram's death was not the result of self-induced hypoglycaemia and irreversible brain damage accompanied by prolonged unconsciousness which led to his death in the ordinary course of nature by pneumonia. We accordingly decide that the prosecution has proved beyond reasonable doubt that Russel's death was not the result of his own act or suicide."

"The next possible factitious cause of Russel's death is that of accident by his own hand. Could he have mistakenly and quite accidently swallowed anti-diabetic pills or tablets that may have been lying about in his home or to which he may have had access accidently? We have already referred to the evidence of the prosecution that the first accused was a diabetic properly taking anti-diabetic drugs and that he had bought himself some in April 1978 and more on 12.7.1978. In view of the scientific evidence already referred to that any drug that he may have taken prior to his deep coma of 18.7.1978 could not possibly have been the cause of repeated hypoglycaemic attacks observed on 26.7.1978 onwards for a week, safely rules out the possibility of his having accidently taken these drugs before his admission to hospital on 18.7.1978."

"Furthermore, this Court has decided that the prosecution has proved beyond reasonable doubt that there were several hypoglycaemic attacks, which Russel suffered at the Vicarage in June and July and that as a result of two of these attacks he had to be hospitalized deeply unconscious. It is difficult to believe that an accident could have repeated itself so many times. This fact of repetition satisfactorily rules out the possibility of accident in our view. We therefore decide that the prosecution has proved beyond all reasonable doubt that the hypoglycaemic attacks Russel suffered before his death and the stage of irreversible brain damage are not the result of an accidental act by himself. For these same reasons we also rule out the possibility of a misadventure by an act done by himself."

"This leaves us with the question of homicide. We have reached the stage in our judgment where we considered it proved and established by the prosecution beyond all reasonable doubt that Russel's hypoglycaemic condition and irreversible brain damage leading to death in the ordinary course of nature on 10.8.1978, was not the result of any natural cause and was also not the result of suicide or accident or misadventure by reason of his own act."

"In the result we are left with the question of induced hypoglycaemia, which may amount to homicide, if the requisite *mens rea* on the part of the person or persons who induced hypoglycaemia and irreversible brain damage could be established by the prosecution to the satisfaction of this Court. Is there evidence that this exogenous, factitious, induced hypoglycaemia was the result of an intentional, deliberate and conscious administration to Russel of an anti-diabetic drug or insulin injection by some person or persons?" (*Mens rea* is the intention or knowledge of wrongdoing that constitutes part of a crime.)

"In other words, the prosecution must establish not only that his drug or insulin was administered to Russel but that it was done not by mistake and not by accident on the part of the person or persons responsible and that it was intentionally and purposely done in order that Russel would die. In considering this question of intentionally induced hypoglycaemia, the prosecution has pointed to the evidence of the medical witnesses that from 26.7.1978 Russel suffered hypoglycaemic attacks whilst deeply unconscious in the hospital and the prosecution has submitted that upon the facts and circumstances, it is clear that those attacks have been induced by introducing anti-diabetic drugs through the unconscious patient's nasal feeds."

"It was the evidence of Dr. Nagaratnam that those attacks of hypoglycaemia have been induced if natural causes are ruled out. Now this Court has ruled out any natural cause has been responsible for the deceased's hypoglycaemia. So in these circumstances we will consider the evidence available to the Court regarding these repeated attacks of hypoglycaemia in the hospital. It has been the evidence of Dr. Wijesiriwardena, Dr. Banagala and the nurses who have testified before us that they saw signs of hypoglycaemia - repeated rapid pulse and sweating. These signs were treated with 50% dextrose and they subsided. No other treatment was given to them except sugar. We are satisfied beyond reasonable doubt that they were indeed signs of low blood sugar in all the proved facts and circumstances in this case."

"The question is how did it happen? In the light of our findings that there was no natural cause and the opinion of Dr. Nagaratnam, we proceed to consider the documentary evidence and other oral testimony regarding his matter. The entries in the BHT and the FBC bear out the oral testimony of the doctors and the nurses about the fact of these hypoglycaemic attacks. Our attention has been drawn by the prosecution to these attacks."

"On 26.7.1978 at 9.30 a.m. are entries of rapid pulse and sweating made by Dr. Wijesiriwardena – he has given 50% dextrose and the signs have subsided. On 27.7.1978, Dr. Banagala said he noticed an attack at 9.30 p.m. and he has also given the same treatment and got the same response. On 28.7.1978 there have been three separate attacks observed by Dr. Wijesiriwardena at 8 a.m. at 3 p.m. and at 10 p.m. and on each occasion he has given the same treatment and the signs have subsided. On 29.7.1978 and on 4.8.1978, Dr. Banagala has observed attacks and treated with dextrose when the attacks subsided. Dr. Banagala has told us that there were still other occasions where he observed signs of hypoglycaemia, which he treated during this period but did not make an entry in the BHT. Nurses Ranaweera, Manawadu, Sugathapala, Wanigaratne and Fernando supported the fact of these signs and the treatment given and the fact of the disappearance of the signs upon the treatment. We accept the evidence of these nurses on this matter," Mr. Bandaranayake said.

CONTEMPORANEOUS ENTRIES

"Contradictions that have been proved by the defence by way of omissions do not touch this aspect of their evidence. The prosecution is not here seeking to relate a particular attack or hypoglycaemia with any food that was given to the patient. The prosecution is merely seeking to establish through the evidence of these nurses supported by the contemporaneous entries in the BHT and the FBC that such attacks did in fact take place and subsided with dextrose."

"Now we have a further proved fact that during the period of this second hospitalization, Russel was on normal diet from 19.7.1978 onwards until his death, normal foods in liquid form. That is the evidence of both the doctors as well as the nurses which also we have accepted and their oral testimony supported by the contemporaneous entries in the BHT and the FBC that foods such as milk, soup, eggs, fruit juice, water, saline and dextrose were given. There is also the evidence that the hospital allows patients to be brought foods from outside by their relatives and friends in addition to the foods provided by the hospital. This fact is not in dispute but we say we accept the evidence on this matter and decide that food was indeed made available in liquid form to Russel during his period of unconsciousness both from the hospital as well as from home."

"The nurses have told us that the first accused brought food for Russel daily in a basket, sometimes several times a day and that they gave these foods to Russel through the nasal tube. The foods were liquids such as milk, soup, Marmite, passion fruit juice, milk, egg, etc. We accept this evidence of the nurses for the following reasons:-

1. The hospital authorities permit foods to be brought to the patients from outside.

2. The first accused admitted the patient and his name is given as the next of kin on the BHT.

3. The evidence of other witnesses, which we have accepted is that at all relevant times in this case Russel was living at the Vicarage and was brought unconscious from the Vicarage by the first accused and admitted to hospital on two occasions in June and July. Entries in the BHT support this fact.

4. The second accused is the wife of the deceased who also lived in the Vicarage at all relevant times and was often seen accompanying the first accused visiting Russel in the hospital. In these circumstances it is quite a natural thing that the accused in this case would bring food to Russel while he was lying unconscious in the hospital when normal liquid foods were allowed for him.

5. As a priest, the first accused had access to the hospital to visit patients at any time.

6. The first accused and the second accused lived in the Vicarage, which was only a short distance away from the hospital where Russel was warded, perhaps half a mile. So there was easy access for these accused to bring meals for Russel from their home and visit Russel even several times a day. Living so close to the hospital one would expect that it would be convenient for the relatives to look after their patient personally with regards to things like food. So having regard to the proximity of the hospital where he was staying to his home, it is quite natural that the accused would bring food to Russel even several times a day."

"So, on the evidence in this case upon a consideration and examination of all the circumstances, we believe the nurses when they say that they saw the first accused daily bring food to Russel in a basket and that those food consisted of the liquids that we have mentioned and that the nurses introduced those foods into Russel's nasal feed tube."

NO NATURAL CAUSE OR DISEASE

Mr. Bandaranayake said that, "The Court has already come to a conclusion upon evidence that the prosecution has proved beyond all reasonable doubt that no natural cause or disease was responsible for the hypoglycaemic attacks suffered by Russel and observed and diagnosed by doctors. The Court has also held that the prosecution has proved beyond reasonable doubt that the death is not a case of suicide or accident or misadventure occasioned by anything done by Russel himself. We have come to a conclusion and it is our judgement that the prosecution has proved beyond reasonable doubt that in all the circumstances of this case and all the proved facts the hypoglycaemic attacks have been induced by a blood sugar reducing agent, administered to Russel by some person or persons."

"There is evidence that the first accused was a diabetic. Dr. Lakshman Weerasena who testified before us told us that the first accused was introduced to him as a priest in 1976 by one Victor Gamalathge and that since that time he was the general practitioner attending to the medical needs of the first accused and his family. He said that the first accused was a diabetic and that from about 1976 he prescribed glibenclamide which is an anti-diabetic drug to control his diabetes. He said that drug is known as Euglucon and marketed under different names and the strength of the tablet was 5 mg, and that he had prescribed half to one tablet per day with restricted diet for the first accused and that he gave him a prescription at that time. In 1977 there was a short period of shortage of the drug due to government restrictions."

"But thereafter it was freely available in the market. On being asked whether the first accused ever discussed the effects of this drug with him, the doctor said that on some occasions the first accused had complained of feeling hungry, giddy or drowsy and he had asked him to reduce the tablet from one to half and that the first accused himself used to check his urine. The witness told us that he had also asked the first accused when he was feeling hungry to reduce the tablet and to take some sugar. The witness further told us that he prescribed Euglucon to the first accused at the first visit to his clinic with Victor Gamalathge in 1976. We believe Dr. Weerasena on this matter and he has not been contradicted in any event on this aspect of the case."

"We have held it to be proved that Russel had continued hypoglycaemic attacks in hospital from 26.7.1978 for some days. It is a proved fact that neither insulin nor any other anti-diabetic drug was given to Russel as part of his treatment recommended by the doctors and administered by the hospital authorities. This finding is supported by the oral testimony of those who attended on Russel and by the entries in the BHT and in the FBC, which contained no reference whatsoever to such a thing being administered to this patient. So if no injections of insulin were given by the hospital and no injections have been seen to be given by anybody, which in fact we believe and hold to be true, the blood sugar reducing agent must be introduced to Russel through the nasal feed."

"What can be introduced in that manner would be an anti-diabetic drug. We have the evidence of Professor Jayasena how an anti-diabetic tablet can be crushed and put into liquid and pass down the tube so that it will get absorbed in the stomach. It was the opinion of Dr. Nagaratnam that hypoglycaemia in all the circumstances in the hospital must have been introduced through the nasal feed, if a natural cause for hypoglycaemia is eliminated."

"Now we consider it too remote and extremely unlikely and highly improbable that such a drug would reach Russel's nasal feed from the kitchen of the hospital. It is unlikely that foods sent from the hospital kitchen to the ward could specially have contained a drug. The hospital kitchen caters to thousands of patients each day. A poisoned liquid food reaching the same patient in a ward each day for several days and sometimes even several times each day is in our view extremely remote and unlikely," Mr. Bandaranayake said

BROUGHT UNCONSCIOUS TWICE

"There is no evidence that any person at the General Hospital even knew Russel Ingram. There is the further fact, which we have held proved beyond all reasonable doubt both from oral testimony as well as the documents produced in this case, that Russel was brought unconscious twice to hospital from the Vicarage and on both occasions with low blood sugar, causing the unconsciousness. Those states of unconsciousness caused by hypoglycaemia could not possibly have been brought about through the media of hospital food. In these circumstances we rule out the possibility beyond all reasonable doubt that Russel's hypoglycaemic attacks in ward 18 were induced through foods sent to him from the hospital kitchen."

"Still we have the fact of repeated hypoglycaemic attacks in late July 1978. Upon the evidence in this case and upon all the proved facts and circumstances, the only other way in which an anti-diabetic drug could have been introduced into Russel's nasal feed was through the food brought to him by the first accused and which was given to him. That is the only reasonable rationale convincing and compelling inference that this Court can reach upon the evidence. Here was the opportunity for an anti-diabetic drug to be administered to Russel to cause the signs of hypoglycaemia observed and treated. So the only inference that we can reach upon the evidence is that the food brought by the first accused and administered to Russel in the hospital contained a blood sugar reducing agent, an anti-diabetic drug that caused the recurrent hypoglycaemic attacks observed between 26.7.1978 and 4.8.1978."

"We hold it has been proved by the prosecution to the entire satisfaction of this Court that those hypoglycaemic attacks were induced by the first accused by the systematic introduction and administration of an anti-diabetic drug via the media of the feeds he brought from the Vicarage and were given to Russel. So now on this question of malicious intention, the prosecution has pointed to three circumstances and asked the Court to draw the inference that an intention to cause the death of Russel has also been proved."

Mr. Bandaranayake said that those circumstances are:

(a) That Russel has been proved to have suffered unconsciousness due to hypoglycaemia on the 26th of June 1978 at the Vicarage, from where he was brought by the first accused and admitted to ward 44, where he was found deeply unconscious and it was diagnosed that it was due to hypoglycaemia. The Court has in fact held that to be proved.

(b) The prosecution next points to the second hospitalization and the fact that on 18.7.1978 also Russel was unconscious in the Vicarage and admitted to hospital to ward 18 deeply unconsciousness with irreversible brain damage, and that it was diagnosed again that the state of his unconsciousness was due to hypoglycaemia.

(c) Thirdly, the prosecution points to the repeated attacks of hypoglycaemia at the end of July in ward 18, which also the Court has held it would have been induced through the administration of an anti-diabetic drug through the food, brought to him by the first accused and given to him.

Continuing Mr. Bandaranayake said, "So we have three separate instances where hypoglycaemia has been induced in Russel Ingram by someone. We have already held that the prosecution has proved beyond reasonable doubt that his hypoglycaemic condition was not the result of a natural disease nor was it induced by himself. The Court decided that the prosecution has proved beyond all reasonable doubt that his condition of hypoglycaemia and irreversible brain damage was induced by someone else."

"Now we find that it has been so introduced on three separate occasions. In these circumstances we are satisfied that such several instances of induced hypoglycaemia cannot be explained as having happened by accident. Upon this picture that has been proved to us by the prosecution, by the evidence they have led, it is our judgement that the prosecution has established and proved beyond all reasonable doubt that hypoglycaemia from which he suffered and which was the cause of his ultimate death, was intentionally and deliberately induced by some person or persons."

MURDER

"In the result, it is our judgement that Russel Ingram's death amounts to murder and that these repeated acts of the administration of an anti-diabetic drug is incapable of having been administered with any other intention other than murder and goes quite beyond a mere knowledge that the act would cause death. In the result, the prosecution has proved that his death resulted from the commission of a crime. The prosecution has therefore proved *Corpus Delicti* in respect of his death."

Mr. Bandaranayake then referred to evidence of statements of the accused led by the prosecution under Sections 17, 21 and Section 8 of the Evidence Ordinance.

He said, "The prosecution has led the evidence of statements made by the accused which this Court has admitted in evidence in these proceedings. The prosecution points to two ways in which the statements could legitimately be used by Court, if proved:

(1) As admissions of facts and events, or

(2) As conduct showing an intention to confuse, mislead or falsify."

"We are of the opinion that wherever we accept these statements to be proved, we can, (a) either treat them as admissions indicative of truth whenever they are supported or corroborated by other independent evidence tending to show that they are reliable, or (b) that they are circumstances of conduct consistent with intent to mislead or confuse or falsify, when their falsity is manifest or indicated by other facts and circumstances, or the conduct of the accused is demonstrably suspicious or inconsistent with a fair and reasonable inference of innocence."

"We see this need for caution as this case depends almost entirely on circumstantial evidence. Furthermore, it is necessary that it be seen that the Court is not reaching a conclusion upon convenience. We set this standard as appropriate in this case."

Mr. Bandaranayake then referred to Count No. 2 on the indictment, namely, the charge of murder of Russel Ingram alleged against both the accused.

"This count is based on the concept of joint criminal liability of the two accused. When a criminal act is done by several persons in furtherance of the common intention of all, each of such persons is liable for the act in the same manner as if it were done by him alone. This embodies a common sense principle, that if one or more persons intentionally do something jointly, it is just the same as if each had done it individually. The leading feature is the element of participation in action, the person must actually participate in some way at the time the crime is committed. It implies acting in concert and it must be distinguished from similar intention."

COMMON INTENTION

"Furthermore, the case of each accused must be considered separately. One must be satisfied that the accused was actuated by a common intention with the doer of the criminal act at the time the act was committed. If there is no evidence of common intention or a reasonable doubt about it, the charge cannot lie against anyone except the actual doer. In such a case the co-accused would be liable only for an act committed by him, if any. There must be evidence either direct or circumstantial either of a pre-arranged or pre-conceived plan or a declaration or of some other significant fact at the time of the commission of the offence showing a common intention."

"Mere presence is insufficient unless it is a presence that contributed in some significant way towards the commission of the crime. The inference of common murderous intention should never be reached unless it is the only deducible inference in the circumstances, an inescapable inference. In this setting we have to consider the evidence that has been proved in this case by the prosecution and in doing so we will consider the evidence against each accused separately on the charge of murder and we will decide whether the evidence warranted an inference that they acted jointly in concert with one another in full knowledge of the purpose for which they were acting."

"We shall take the case against the first accused first. The case for the prosecution that has been presented before this Court depends on circumstantial evidence. The deceased Russel Ingram was the husband of the second accused. So in considering the case against the first accused, the Court must examine all circumstances showing a relationship between the first accused and the deceased. The Court naturally in a criminal case such as this, would look if there was any motive for the first accused to kill the husband of the second accused. We know that the law does require the prosecution to prove a motive in a criminal case but in a case of circumstantial evidence it is prudent to our opinion for a judge of facts to examine the evidence, to ascertain whether there was some motive and the absence of motive in such circumstances would be a matter favourable to the defence."

CAUSE OF DEATH

"The cause of death that has been established in this case is that an anti-diabetic drug was administered to Russel without his knowledge over a period of time, which resulted in an irreversible course of nature as a result of prolonged unconsciousness. So the method of murder becomes a significant fact in considering the question as to who could be held responsible for such an act. The administration of a drug over a period of time as has been proved in this case drives one to an irresistible inference that the party responsible for the administration of such a drug was known to the deceased and that the deceased kept his company over that period of time. The killer must have an opportunity to administer the drug," Mr. Bandaranayake said

"In these circumstances, evidence relative to association becomes relevant to the question of opportunity. Evidence relating to association also becomes relevant to the question of motive. Evidence showing knowledge and action of such drugs and evidence showing access to a possession of drugs becomes also relevant to the question of administration. In this setting, we will consider the evidence against the first accused. It is the evidence that Russel came into the life of the first accused around the month of August 1976 when he found himself without a job and had to return from Kandy and live with his parents in Colombo together with his wife, the second accused, who was also unemployed. They had three children. Now it was also the evidence in this case, which is not contested that the first accused was a clergyman who indulged in what was known as exorcism, of driving away evil spirits; that he visited homes and that he conducted exorcism services on Thursday evenings at St. Paul's Church in Colombo 10."

"We find from the evidence that the deceased and his wife, the second accused, attended these Thursday Services about August 1976 and that is the introduction of the deceased as well as the second accused to the first accused. Thereafter, the first accused employed the second accused as his typist. It was at that time that he was supposed to be writing a book. All these peripheral facts are not contested in this case. This is a part of the uncontested evidence and we hold it to be proved beyond reasonable doubt. From these early beginnings it is the evidence which we accept that second accused progressively began to play a prominent role at the Thursday Services which means that she had the confidence of the first accused."

"Thereafter we have it that in 1977, the first accused became busy with two things.

(1) He was given a responsible portion of the preparations that had to be made in regard to the consecration of the Bishop of Colombo due to take place in January 1978.

(2) The first accused was invited to go on a world tour and he had to make preparations for that too. So we find that the second accused played the role of secretary/typist for the first accused."

"We see this association, which is the background to the terminal point of the charge of conspiracy that had been laid against these two accused on Count one of the indictment. According to the prosecution, the intention and the resolution and the knowledge and the agreement of the accused to commit the murder of Russel began on or about the date of 8th July 1977. The prosecution by its evidence has been able to relate that date to a significant event and that is the hospitalization of Russel Ingram at Durdans Hospital. So we find the association between the two accused has developed up to a point where the first accused intentionally and voluntarily involves himself with Russel in admitting him to the Durdans Hospital with the assistance of a parishioner Mr. Wanigasekera. Russel had recovered in four days and was seen to be leading a normal life. Munilal Peiris says so."

"Thereafter, we again find that the first accused has involved himself voluntarily with the affairs of Russel. In that he spoke to witness Weeraman, the Managing Director of Independent Newspapers and asked him to give Russel Ingram a job and Mr. Weeraman obliged the first accused and employed Russel in a probationary capacity in late November 1977. Mr. Weeraman says that Russel was quite healthy and that Mr. Weeraman confirmed him in his post on 1.1.1978. Mr. Weeraman says that Russel participated in the activities of the Social Club and he was a member of their Cricket Team, which also shows that Russel was well and actively doing his work competently and to the satisfaction of his employer. One must remember that having regard to the cause of death and the nature of his illness the fact of his good health prior to June 1978, which was significantly important in this case."

CONSECRATING

Mr. Bandaranayake said that both Russel and his wife and the first accused and his wife played their part in the consecrating of his Lordship, the Bishop of Colombo, and that on the 4th of February, the first accused and his wife departed Sri Lanka on a world tour leaving the second accused and Russel Ingram in charge of the affairs of the Vicarage.

"That event, which is uncontested in this case and which we accepted proved shows that the first accused had confidence and had regard for the second accused and placed her and her husband in charge of his home in his absence. They were entrusted with the task of looking after a boarder who lived in the house at the time and to provide meals for that boarder and to see that the premises of the church and the Vicarage were kept in proper order. Munilal Peiris had testified before this Court that during this period he was living in Moratuwa and he visited the Vicarage and found the second accused was managing the affairs of the Vicarage satisfactorily. The next significant event is the departure of Munilal Peiris from these shores to the United Kingdom on the 29th March 1978."

"Russel Ingram and his wife attended that party and he was found to be quite in good health. Thereafter Cora Ingram, his mother tells us that she visited the Vicarage on 18th April 1978 to celebrate the Wedding Anniversary of the second accused and Russel Ingram and that he was in good health. This is followed by the evidence of Chandrakanthi Dharmadasa who has told us that up to the time that she left the Vicarage on or about 26th May 1978, Russel Ingram was in good health."

"Upon all these facts, which we hold to be proved beyond reasonable doubt there is amplitude of evidence coming from several witnesses who spoke of the good health of Russel up to this point of time which provided Court with an opportunity of comparison. All these witnesses have been consistent on this question as to the good health of Russel. We have no hesitation in accepting the testimony and we hold that fact to be proved that up to the end of May, Russel was in good health, going about his employment in a satisfactory way to the satisfaction of his employers up to the end of May 1978. A fact that must be emphasized at this point is that Russel and his wife were living at the Vicarage definitely from 4th February 1978 up to 9th June 1978. That is the established fact in this case."

"The next significant fact that should be mentioned at this point is that the first accused returned alone to Sri Lanka and into the Vicarage in about 25th April 1978. Russel was found to be ill for the first time in 1978, stuporosed on 9.6.1978. In the result it becomes important for the Court to consider the conduct of the first accused since his return to Sri Lanka on 25.4.1978 and Russel falling ill at the Vicarage on 9.6.1978. The prosecution placed evidence before us regarding the conduct of the first accused in this period."

Mr. Bandaranayake said that the prosecution has placed the evidence of Dr. Dayasiri Fernando, a relation of the first accused, and in this connection at an earlier point of this order, the Court has stated that Dr. Dayasiri Fernando's evidence falls into two categories - evidence of fact, and opinion evidence.

"Now we consider this evidence as to facts. He said he was working at the Accident Service of the General Hospital, Colombo and somewhere in late April or early May 1978, the first accused met him on the corridor of the Accident Service building, which is situated in Ward Place, which is a parallel road to Regent Street. He said that Dr. Joseph asked him to meet and discuss and consult him as he was fully qualified in the field. The first accused said that he had a lodger who was ill and he described the illness. The salient points of the description were that the patient went into states of reduced consciousness associated with loss of consciousness and associated changes of blood sugar, sometimes high, sometimes low, together with behavioural disturbances."

INSULINOMA

"Dr. Fernando said it was a good description and also said that he told the first accused at the time it was a classic case of insulinoma. He also told the Court that he advised the first accused to admit the patient to a medical ward at the General Hospital as the new Gastroenterology Unit that was being set up at Colombo South Hospital was six miles away and which Dr. Fernando was going to head, was not yet ready. He says that he assumed duties at this Unit on 23.6.1978 and he said that visit of the first accused to the Accident Service and this conversation took place long before that."

"Now Dr. Fernando says the date of his conversation as to the time that he was working in the Accident Service was before he was appointed the Resident Surgeon of the Accident Service on 17.5.1978. In the circumstances we accept Dr. Fernando's evidence in regard to the probable time of this conversation because we are satisfied that Dr. Fernando has cogent means by which he is able to give us the date and those means are a significant event in his life where he was appointed a Resident Surgeon of the Accident Service in Ward Place. He is confident that this conversation took place before that date. We have had the advantage of seeing this witness in the witness box and we are confident that he is speaking the truth on this matter."

"So, we find from the period of this conversation that the first accused happened to know and was able to give a good description of what is called 'Insulinoma', was soon after the first accused returned to Sri Lanka while Russel was living in his home in the Vicarage. This evidence also shows another very important matter and that is that at the time of this conversation, at the time the first accused told Dr. Fernando that Russel is a lodger was having all these symptoms. Russel, as far as the evidence goes, was in good health and doing his job as an Advertising Agent for the newspaper."

Mr. Bandaranayake said that the evidence from Mr. Weeraman was that from the month of January to June 1978, Russel has been working almost all that time.

"The evidence regarding the attendance of work and having regard to his good health, especially in this critical period coming from his mother that he was well on the date of his Anniversary in April, and that of Chandrakanthi Dharmadasa that he was well on 25th of May shows a contradiction."

"How is it that the first accused came to describe an illness to Dr. Fernando, which Russel Ingram was not suffering from? Upon the evidence that we have, that is significant conduct against the first accused in regard to this period. The conduct of the first accused arising out of the testimony of Dr. Fernando is in the teeth of the evidence of good health of Russel Ingram during this period."

"We like to point out that it has been the evidence of Parker Ingram that all his sons including Russel Ingram were healthy fellows; there was never an occasion to have a family doctor because his children did not fall ill. He told this Court that Russel Ingram had his schooling at Wesley College where he represented the school in the Stubbs Shield Inter School Boxing Tournament; that he played cricket and athletics and that he was a good sportsman and that after leaving school he played cricket at club cricket level for the Boras Cricket Club. His father said that Russel Ingram also visited Mt. Mary's Railway Sports Club at Welikada. Upon the foregoing, this Court observes that there was a connection between the first accused and the deceased and that the deceased was living in the home of the first accused along with the second accused. This establishes beyond all reasonable doubt that the first accused was proximate to and in that sense had an opportunity of administering food to the deceased."

"At this point of time in the narrative we come to a striking event and that is that this healthy man who was going about the affairs of his life as best he could, suddenly could not go to work, had to get into bed and his father had to be summoned to his bed and when the father so came, the second accused told him that Russel has been in 'stupor', which in ordinary layman's language is a state of unconsciousness. This evidence of Parker Ingram we believe. This evidence has not been contradicted in any way. It is not evidence directly connecting the first accused with the crime and we have no hesitation in accepting this item of evidence as being truthful. So that upon this admission of the second accused who was the wife of the deceased, we have this fact that on the 9th she said that Russel had been unconscious," Mr. Bandaranayake said.

"We have no evidence as to when he became unconscious or for how long he had been unconscious but he had been to work on the previous day. We see from the register that he has not taken leave for the 8th June, that he has taken leave for the 9th June. So what is relevant here is that upon the evidence this healthy Russel has been found unconscious and has been kept in the Vicarage. The General Hospital is a stone's throw away. If his state of health was so obviously bad, that they felt the need to inform his parents one wonders why at the same time he was not taken to hospital, but we have some evidence on this event, which we will consider in the course of this order, and that is that, the first accused and second accused told Alex Parker Ingram that Dr. Weerasena was treating Russel. We feel it is fitting at this point to deal with this matter straightaway."

"It has been the case for the prosecution through the testimony of both the Ingrams as well as Jackson that the first and second accused made out that Dr. Weerasena was treating Russel at the Vicarage in June and July 1978. Dr. Weerasena has quite unceremoniously rejected this evidence and denied that he did so. Dr. Weerasena says he treated Russel in 1976 once for some sores that he had, by giving him some ointment. This fact he remembers because it was the first accused who brought Russel to his clinic at Kollupitiya and that was done soon after he met the first accused who had been introduced to him by Victor Gamalathge. The first accused developed a relationship with him and got him to give him his note paper book as well as to give him a certificate concerning a claim that he had stigmata," Mr. Bandaranayake said.

"So in this context we would like to state that we believe Dr. Weerasena when he says that he did not treat Russel Ingram during this period. The witnesses who have testified before us namely the relations of Russel and relations of the second accused, regarding the events in the month of June and July have told us that no doctor visited Russel and treated him. Having regard to the conduct of the first accused in regard to the history that he has given to the General Hospital authorities upon Russel's admission to hospital, which bears no reference to the fact that Dr. Weerasena had treated Russel, having regard to the proved fact that the letter of admission that he got on 26.6.1978 was from Dr. Joseph, and not from Dr. Weerasena, we are confident that Dr. Weerasena is speaking the truth when he says that he did not treat Russel at those periods in June and July 1978 relevant to this case."

PANCREATIC DISORDER

"Being satisfied of that we return now to the 9th June when Alex Ingram visited the Vicarage and finds his son sick in bed and he says that upon his asking Russel what was wrong with him, the deceased replied, 'Daddy, I can sleep, sleep and sleep', to which the first accused had replied, 'No man, he is having some pancreatic disorder. An operation has to be done. There is no other treatment.' First accused told him on 9.6.1978 that he consulted one Dr. Lakshman Weerasena and that doctor had prescribed some pills. First accused also said that it was something like Disprin, but it was not medicine. Alex Ingram accepted this statement of the first accused and matters rested at that. Alex said that the first accused prepared Russel's food and even fed Russel. 'He prepared something like mincemeat and fed Russel. Food was prepared specially for my son. My son took one or two spoonful in a disgusted mood'."

"The defence has pointed out to Court that Alex Ingram when he made a statement to the police in connection with the inquiry omitted to mention to the police either;

(a) that the deceased told him that he can 'sleep, sleep and sleep';

(b) that the first accused prepared food specially for Russel on a stove; or

(c) that the first accused fed Russel."

"The defence says that the omissions are amount to contradictions and that having regard to the cause of death they are all important matters in regard to the testimony of Alex. The defence has also pointed out to Court that Alex Ingram made a statement to the police several months after the death of his son and therefore, that in the circumstances it is a belated statement and should be so treated. In the result the defence says that the testimony of Alex Ingram is rendered unreliable on important matters. We have had the benefits of having Alex Ingram testified before us upon oath."

"Alex is a man who has spent long years in the public service of this country. He is a retired engine driver. He also appeared to us to be a fairly educated person and content to live out his life in the circumstances in which he is in an honourable way. He is a familied man who says he accepted what the first accused told him because he was a priest and he appeared to be quite confident about what he was saying and doing."

"His son Russel showed confidence in the first accused. It was in these circumstances that he also did not do anything meaningful to take Russel out of this Vicarage and put him in the hospital. We believe Alex's evidence that at the first instance he was invited to the Vicarage that day. That was not a casual visit because his visits are coincided with the fact that Russel Ingram has taken leave for that day. We do not accept that his visit was a coincidence when he says it was not. He has impressed us as a fair, honest witness in spite of the fact that it was his son who was involved in this case."

"So in this context, this man who was invited says that he stayed for 3 or 4 days and that fact is also supported by reason of the fact that Russel has taken leave from his workplace for the 9th, 12th and 13th. It is too farfetched for us to think that Alex knew that when he was testifying that he will support the entries in the personal file of Russel kept in the Independent Newspapers."

"So when we look at the evidence intrinsically we feel it is safe to accept Alex's testimony upon the circumstances under which he went to the Vicarage on that occasion. Having gone there on invitation, he speaks of a succession of events that took place during the next few days. It is established having regard to the leave taken that Russel was ill. We see this because we believe Alex when he says that Russel was ill. That is why he could not attend work. He was told that Dr. Weerasena is the doctor attending the patient and that such a patient should have a regulated controlled diet," Mr. Bandaranayake said.

"A person sick enough to go into a state of unconsciousness is not given normal food. So it is our common experience that such patients should be given an appropriate diet. In these circumstances Alex has told us that indeed the first accused gave a regulated diet to his son. So when we look at the testimony intrinsically we do not see any improbability simply because he has omitted to mention this in his statement to the police. That is not a good enough reason for us to say that this man has intentionally added a significant item of evidence to blacken the case against the first accused. So in the testimony that Alex has given us so far, he has told us of a symptom that was felt by his son and he has told us of the conduct of the first accused in regulating food for his son. Feeling sleepy obviously is a symptom known to the person who is sensing that. When we examine this evidence intrinsically we are confident Alex is speaking the truth. We believe his evidence. We have no hesitation in accepting that he has given reliable testimony to the Court."

SWEATING PROFUSELY

"The next important significant item of evidence also comes from Alex Ingram and this is in regard to the incident that took place the following day, namely 10.6.1978 where Alex says that the first accused took pills out of his pocket and that there were 4 pills and a capsule and that he gave them to Russel who consumed them and that about ten or fifteen minutes later Russel started sweating."

Mr. Bandaranayake said that what is important in this evidence is firstly, the first accused administered pills to Russel, and he was sweating profusely, which according to medical evidence that we accept, is a clear sign of hypoglycaemia.

He said, "The defence points to the omission in regard to this testimony to this extent that they say that the witness has not in his statement told the police that the first accused took the pills out of his pocket. We keep in mind the defence submission that the statement of this witness is a belated statement; that they had every opportunity to make a statement to the police soon after the death of Russel; that it is in evidence that his wife suspected that something was wrong in relation to Russel's death and that she had complained to the Coroner and that there had been an inquest and that in these circumstances waiting till April 1979, should raise a reasonable suspicion in the mind of the Court as to the reliability of his testimony."

"Bearing these submissions in mind and bearing in mind the impression that this witness created at the time he gave this testimony, we accept his evidence as reliable. As we said before, if Russel was ill enough to be in bed and being told that he is being treated by a doctor is quite the thing to be accepted that some treatment be given to Russel. There is nothing surprising or inconsistent for pills to be administered in the context of what the first accused had said, which we accept, so that when we look at this evidence intrinsically we are confident that Alex is speaking the truth and we therefore accept his testimony as proved in this case, which means that this Court accepts that the first accused administered pills to Russel on 10.6.1978 and that he collapsed, began sweating profusely 10 minutes thereafter."

"Alex has told this Court that Russel went back to work about the 14th and that he himself went away. He is not certain of the dates but Mr. Weeraman confirmed that Russel returned to work which again points to a significant fact and that is that he recovered after being stuporosed after being given pills and after being given mincemeat. He appeared to be sufficiently well to go and attend to his work. We next come to a further significant fact, which is a claim by the first accused that he got into trances and he had some supernatural guidance."

FATHER WAS IN A TRANCE

"In the first place there has been the evidence of his children. Munilal Peiris and Malrani who have spoken to the fact on several occasions too their father has claimed to have connection with a supernatural power, so that intrinsically when we approach this evidence we find that Alex is not speaking of something unusual to the first accused. Alex Ingram has told this Court that on the 10th June in the evening at about 8 p.m. at the Vicarage first accused was in his bedroom on his bed, which was in the room next to where Russel was and that first accused was lying on the bed motionless and he thought he was dead."

"So naturally in such circumstances we believe that he must have had a look at this man at which point the second accused had alleged to have told him that 'Father was in a trance'. We believe this evidence and we will give our reason as to why we accept this testimony. From this point we infer that the second accused was in the bedroom with the first accused. Alex said that the first accused was making sounds which gave him the impression that he was in conversation with someone. Second accused put off the light and lighted a red bulb like a night lamp so that there was sufficient light in the room to observe what went on."

"Alex continues and says that the first accused mentioned the name Michael and while stroking his abdomen said 'Pancreas, pancreas'. This behaviour went on he says for twenty to twenty five minutes and the second accused and Russel were there and Russel was with hands on the first accused's body while the second accused announced that the first accused was in a trance. Then at some point second accused brought a bandage and some rectified spirit and took the palm of the first accused on to her thigh and starting rubbing the palm with the spirit saying 'This is the place where the wound is'. Witness continued that he was very close by but did not see a wound on the palm. There was no blood on the palm. We were told that once the first accused started the services in church that it was claimed that his palm starts bleeding and that is why the second accused was bandaging the palm. Alex continued this testimony by telling the Court that on the following day first accused told him that he conversed with angels and that he was given very bad news that there was a crisis."

"Now the defence rigorously attacks this evidence as unreliable on two grounds that Alex Ingram did not mention to the police that he witnessed that first accused getting into trances and uttering any words or doing anything. Secondly, the defence says that in any event Alex's statement to the police was belated. Thirdly, the defence says Alex had an opportunity to read the newspapers as this case was given much publicity after its commencement and the opening address of counsel for the prosecution was published in the newspapers and the testimony of Malrani and Munilal were taken and excerpts of this also appeared in the newspapers. So the defence says Alex had an opportunity to come to know alleged trances of the accused and that in these circumstances it is dangerous for the Court to rely upon this evidence as it could well have been made up by the father of the deceased to mislead the Court and prejudice the Court against the accused."

Continuing, Mr. Bandaranayake said, "We have examined this testimony with great care. To begin with while Alex was informing the Court of this episode which he claimed to be true, he said that he even made a note of this event in his personal diary and he offered to produce his diary before the Court for the inspection of Court. As he was given time to do this and he did in fact bring a diary to the Court. As it was highly a personal thing, it had not been scrutinized by the police in the course of the investigation. The Court looked at this relevant entry only and handed the diary over to the defence to enable them to cross examine the witness. Now Alex Ingram has told us that he had not given particulars of the entire incident that took place but that he has made a reference in this diary contemporaneously to the fact that the first accused told him something and that this present testimony is about that matter. The cross examination of this witness bears that out. He has not referred to the fact of the trance or the fact that the first accused stroked the stomach or the first accused uttered those words."

"So that defence says that this testimony is unreliable. For one thing, we see that this diary is a personal diary of the witness, which would usually contain a summary of events significant to him relating to his day to day life. It is not for us to say what particulars a person should write in this own diary. For the man who had made an entry of the fact that something was said, the question arises whether a Court is entitled to expect him to set down all the particulars also of what was said."

"As we said before we have had the opportunity of observing the demeanour of this witness. He has had the opportunity of being at the Vicarage. He has had the opportunity of seeing things that happened in this bed room of the first accused because he says his son was also there. The witness goes further and says that the deceased believed in the first accused and that is also important in this case that he accepted what the first accused was doing and he was thankful to the first accused for what he was doing," Mr. Bandaranayake said.

SPIRITUAL MESSAGE

"So we have the evidence of Alex Ingram on one hand telling us that this trance took place and that he is believing him and accepting his conduct. Then he has gone on to describe the conduct that his son accepted and reason for his acceptance, namely it was because of a spiritual message and it is in those circumstances that he described to this Court what took place. The defence wishes the Court to believe that this witness is adding to his evidence as he goes on. As opposed to that, Parker Ingram wishes the Court to accept his evidence by describing why he believed the first accused. It is a fact before us that the Ingrams are relations of the deceased Russel and that they all accepted the conduct of the first accused and they believed that Dr. Weerasena was attending to Russel and treated him. Therefore, we feel it is safe to accept Alex's testimony in this matter both as conduct of the first accused as well as to show a reason as to why the deceased accepted this conduct and had confidence in him. So when we examine this testimony intrinsically we do not have a good reason to doubt its credibility."

"We are convinced that he has spoken the truth before us and we accept and adopt his testimony on this matter. The inference that the prosecution wishes us to draw is that the first accused was introducing the subject of an element related to the functioning of Russel's pancreas which was responsible for causing his sleepiness, lethargy and sickness. It has to be taken in the context of the first accused's earlier statement previously made that Russel was suffering from pancreatic disorder for which there was no treatment other than an operation. In this sense we see the consistency in the conduct of the first accused in conditioning the mind of Russel and his relations into accepting that he had a natural disease of the pancreas."

"We also bear in mind that Munilal Peiris has told this Court of a trance that his father got into in the second half of April 1978 after which he told them that the angel told him that Russel was ill. So we see that the conduct of the first accused in regard to the message through the medium of trance is deposed to by these totally unconnected witnesses, Munilal Peiris and Alex Ingram. The suggestion by the defence is that Alex Ingram is testifying simply because of something he has read in the papers. We do not consider it something that can be taken seriously. This question of the trance is relevant in this case having regard to the first accused being known to be a person allegedly dabbling with the supernatural. He is so interested in the subject that he has even started writing a book. So it is in this context that we have to view this evidence of this witness. According to the prosecution he is attempting to condition the mind of the people into accepting that his victim was in fact unwell. So when one is involved in a question of the supernatural it is not contested except by its non-believers and the evidence is that the Ingrams are Christians."

"We also have the evidence of Alex Ingram that on the 24th, Russel was unconscious in the morning. He remembers the first accused feeding Russel with a spoon. First accused said that there was no need to get down a doctor as there were pills given on the recommendation of Dr. Weerasena and what is required was an operation. As stated earlier Dr. Weerasena has vehemently denied that he recommended pills for Russel Ingram. It is also in evidence that these pills which were referred to by Russel have been white in colour and were similar to Disprin and the pills were taken out of his pocket. If these pills were similar to Disprin and harmless it is strange that they should be produced from the pocket of the first accused without the foil, which suggests that he had removed the pills from the foil earlier."

"We believe Dr. Weerasena that he did not prescribe any medicine for Russel during this period. This is supported by the fact that the first accused got a letter of admission to admit Russel to hospital from Dr. Joseph on the 26th. That has been produced in this case as P14 which fact strongly suggests that Dr. Weerasena was not the doctor who had been treating him. Furthermore, he has not given any history to the hospital to ward 44 that Dr. Weerasena had been treating this patient."

"Furthermore, he has not produced any letter from Dr. Weerasena. In these circumstances we are satisfied beyond any doubt that Dr. Weerasena has nothing to do with those pills administered to Russel for unimpeachable reasons. In this connection we bear in mind that Alex Ingram has failed to mention in his statement to the police that he has seen the first accused taking pills out of his pocket. We are satisfied that Alex Ingram has spoken the truth in these matters, that the first accused said they are on the recommendation of Dr. Weerasena."

ARE YOU MAD?

"Alex Ingram also stated that after Russel Ingram was admitted to hospital on 26.6.1978 the doctor has told the nurses to administer 10% dextrose drip to Russel at which stage the first accused had flared up and said, 'Are you mad?' He had also told the doctor that sugar is poison in this case and the lady doctor in turn said, 'Are you trying to cause further brain damage?' at which stage the first accused had remained silent. It is in evidence that the first accused right throughout had said that sugar was bad for Russel's condition. It was urged by the defence that in his statement to the police Alex Ingram had not mentioned that the first accused had stated that sugar was bad for Russel, but the evidence of Dr. Ruwanpathirana is that the first accused had told her that sugar was bad for Russel. Dr. Ruwanpathirana has no personal interest in Russel Ingram in this case. She is employed in a government hospital. This fact that she deposed to in this Court we consider as detail, which cannot create any substantial doubt as to the veracity of her testimony."

"This is the kind of fanciful doubt that we are not entertaining. Both, Dr. Ruwanpathirana and Alex Ingram have referred to the fact that first accused said that sugar was bad for Russel. Furthermore, Alex Ingram is a lay witness who does not understand the significance of the effect of sugar on the human body. In the circumstances we feel that his failure to mention this matter to the police is of no significance. It is also the evidence of Alex Ingram who says that the first accused had told him 'I told you. I told you they are giving dextrose and that will be his end,' referring to Russel."

Mr. Bandaranayake said that the medical evidence reveals that administration of dextrose in the hospital resulted in Russel becoming conscious after his admission to hospital in an unconscious state. He said that the facts show that the administration of dextrose in fact revived Russel.

"The first accused has said that dextrose was in fact bad for him. Having observed Alex Ingram in the witness box we do not consider that he could have spoken to a matter or incident regarding the utterances of the first accused about dextrose if it had not in fact taken place. We are satisfied beyond reasonable doubt Alex Ingram was speaking the truth in this connection. Several doctors have spoken to the good knowledge that the first accused had on medical matters and we are satisfied with the evidence of such witnesses. Therefore, the utterance of the first accused that sugar was very bad for Russel would indicate that the first accused was in fact trying to cause harm to Russel and divert medical treatment being given to Russel. According to Alex Ingram the first accused had told him not to worry as he was guided by an angel."

"Alex Ingram also stated in evidence that, Russel was taken to a psychiatrist on the 13th and at the request of the doctors that he had got down the second accused, who came in a taxi and had answered the questions put by the doctor. The first accused had, according to Alex Ingram, come soon afterwards and had told 'I do not know what she will go and say' and rushed into the room where the doctors were. This is rather a significant remark for there is no reason for the first accused to be apprehensive what the second accused would have told the doctor, if in fact the truth could in no way be incriminating. Having observed the demeanour of Alex Ingram we are of the view that he would not go to the extent of giving false evidence on this matter."

"We accept his evidence on this point. According to Parker Ingram after the son was admitted to hospital on the 26th and when he returned to the Vicarage the first accused has told him that he need not wait and asked him to get back saying that Russel will be looked after. This evidence, which we see no reason to disbelieve and which we accept, shows that the first accused had in the presence of Alex Ingram given certain medicines to Russel informed Alex Ingram that he was receiving medical treatment and also told him that the angel was guiding him and had further warned Alex Ingram of the outcome of the trance."

MOTHER TOOK CUSTARD

"In our view the first accused has merely by these actions prepared the ground to show that he would render whatever medical care he could to Russel and that the death of Russel would be a foregone conclusion. There is also the evidence of Alex Ingram that when his wife took custard to be given to Russel the first accused had objected to it. The evidence of Cora Ingram too shows that she had taken the custard to be given to her son but the defence pointed out that no such mention had been made to the police in the statement by Cora Ingram. Considering the social background of Cora Ingram and Alex Ingram and having observed the demeanour, we do not think she would have realized the significance of mentioning about the custard. At that stage she certainly would not have considered the significance or importance of this item."

"We also examine this evidence intrinsically. We consider it likely that this lady, Mrs. Ingram would make custard and take it for her son because that is precisely the social background to which she belongs. They are not Sinhalese people. They have settled in this country at some point and they are English speaking people, that it is customary for such people to make things like custard. That has been our experience and so we accept her testimony that she took custard to her son. We are quite satisfied that she did not realize that custard contains sugar and that was the best possible thing that she could have taken to her son in the circumstances."

"In regard to the period of his second admission the evidence is that Cora Ingram has visited the Vicarage once. She appeared to be rather confused about that day but when we take her evidence it fits into the setting that visit would have been on the 26th June, the day that her son was hospitalized. The Court does not have material from her concerning the period 9.6.1978 to 26.6.1978 during which her son remained in the Vicarage."

Mr. Bandaranayake then considered the testimony of Bridget Jackson.

"Her evidence is of a significant nature, pertinent to the case against the first accused. Her testimony becomes important with regard to the events that took place in the Vicarage on 16.7.1978. Her position is that she visited the hospital intending to see Russel because she did not know at that time that he had been discharged but she went to the Vicarage first to ask the second accused for the pass. When she went to the Vicarage she was informed by the first accused to come into the house and there she found Russel lying in bed. He looked sick. She questioned the deceased asking what was wrong with him and Russel said that he did not know and then she questioned him as to why he says he does not know what was wrong with him and Russel replied "When I take this mixture and tablets I feel drowsy.""

DYING DEPOSITION

"This testimony was led by the prosecution as a dying deposition setting out alleged circumstances of the transaction which resulted in his death. We accept this testimony. It becomes probable circumstances in this case. We are alive to the fact that such a statement has not been made in our presence and that it is not upon oath and has not been subject to cross examination. We also have to bear in mind whether she could have any particular reason to utter falsehood. We have also got to test the credibility of the witnesses who spoke to the facts and that of Bridget Jackson. So bearing in mind all these matters of law that arise upon this item of evidence we are told by the defence that this witness has not referred to this fact when she made a statement to the police and that therefore, this omission amounts to substantial contradiction because it is on an important matter in this case."

"Bridget Jackson said that she found the deceased lying in bed. In fact she has gone to see him in hospital and had found him at home, which means that she knew that he had been sick; she had in fact visited him in hospital in June and she suddenly finds now that he has been well enough to be allowed to come home. This is a fact that she had not known when she came to the hospital. When she came home she asked Russel 'Why are you looking sick?' It is quite natural that Russel should have replied. We also have to consider this evidence in the background of other evidence regarding the conduct of the first accused in the Vicarage where Russel was living."

"We have already dealt with Alex Ingram's testimony, that he saw the first accused giving pills to Russel. In this sense there is therefore, a consistency when a witness says, well the deceased said that someone was giving pills to him. We also place this testimony of Bridget in the context of Dr. Joseph's evidence that he found brain damage in Russel on the previous day, 15.7.1978. He has told us how he fixed this date and we accept it as reliable that Russel could not work a simple arithmetic sum. We cannot view evidence in a vacuum. We believe Dr. Joseph in regard to the testimony he has given."

"It is this same Dr. Joseph who saved Russel's life by giving a letter of admission in June or so he said, because he did a favour to the first accused by giving a letter without seeing the patient. He told us how he came to give P14. We believe him. When we look at Bridget Jackson's evidence, in the absence of medical testimony in this case her evidence would amount to nothing. The defence also attacked the evidence on the basis that it is belated and that she has had time to prepare her testimony; that she comes into the witness box at a time when the newspapers of the country carried the opening address of the counsel for the prosecution; that she therefore had plenty of time to concoct evidence," Mr. Bandaranayake said.

"The submission of counsel of the defence that she might have been influenced by newspaper reports is unacceptable to us. Bridget also is a sister of the second accused. We bear that in mind in assessing her testimony. Furthermore, when we examine the statement of the deceased intrinsically we find that it is probably true because in fact he has been killed by the administration of anti-diabetic drugs. In all these circumstances, we accept the testimony of Bridget Jackson without hesitation that the deceased in fact uttered these words."

GREEN VEGETABLE CURRY

"The next fact that we will refer to in this context is that Russel was given lunch on 16.7.1978 by the first accused which Bridget Jackson observed. There was rice, pumpkin, meat curry, *mukunuwenna mallun* (a green vegetable curry), which means that there was plenty of carbohydrate in the food, which amounts to that there was sugar in the meal. After the rice meal Bridget says that the first accused fed him with ice cream which again is sugar. When we look at the extracts of P40 produced by the prosecution we find that the book says that one of the antidotes for hypoglycaemia is ice cream because ice cream immediately starts elevating the blood sugar level. We know that the first accused had a book, which was lost and that P40 is the replacement for that book. We accept the evidence of Bridget Jackson that the first accused gave Russel lunch that day and just as much as Cora Ingram says that she gave custard to Russel, Bridget Jackson says that the first accused gave ice cream to Russel. But one sees this significant fact that if one administers an anti-diabetic drug and also administers ice cream, the blood sugar level fluctuates and this precisely is what Dr. Joseph says the first accused told him on the telephone in June."

"So when one looks at all these circumstances one is satisfied that this lady Bridget is speaking the truth. Now the next matter we might mention is that Bridget says that after feeding Russel, the first accused and second accused had lunch in the dining room and Bridget remained in their company. Although she did not have lunch for herself as she had an early lunch that day Bridget speaks of the conversation that place at the dining table, where she says the first accused told her that Russel's condition was very low and that he might pass away at any time and that he will not recover. First accused has also said if Russel dies he wanted to bury him in his ground. Bridget has said why not in Ingrams' grave (their mother's grave). Then the first accused said 'No, no, he can be put in my grave'."

Mr. Bandaranayake said that the prosecution relies on this testimony as evidence of conduct of the first accused as well as admissions and the prosecution asked to Court to draw an adverse inference from these circumstances.

"The defence has pointed out that the witness is a belated witness. Defence also suggests that Bridget had reason to be angry with the second accused because some accusation had been made against Bridget's son in the past regarding some theft. Bridget denied that her son was ever suspected of a theft by breaking a wardrobe. Bridget denied that she had reason to falsify testimony. She has not spoken of any act or omission. She spoke of a general conversation and she says she was surprised because it was soon after Russel had his lunch. So there is no reason for anybody to think in terms of Russel's death and so she remembers this conversation. In the circumstances and having observed the demeanour of Bridget, we are satisfied that she is not making it up."

"We now pass from lunch to tea time about 3.30 p.m. Bridget is in the room with Russel because she was dressing a wound of one of the children. She had gone to the room at the request of Russel. She said while she was there some incident took place and that is that the first accused brought some tea for Russel and he also asked the second accused who was present 'Where are the medicines?' to which second accused replied, 'Why father, you are the one who has the medicine'. Then, the first accused took some pills from his pocket. There were four tablets white in colour without a cover, two green tablets and a capsule. These pills were in polythene bag in his pocket. He then gave the pills to Bridget and asked her to give them to Russel. Bridget tells us that she refused to do that saying she has a fear of it getting struck in his throat. At that time Russel was lying on the bed and Bridget refused. Then the first accused gave the pills to Russel who swallowed them with the tea."

"Bridget said that she did not speak anything because she had been told that is the medicine. Ten or fifteen minutes later, Bridget tells us that Russel collapsed sweating. He appeared to be in pain and he passed urine on the bed. He was struggling and then he became unconscious. Having given the tablets the first and second accused left the room. Then according to Bridget she had gone to the dining room and told the second accused that Russel had passed urine and was struggling and asked why the tablets were given to which the second accused did not reply."

Mr. Bandaranayake said that according to Bridget, Russel remained unconscious up to the time he was removed to hospital in the morning of 18.7.1978, which means that he never recovered consciousness during the rest of his life.

"In regard to this testimony, the defence has pointed out the fact that she has omitted to tell the police that the first accused first offered her pills and told her to give the pills to Russel. We cannot consider this as a substantial contradiction in regard to the fact that the first accused administered pills to Russel. We regard it as a descriptive detail and we do not expect a witness making police statements to give every single detail connected with the items of evidence. Even if Bridget had administered the pills, it would not make a difference to the case against the first accused. In the circumstances we accept this evidence as satisfactory and credible and we adopt it as a proved circumstance in this case."

"We bear in mind the general submission of the defence that the testimony of Russel's relatives is belated. Those have been made in 1979. In all the circumstances in this case we do not consider that delay to be fatal to the question of the credibility to the testimony of these witnesses. We view this evidence that we have accepted in the context of the fact that when Russel was discharged from hospital on 14.7.1978 as is proved by 1D21 that no continuing treatment had been prescribed for him. In the result there was no necessity to give Russel any pills on that occasion. Prosecution points to the conduct of the first accused as incriminating."

"We next proceed to the testimony of Bridget who says that when she observed all these signs of Russel - sweating, urinating, going unconscious - she told the second accused to get a doctor and the first accused replied 'We will see, we will see, we will see' but did not get down a doctor. Bridget left the house at 4.30, went home and returned to the Vicarage about 6.30 with her husband, Russel Jackson."

CONTRADICTION IN THE TESTIMONY

"Russel was still unconscious on the bed in the identical position. She questioned the first accused as to whether a doctor had been brought to which the first accused replied' 'Doctor is gone; I will get him admitted to hospital on the clinic day.' We know from the other evidence that Dr. Sheriffdeen's clinic day was Tuesday. Now Bridget says that her husband changed him into another sarong and also adjusted him and put a tube for the purpose of passing urine. In regard to this matter the defence points to a contradiction in the testimony, on this point about the urinal, arising between the husband and wife. The defence points to the fact that Russel Jackson has said that there was a urinal, when he came. We fail to see contradiction. If in fact Russel Jackson changed Russel Ingram's sarong, we would expect Mrs. Jackson not to remain in the room at that time and so she would not know where the tube is connected or whether it had been connected. The only man who could have seen that is Russel Jackson because he was changing the sarong and he says the tube was connected. She also has told us that they stayed in the night and in the course of the night her husband went to pray for Russel to the room where Russel was. Bridget says that Russel was in the first accused's room."

"Russel and the children slept in the first accused's room that night and on the next night too. On the 17th morning the Jacksons left the Vicarage and Russel was still unconscious. Bridget says that they returned in the evening on the 17th and found Russel still unconscious in the same position in the first accused's bedroom. The witness thereafter gets on to the events of the 18th when she says that Russel was still unconscious and he has taken to hospital by her husband

and first and second accused at about 7.15 a.m. by ambulance and before that first accused said some prayers. They returned from hospital having admitting Russel in about forty five minutes and first and second accused went away saying that they were going to the Food Commissioner's Department to get the second accused's and children's rice ration books changed to the Vicarage address."

"She said that the second accused gave that information. The prosecution pointed to the conduct of the accused of placing the unconscious Russel in the hands of the hospital authorities and going about on a mundane errand. When considered in the context of the seriousness of Russel's condition at that time, because we know that he had a low blood sugar level that morning upon admission and that had it not been for the immediate infusion of dextrose he would have been dead. So, the prosecution says in such a condition having had this unconscious man with them for two days they did not show any concern. The prosecution says that these events of both accused were common intention as well as conspiracy."

PLACED A RING

"We next come to the testimony of Bridget Jackson as the second act that took place in the Vicarage on the day Russel died. She says that the two accused were in the dining room and there were other visitors, and in the presence of everyone the first accused took out a ring, which was gold in colour and placed on the second accused's ring finger. She said that the second accused allowed the ring to be put into her finger without protest and kept silent. Witness says that she was shocked by this conduct. Having placed the ring on the second accused's ring finger the first accused said, 'Don't worry Dalrene, soon I will be in the same condition as you', and stroked her shoulder and walked away. The defence has pointed to an omission in the statement by this witness to the police, about the statement Bridget says the first accused uttered after placing the ring on her ring finger. That is the only contradiction in regard to this item of evidence. This matter has been more fully considered by us in another part of this judgment as it is relevant to the question of conspiracy by the first and the second accused, which is the charge alleged on Count three of the indictment where they are charged with the murder of Mrs. Peiris."

"It is the case for the prosecution that evidence in this case relating to the conspiracy charge is part and parcel of one continuing transaction. The episode about the ring is relevant evidence against the second accused on the charge mentioned. For this reason we have gone into this item of evidence more fully and given our reasons for accepting it. Suffice it to say here that we accept the testimony of Bridget Jackson that the first accused placed the ring on the second accused's finger and she accepted that ring on the date of her husband's death as proved circumstances against both accused."

Mr. Bandaranayake then considered the testimony of Russel Jackson, which also concerns his stay in the Vicarage on the nights of 16.7.1978 and 17.7.1978 and the circumstances of Russel's hospitalization on 18.7.1978.

"Russel Jackson told us that he went to the Vicarage on 16.7.1978 in the evening consequence to telephone call by the first accused who asked him to come there. He found Russel unconscious, breathing heavily and very ill. He asked the first accused why Russel has not been taken to hospital and the first accused said that he was waiting for the clinic day. He changed Russel's sarong at the request of the first accused. He carried Russel to the first accused's bedroom and put him on the first accused's bed. When they retired to bed that night he and his wife were occupying a room on the other side of the house. Before he retired he wanted to say a prayer for Russel Ingram. So he went across the hall and wanted to enter the bedroom. He told us that he is a lay-preacher of Christian denomination. But when he went to the first accused's bedroom he found it locked. Therefore he announced himself and the first accused opened the door having first unlocked it. He found both accused in the bedroom and the unconscious Russel and the children. He said his prayers and came out."

Mr. Bandaranayake said that, "The prosecution points to this evidence as evidence showing the relationship between the two accused which really asserts and that they are sleeping together in a room with an unconscious person and children is sufficient material upon which a Court can draw an inference of adultery. If this had been in a divorce action it would have been in evidence which a Court have to believe."

"The evidence would have taken into account upon such a charge but it is not necessary for us to go that far. It is certainly suggestive of sexual intimacy if believed. The defence criticizes the evidence on the basis that Jacksons had omitted to tell the police that the first accused pulled down the bolts and turned the lock and then opened the door. We do not consider this as a serious substantial contradiction. No one expects people to go to those lengths in making a statement to the police. The defence also criticizes this testimony on the basis that it is unlikely that if the accused were joined in a criminal endeavour that would invite a witness to come and watch their criminal activity. Jackson was criticized on that basis. In considering this criticism that the Jackson's testimony is unreliable on this basis, we have to look at the matters, which strongly suggest as relevant upon this question."

"One such matter we think is the method of murder. We are satisfied that an anti-diabetic drug was administered to Russel Ingram over a period of time and that the doctors themselves were perplexed during his lifetime as to the cause of several attacks of hypoglycaemia and unusual periods of reminiscences, unusual attacks during a period where he was getting consistently high dosages of dextrose. Upon the evidence we believe, we realize that the method of the murder has been surreptitiously to administer the drug making the victim and his relations believe that there was a natural cause making him ill and thereby allay any suspicion that might arise out of his sickness. So, if one is bent on committing murder that will go unrecognized as a crime, it would be quite consistent for the murderer to create evidence to support a view that there was indeed a natural cause for his sickness. So, when one invites witnesses to one's house one can influence them into believing that in fact the patient is ill and is being medically treated. So that when the patient dies everyone will be satisfied that he did not die of neglect and there will be no suspicion whatsoever attached to his death."

"So in these circumstances, when we view the evidence in this context, the criticism of the defence does not create any reasonable doubt in regard to the credibility of this evidence. We believe Jackson when he says that the accused slept in that room that night behind locked doors knowing Jackson to be a preacher and knowing that they were in the house and knowing that Russel was unconscious there was a great probability that the visitors might want to see how Russel was in the course of the night and therefore there was a great likelihood that one of them might come into the room in the night to see how Russel was and that might turn out to be unsatisfactory."

"In the result it is not a strange thing for them to have locked the door and this is precisely what Jackson says and that is all he says. By this conduct the prosecution wishes the Court to believe that there was intimate relationship between the two accused. If for instance, that Jackson had not been invited to spend the night and nobody had been invited to spend the night it might have been inconvenient if Russel had died in the Vicarage. Jackson says that the following night also second accused slept in the room with the deceased and on the 18th morning they took Russel to the hospital."

EXORCISM SERVICES

"We have already referred to the fact in this judgment which is mutually accepted evidence as to how the second accused started attending the first accused's Thursday Exorcism Services and then she became his typist/secretary in about September 1976. From then on she was seen to take a more prominent part at the Thursday services. With the oncoming event of the Bishop consecration she involved herself more and more with the life of the first accused by helping him in the secretarial work connected with that event as the first accused had been given a role to play in the preparation for that ceremony, the evidence was that he was placed in charge or organizing the consecration and foreign dignitaries were invited and expected to attend. In this setting it is a safe inference that she came to see much of him, spent a lot of time with him, became quite friendly, was given free range in the house, probably shared meals, got to know the deceased Mrs. Peiris also well and became more or less what one can term an insider in this household."

"Malrani left for the UK in 1977. Munilal married and lived in Moratuwa. Mihiri was married and living in Wales, so that really it was the first accused and his wife who were left at home with a boarder. Now it is the evidence that the first accused was also writing a book and the second accused was typing the manuscript. Mrs. Peiris was employed and going for work in the afternoon. Russel in 1976 and sometime in 1977 lived at Athurugiriya with the second accused but we know for certainty that both Russel and the second accused were at the Vicarage on 8.7.77 because that was the day on which witness Wanigasekera took Russel, who was looking quite ill and helpless at the Vicarage, to the Durdans Hospital."

"That fact is proved by the production of Exhibit P46, the BHT of the Durdans Hospital. This fact is a relevant fact upon the conspiracy charge laid against the accused in respect of the death of Mrs. Peiris but it is also relevant here as showing an association between the accused, which has grown to such an extent that the first accused gets obliged to Wanigasekera to admit his secretary's husband at a private nursing home, when the free General Hospital is very close at hand."

"So upon this evidence we see a close concern in the welfare of the second accused's family being displayed by the first accused. There is evidence that Mrs. Peiris went in the car to Durdans, but Wanigasekera says it was the first accused who decided against the General Hospital. It has not been supported that Mrs. Peiris wanted this done. All the while, preparations are also afoot for the first accused and his wife to go on a world tour in early 1978. We have satisfactory evidence that the second accused and her husband were left in charge of the Vicarage in their absence. In the meantime the first accused has found a job for Russel also from November 1977."

"Here from the evidence placed before us, the inference is irresistible that it was the association that had developed between the accused which was the real reason that the Ingrams were chosen by the first accused to look after the Vicarage during their absence. Russel was employed. After the first accused and Mrs. Peiris leave, the second accused would be free to look after household affairs. We cannot infer upon the evidence that the first accused chose Russel for this task. There is no evidence of any particular direct connection between Russel and the first accused. The evidence is consistent only in the position that it was the confidence that the first accused had in the second accused, which prompted him to take the course of action he took."

Mr. Bandaranayake said, "It was the evidence of Munilal that he had dealings with the second accused about letters connected with the Vicarage, the care of the boarders, etc. not with Russel. It also provided a home for the Ingrams. She was the secretary/typist, not Russel. She helped at Thursday services. Russel was merely about the place."

"The first accused returned to Sri Lanka on 25th April 1978. On 26th June, Dharmadasa saw Russel looking quite well. He has been going to work regularly since November 1977. The leave he took in the seven months is in evidence and it is not much. Suddenly on 9th June 1978, he is found to be quite ill at the Vicarage in the company of his wife and the first accused. That is the evidence of Alex Ingram, whose evidence we accept and we have given our reasons for our findings dealing with the evidence against the first accused on this Court. It is convenient to point out that from this point we will refer to specific items of evidence, which we hold to be proved facts in this case and for which we have stated our reasons in that point of our order dealing with the charge of murder of Russel Ingram against the first accused. We have considered the defence in coming to our findings and we do not propose to recite them again here. On 9th June 1978, when Alex visits his son because he was ill and found him in bed with his hand across his face and Alex shook him and asked what was wrong with him and Russel told him 'Daddy I can sleep, sleep, sleep'."

PANCREATIC DISORDER

"He did not think much. Upon questioning the second accused she tells Alex that Russel had gone into a stupor. The first accused tells Alex that Russel has a pancreatic disorder and that an operation is the only treatment for it, and that no other treatment was available. Now this must necessarily be known to the second accused because in these circumstances, we are entitled to conclude that they themselves had conducted the matters. Their statement were made in the presence and hearing of the second accused. The first accused further said that he himself was following the case and until Russel was taken to hospital. Alex asking whether a doctor was attending the first accused had said that Dr. Lakshman Weerasena was attending."

"Now being in a stupor means to us laymen that one is senseless or unconscious. So if she found her husband senseless or in stupor, one would expect any normal person to call in medical aid, especially if he has an organic disorder. Having regard to the human background of the Ingrams, one finds it difficult to understand why she did not go for help to the General Hospital, which is so close by from the Vicarage. The Out Patient Department is perhaps less than half mile away according to the evidence and probably visible because it is a straight road. Ordinary prudence would prompt one to do that. But now she does not do that. She allows the first accused, who is not a doctor, to care for a stuporose patient upon so called telephone conversations. She summons Alex Ingram to see for himself that Russel is ill. So suddenly from good health, Russel is in stupor."

"Alex remained at the Vicarage for about four days because of Russel's condition. On 10.6.1978 the first accused pulled out pills from his pocket, four pills and a capsule and gave it to Russel who after consuming it started sweating about ten minutes later. The first accused had said that Dr. Weerasena had prescribed these pills and that they were no medicine but just like Disprin. Now this if true, must also have been known to the second accused. Alex said that they had no family doctor as all his children were healthy. That day by evening Russel was out of bed. The first accused fed him liver and he ate about a spoonful. Alex said that Russel's condition was fluctuating sometimes drowsy, sometimes all right. Alex says the four days he was there a doctor did not visit. When he saw the first accused giving the pills the second accused would have been in the kitchen. Alex says he asked the first accused to take Russel to the General Hospital but he said they would mess the case up. The first accused also said that sugar, carbohydrate and glucose were poison for Russel and that rice was bad for Russel. So one would expect him to say this to the second accused too."

"Alex says that to an extent he believed the first accused and Russel had faith in him. The first accused prepared all his meals. But in the background of association the second accused was an insider. It is evident to us that Alex is doing so because the second accused the wife accepted it. Russel did not go to the kitchen and eat on 19.6.1978. Russel became boisterous and took a knife and tried to attack him but later quietened down and went to sleep. His behaviour was quite irrational. Witness has seen the first accused sitting by Russel praying and with a stethoscope. Alex said that the first accused was also constantly phoning people and giving the impression he was speaking with doctors."

NO DOCTOR VISITED RUSSEL AT THE VICARAGE

Mr. Bandaranayake said, "What was important to remember was that in spite of all of this, no doctor in fact visited Russel at the Vicarage or treated him at all. The second accused was in the house. She knew very well that it was the first accused who was controlling everything. The first accused had used the names of doctors Weerasena and Joseph in connection with treatment for Russel in June/July 1978. But yet even with signs of mental disturbances she does nothing. She has been told that the pills he is giving is just like Disprin. But still with all these signs of serious sicknesses she does nothing. Both doctors have testified before us and both have emphatically denied treating Russel or advising the first accused about treatment."

"We believe Dr. Weerasena and have given our reasons. If he made out to Alex that Dr. Weerasena was treating, why did the first accused get a letter -P14 - from Dr. Joseph? Dr. Weerasena's name was not mentioned in the history given to the hospital on admission. No history is given of a private practitioner treating Russel at the Vicarage or any reference to drugs given. The second accused is witness to this conduct. She is the wife of the patient in the house. She knows Dr. Weerasena has not treated her husband and that Dr. Joseph has not treated her husband either. We have found evidence that Russel was unconscious at the Vicarage from 24.6.1978 up to the time of admission to ward 44 on 26.6.1978, when he is found to be deeply unconscious. She shows no alarm. She knows that no one except the first accused is administering pills to him. As long as Russel's wife accepts the situation we see that the senior Ingram can think little about it. He is a railway pensioner having been an engine driver."

"We find her conduct in just allowing the first accused to treat an unconscious husband for days is quite incapable of an innocent explanation. She must have known in the circumstances that no medical attention was being given to Russel in fact. She must have seen that Russel was not getting better but worse. She is herself the daughter of a government nurse. One would expect her as a wife to bring a doctor to the house when her husband is unconscious for such long periods. Her conduct in not doing so is inconsistent with any reasonable theory of ignorance or innocence. There was no lack of opportunity either with the hospital so close by. Any innocent wife would have shown alarm or insisted on proper visible medical attention. But the inference we draw is this, which we think is a fair inference, and that is that as long as she does not show suspicion or anxiety and remains calm and shows confidence in the first accused. Russel's parents would accept it. The reference of her quality participation is inescapable. We next find that Russel is hospitalized on 26.6.1978 and returns home well on 14.7.1978 to the Vicarage. No continuing therapy has been ordered by the hospital. But again on 15.7.1978 Dr. Joseph finds him with brain damage unable to reason," Mr. Bandaranayake said.

"Next we have the evidence that Russel fell unconscious after the first accused administered pills to him on 16.7.1978. He collapses sweating at about 3.30 and is unconscious. Jackson has to come and change him as he has urinated in his bed after the pills and the second accused was informed of it and asked to fetch a doctor. But she does nothing. She does not even bother to change his clothes. She allows the first accused to fix a urinating apparatus to Russel. She allows Russel to be taken to the first accused's bedroom unconscious and she sleeps two nights with her unconscious husband in that room with the first accused and the small children behind locked doors. She does not call in a doctor or take Russel to a doctor or to the hospital but allows him to remain unconscious on that bed for two whole nights and one and a half days and admits him to hospital on the 18th morning when Russel is found to be at death's door and immediately leaves the hospital with the first accused," said Mr. Bandaranayake.

"This we consider to be callous conduct on her part. Later she is seen visiting Russel in the hospital in the company of the first accused and it is a proved fact that the first accused administered anti-diabetic drugs to Russel through those feeds. We also have evidence, which we accept that the second accused had read the book 'Body, Mind and Sugar', which contains information understandable by a layman about the condition of hypoglycaemia the need for blood sugar and how it is regulated that after meals particularly carbohydrates like rice it is high, that after sugar and ice cream meals it rises, and that insulin and anti-diabetic drugs lower it. She must know having regard to the very close association that she has had with the first accused for nearly two years, that he was a diabetic on Euglucon, an anti-diabetic drug given to diabetic patients to reduce the blood sugar level."

"He has bought fifty tablets of Euglucon on 11.7.1978 during the relevant period. It is indeed a safe inference that this Court comes to upon all of these circumstances that she would have known that such a drug given to a normal person would reduce the blood sugar to hypoglycaemic levels. Now, all the signs and symptoms that Alex Ingram has observed in Russel - sleeping much and looking drowsy, sweating, slurring of speech and state of unconsciousness - must surely have been observed by his wife who was in the house and they are all symptoms of hypoglycaemia."

STUPOROSE

"Surely, she must have talked to Russel and found out his symptoms and seen the signs herself and discussed it with the first accused. She has used the word 'stuporose', which is not a common word used in ordinary conversation in this country. This we say from our experience of our society. One would normally expect a common word like 'unconsciousness' to be used. But the word 'stuporose' is used in the book 'Body, Mind and Sugar' to describe a state of unconsciousness."

"It is our considered view that the second accused knew very well that Russel was having symptoms of hypoglycaemia. This is an irresistible inference upon all the proved circumstances. She must in the circumstances have also known that he was administering pills like Disprin. The failure to call in medical help or take him to the hospital is conduct on her part that clearly shows that she participated and helped the first accused to administer anti-diabetic drugs to Russel, which we hold as proved in this case. Sleeping with her unconscious husband behind locked doors with the first accused in the same bedroom is clear evidence in our view of sexual intimacy with the first accused. This she has done on two consecutive nights whilst her husband was lying helpless and unconscious beside her. All this happens in the sanctuary of the Vicarage."

"She then abandons her husband to doctors and leaves the hospital in the company of the first accused when she must know that he is critically ill. After his death in the teeth of accusations by her mother-in-law that there is something suspicious about the circumstances of Russel's death, she allows the first accused to put a ring on her ring finger on the day of the death in front of others."

"Earlier on 16th July 1978, she calmly allows the first accused to discuss things connected with Russel's death and burial at a time when he had just had some lunch and ice cream. The witness, her sister is surprised. Later we observe a continuing close relationship with the first accused."

"Russel's funeral is taken from the Vicarage and there are strained relations with the Ingrams. The seven day almsgiving is also taken from the Vicarage and the Ingrams are not invited. Russel is not buried in the Ingrams' grave. There is further evidence of a continuing relationship with the first accused. She opens a joint bank account with him on 5th December 1978. He finds accommodation for her in an annexe in Nugegoda and he pays the rent for three months in advance. The prosecution has suggested a motive in this case and points to the evidence of the conduct and the proved state of the accused's relationship with each other and has submitted that an amatory motive is supported on the evidence."

Mr. Bandaranayake said that, the evidence relating to their sharing the same bedroom, the evidence of their companionship as shown up by the evidence of the nurses and doctors, the evidence of close association and the fact that they were living together in the Vicarage in the absence of the first accused's wife, Russel being drowsy, sleeping, stuporose and unconscious often, and the evidence of the first accused putting a ring on the second accused's finger on the day Russel died, are entirely consistent with the existence of an amatory relationship.

He said, "We hold that fact proved that the second accused had a strong motive to kill her husband because the first accused had come into her life in a very meaningful way. We have no reasonable doubt about this. We hold that the prosecution has proved that the second accused has a strong motive to kill her husband."

"We next find that the second accused has been present on several occasions when significant things happened to her husband as described in the evidence. An important aspect of this case is the method used by the first accused to commit murder. We see that he has administered an anti-diabetic drug to the deceased in a particular way. Not just in one large dose which could well have resulted in death. That is the evidence before us about the drug Euglucon. The first accused has used a method where discovery becomes difficult and is certainly not apparent at first sight. By a slow process, which suggests administration in small doses over a period of time, he simulates a natural illness. All he is doing by the use of this drug is to stimulate normally functioning glands to secrete excessive quantities of their secretions, in this case the hormone insulin, which would then normally bring down the level of blood sugar and cause drowsiness, depression and as the blood sugar drops according to dosage the victim can get unconscious or even die."

"Now, there are known natural diseases, which have the same effect of increasing the insulin level of the blood, which counters the glucose level and brings it down with identical results. These diseases have been discussed in this judgement dealing with the cause of death. This method needs careful preparation and planning."

SPECIALISED TREATMENT AND MEDICAL CARE

"The victim must be near at hand and the opportunity to administer the drug must be available without raising the suspicion of the intended victim or his relatives. So in the case of an intended victim, who is a married person and who is not in your household, that person has to be invited into your home. The home is the best place to carry out such a plan because you have privacy. Now, to carry out such a plan you need time and an opportunity to care for the victim, in case he gets bad until the time is ripe, until those close to the victim are satisfied that he really is ill and is in need of specialized treatment and medical care to make him sick enough to be hospitalized without arousing suspicion."

"It will be seen that when one is bent on manipulating a person's blood sugar level, one must also have control of the intended victim's food, and the drug must be consumed by him unknowingly. Now in order to accomplish all of these things in respect of Russel while keeping him at the Vicarage, the Court observes that it could not have happened, it could not have been done without arousing suspicion or without hindrance and interference, without the support of the second accused."

"If she was not in the picture, if she was a totally innocent bystander the chances are that she will interfere or forcibly remove Russel to hospital or call in a doctor. One intent on murder in this way will not in our view run the risk of exposure of failure. So it is a factor of great importance of the murderer to get the support and connivance and agreement and assistance of the second accused. He could not have administered the drugs and simulated a natural disease in the face of Russel's parents and relatives without her support and connivance."

"This is the irresistible inference we draw from the proved facts and circumstances. We are convinced that all the things that happened to Russel could not have happened without her help and support. The proved circumstances in our view point to the existence of a prearranged plan between the first accused and the second accused to murder Russel Ingram. Without her agreement in the plot she could easily have resisted or prevented or disturbed the acts of the first accused. She could have taken Russel away or not brought him back after the first hospitalization. But she does not."

Mr. Bandaranayake said that she was with the first accused and allowed him to do as he liked. She prevented suspicion being aroused.

"She called Russel's father and later her sister was let into the Vicarage to witness Russel being ill and joined the first accused in pretending he was being cared for. She was present in the house when the first accused last administered a drug to Russel at the Vicarage on 16.7.1978 when he fell unconscious. He was never known to regain consciousness. She was present in the house when Russel was removed from the Vicarage unconscious on 18th July 1978, when Russel was found to be brain dead and he died from prolonged unconsciousness arising out of that condition."

"In the circumstances we are convinced that the second accused jointly committed the murder of her husband Russel Ingram with the first accused in furtherance of the common intention of both of them. We hold it proved that his intention to murder Russel was known to her and they both agreed and shared the intention. This is the only irresistible inference this Court can draw upon a consideration of all the proved facts and circumstances. An inference consistent with her innocence or consistent with any reasonable theory of her innocence is incapable of being drawn by this Court upon the evidence."

"The defence says that all of her conduct is consistent with innocence, that she was a poor widow whom the first accused was helping and that she happened to be in the house and was ignorant of the first accused's intentions or acts. We do not agree. We have considered this defence and we reject it as inconsistent with and unsupportable on the evidence and that it does not raise any reasonable doubt in our minds as to the reliability of the prosecution case. Such an inference could be in the teeth of the evidence, unreasonable. The only reasonable and compelling inference in all the circumstances is an inference that she shared a common murderous intention with the first accused to kill Russel and this inference is the only deductible inference upon the evidence. We accordingly convict the second accused on count two of the indictment."

COMMIT MURDER JOINTLY

"We have also to consider the case against the first accused from the point of view of joint participation with the second accused in the murder of Russel. Did he commit murder jointly with the second accused whilst sharing accommodation? Did he make that his intention known to her and that she agreed and joined him in his criminal venture?"

"We have already stated our views that having regard to the method of murder in this case that he would have needed to get her agreement and support to execute his intentions. We are firmly convinced that this result could not have been obtained without her support. All the evidence points to the first accused as the person who administered the drug. He had the drug; he had brought it in quantities on 11.7.1978. The book 'Body, Mind and Sugar' was his and he is known to have exhibited his knowledge of hypoglycaemia and swinging blood sugar levels and insulinoma etc. He takes Russel to hospital twice unconscious from his home and gives the history. On each such occasion he is accompanied by the second accused. Russel is found ill at the Vicarage and the second accused says the father is looking after Russel. She allowed the first accused to prepare all Russel's needs, administer pills to him and allow him to let Russel remain unconscious in the Vicarage."

"All these proved circumstances point to an irresistible inference that the first accused had disclosed his intention to the second accused and they had agreed to a plan to help each other to kill Russel. That inference is irresistible that he shared his ideas with the second accused and both agreed to a course of action and supported each other and even succeeded in passing his death off for a time as due to natural causes. Upon all these proved circumstances the inference that the first accused had a common murderous intention with the second accused is inescapable. We hold it proved beyond reasonable doubt."

Mr. Bandaranayake said that the charge 'conspiracy to commit the murder of Russel' on Count one, was based on the footing that there was an agreement between the accused to murder Russel.

"Conspiracy is generally proved by circumstantial evidence, ordinarily proved by the subsequent conduct of the parties in committing overt acts resulting in the commission of crimes which suggest that they must have arisen from an agreement to bring them about. There must be proof against each conspirator that he had the knowledge of the general purpose of the plot and the common design. There could be different degrees of guilt between persons in the conspiracy and they may play materially different parts."

"We shall examine the evidence against each accused to ascertain if there was a plot to kill Russel and whether each knew of the plot and agreed between themselves to commit the offence of murder. The transaction of criminal conduct in pursuance of conspiracy would be, (a) The formation of intent, (b) Communication and acceptance of intent and, (c) The commission of overt or supporting acts in furtherance of the agreement.

The evidence could conveniently be divided under the following heads:

(a) Association between accused and deceased.

(b) Motive - is there evidence of motive against each of these accused? and,

(c) Opportunity:

  (i) for conspiring and agreeing to murder the second accused's spouse

(ii) agreement on method of killing

(iii) if so, arising out of the method of killing an agreement on building up the infrastructure to facilitate the commission of the offence so that it will go unobserved, undetected and unpunished."

"We have already referred to in the course of this order the evidence regarding the association and relationship that grew between the accused from September 1976 to June 1978. We find there is ample evidence from which the Court can infer safely that the association between the accused was very close by June 1978. The second accused was the wife of the deceased and the deceased was living at material times in the house of the first accused and was quite friendly with him and respected him and was obliged to him for finding him employment. The first accused had put a ring on the second accused's finger on the day of Russel's death and she had not protested."

"As far as motive is concerned there is strong evidence of an amorous motive found by reason of their proved close association and conduct. We refer to the fact that it is proved that the accused were living together in the first accused's house at all material times in the absence of the first accused's wife, who was abroad and that they have been known to share the same bedroom with the unconscious deceased. The case is replete with evidence of their close relationship during Russel's illness. The association between the accused from about September 1976 onwards, progressively growing stronger with time, which is the evidence, the accused had ample opportunity to discuss and agreed to murder the deceased Russel. On this question of agreement a most significant fact is the method of killing. As we have said before, the method adopted namely the slow calculated intermittent administration of an anti-diabetic drug to reduce the level of sugar and again give food to raise the level while keeping Russel at the Vicarage could not in our opinion have been executed and accomplished by the first accused alone without raising suspicion and risking exposure without the support and help of the second accused. It needs planning both to administer the drug and administer food to simulate illness," Mr. Bandaranayake said.

"The first accused in our view would never have been able to disguise his hand without her assistance. This clearly shows that she was a party to the plot. The inference that she agreed to a plan with the first accused to kill Russel is the only deducible inference upon her conduct in permitting Russel to be kept helpless and unconscious for days on end at the Vicarage without admitting him to the hospital only a stone's throw away."

"In all the evidence of this case ordinary prudence would have compelled an innocent wife to get away from the Vicarage with her sick husband and not to continue to allow the first accused to give tablets like Disprin and watch her husband get progressively worse on supposedly telephoned conversation with a Dr. Weerasena. Where was this Dr. Weerasena when Russel was admitted to hospital on 26.7.1978? Dr. Weerasena has categorically denied the allegations and we believe him."

"The second accused must have known that Alex Ingram was sent to Dr. Joseph to get a letter of admission and not to Dr. Weerasena. It is the evidence of Dr. Joseph that he gave P14 without seeing the patient on 26.6.1978. The second accused accompanied Russel to hospital. The defence suggestion that she would not have known and not responsible for the acts of others if any, is not acceptable to the Court upon the evidence in this case. We are convinced that by the conduct of the second accused in approving of the conduct of the first accused that 'Father is looking after Russel and Father knows what to do'. She deliberately and knowingly facilitated the commission of a crime, that she was a willing conspirator in a plot to kill Russel and yet goes unpunished."

"There is also the evidence that she had read the book 'Body, Mind and Sugar', which belonged to the first accused. Here was an opportunity for them to discuss the subject of fluctuating levels of consciousness by the manipulation of blood sugar levels by the administration of anti-diabetic drugs. The proclamation of the second accused that Russel had been stuporosed is significant. The word is found in the book P40."

"The conduct of the second accused in watching Russel being unconscious at the Vicarage is totally inconsistent with her innocence. All the evidence points to the first accused having administered the drug. He has made several statements to witnesses displaying his knowledge of hypoglycaemia which caused the brain damage which resulted ultimately in death from pneumonia arising out of prolonged unconsciousness. He kept Russel in his house along with the second accused. There is no doubt that the accused agreed to murder Russel by the administration of an anti-diabetic drug. That inference is the only irresistible inference arising out of the proved facts and circumstances, which in our view are incapable of any inference based on the hypothesis of innocence."

"We hold both accused guilty of the offence of conspiring to murder Russel in consequence of which conspiracy Russel was indeed murdered. We convict both accused on Count one of the indictment. So here we have evidence, each accused having previously conspired and having caused the death of Russel Ingram that there was to be a continuing transaction and a continuing motive for the accused to cause the death of Mrs. Peiris."

CAUSE OF DEATH OF MRS. PEIRIS

"It is evidence in support of the charge of conspiring to cause the death of Mrs. Peiris. It is our decision upon a consideration of all relevant circumstances that the conspiracy to kill Russel and the conspiracy to kill Mrs. Peiris were part and parcel of one transaction."

After dealing with the death of Russel Ingram, the Court considered the cause of death of Mrs. Peiris who died in ward 47B of the General Hospital on 19.3.1979 after a prolonged state of unconsciousness. Mr. Bandaranayake said that the prosecution must establish beyond all reasonable doubt that a crime has been committed in respect of her death and eliminate any reasonable possibilities that she died of natural causes or that she took her own life or that her death was accidental.

"In an earlier part of this order we mentioned that when a Court considers the question of the cause of death in a case of circumstantial evidence, it is legitimate and often necessary to consider other facts and circumstances, which may at the same time have a bearing as to the identity of the person or persons responsible for the crime. The prosecution relies upon opinion evidence of medical experts together with other proved facts and circumstances including statements of the accused, which may be taken into account either as admissions or as conduct to prove the cause of death. We have already mentioned in an early part of this order that statements of the accused could be taken into account by the Court if proved as admissions against him if their truth is indicated or manifest by reason of support from other independent truthful testimony accepted by the Court; and similarly as conduct showing an intention to deceive or mislead wherever that is intrinsically manifest or otherwise clearly indicated upon a comparison of other proved satisfactory facts accepted by the Court as reliable and truthful."

"It is in evidence that Mrs. Peiris suffered irreversible brain damage and unconsciousness, which state of affairs persisted right up to the 19th of March when she died. It is necessary therefore, for the prosecution to establish beyond all reasonable doubt the cause of irreversible brain damage that the deceased suffered on 31.1.1979 on the cause of the unconsciousness found on that day."

"It is the case for the prosecution that the cause of the permanent brain damage and unconsciousness was the result of introduced hypoglycaemia. In order to prove this, the prosecution would have to eliminate within reason all other causes, which might have resulted in permanent brain damage and unconsciousness. They have to eliminate all natural causes for this condition and they must eliminate all other induced causes as well and establish homicide beyond all reasonable doubt. The medical opinion that has been placed before this Court supports the inference and the finding that the immediate cause of death was the result of double pneumonia."

"So we wish at this point to proceed to consider the evidence, to consider the defence in order to decide whether the prosecution has discharged its burden of establishing beyond reasonable doubt that the immediate cause of the death of Mrs. Peiris was pneumonia, resulting from a prolonged state of unconsciousness."

Examining the evidence, Mr. Bandaranayake said that the deceased Mrs. Peiris was admitted to ward 47B of the General Hospital, Colombo, by the first accused who was accompanied by her relatives at 12.15 p.m. on 31.1.1979.

"The BHT produced in evidence as exhibit P2 supported the oral testimony of witnesses, which was that the first accused took the deceased by ambulance from the Vicarage in an unconscious state and had her admitted to hospital. At the time of admission, the admitting officer who has not been a witness of this Court has recorded her blood pressure as being 100/60, which according to the evidence before us is just below normal range. This item of evidence was elicited by the first accused in cross examination. Although the Admitting Officer is not a witness, the history has been given by the first accused according to the evidence and this page EPGH 9 was produced before the Court and the entry at EPGH9A requiring a doctor to send the patient immediately was also produced by the prosecution."

"These entries have been made in the ordinary course of duty, the document produced before the Court for its inspection and some of the entries in this page have been marked. It is appropriate that we consider these entries. We also find that the first accused has signed on this page on 4.2.1979."

"Dr. Terrence de Silva was the House Officer on duty at that time of admission. He had been at ward 49, which he also overlooked that day and the nurse had come running and showed him the entry at EPGH9A and he came rushing back to Ward 47B and examined the patient. The patient had been admitted to the ward at 12.26 p.m. and Dr. de Silva saw her at 12.30 p.m. At that time he says the first accused was present but he did not know him. The first accused gave him the history, which he recorded on the BHT."

"The first accused also produced before him three documents:

- The letter p13 photocopy,

- The photocopy of GTT report,

- The photocopy of a letter written by Dr. E.V. Peiris to Dr. Lakshman Weerasena."

"Dr. de Silva recorded the history given by the first accused which is found on the reverse of P1 and on pages 2 and 3 of P21. He has written, 'History from her husband Rev. Father Mathew Peiris'. He took the blood pressure of the patient at that time and found that it had dropped to 60/40 (vide entry at EPGH16B), which is a very low pressure. He also took a sample of blood for testing and a urine sample for testing. Dr. de Silva says he asked the first accused whether the patient had taken anti-diabetic drugs at any time on seeing the figures in the Glass House GTT of 29.1.1979 and the first accused told him that the deceased was not a diabetic and that he had not taken any anti-diabetic drugs at any time. The prosecution points to the latter part of this entry and says that is a false representation that the accused has made to the witness in order to disguise its administration."

"There is a comment by Dr. de Silva at 2.45 p.m. (vide – entry EPGH15B) that the first accused gave him a peculiar history of the patient going bad after dextrose and so he minutes, 'Husband has advised not to give dextrose to the patient'. Despite that he says he gave dextrose but he wrote that down because he was not sure if it was some rare disease unknown to him where sugar is bad for a patient. Generally speaking, as far as he knew, sugar is always good for the patient and will not harm even a diabetic patient."

"At 1 p.m. Dr. de Silva says, the patient had still not regained consciousness (Vide EPGH14A). Then he says the first accused told him that the patient's blood pressure falls some more when glucose is given (Vide EPGH 14B). He also says that the first accused gave a history of depression treated with the drug Tofranil (Vide EPGH10C) and also said that the patient felt giddy 2 or 3 hours after meals," Mr. Bandaranayake said

IRREVERSIBLE BRAIN DAMAGE

"The patient had not recovered consciousness for about half an hour after the administration of dextrose and so he concluded that the patient suffered from irreversible brain damage and he therefore told the first accused who was the person who brought the deceased that the patient appears to have permanent brain damage and was unlikely to recover. That is also recorded in the BHT. So we have it that the first accused knew by about 1 p.m. on that day that his wife had suffered irreversible brain damage."

"The blood sugar at admission was found to be 30 mg %, which is hypoglycaemic (Vide entry at EPGH 16B) the normal level of blood sugar is between 60 – 100 mg%. By 11 p.m. the patient's blood sugar had risen to 247 mg% well above normal and the pulse rate was 108 per minute and the blood pressure was 70/40 – still below normal. At 12.10 a.m. on 1.2.1979 a blood transfusion was started and it was over at 4.30 a.m. The patient responded to painful stimuli. At 3.30 p.m. on 1.2.1979 the blood pressure was 100/60, which was the pressure with which she was admitted to hospital at 12.15 p.m. on 31.1.1979. This pressure, it will be observed, has come close to normal in about twenty seven hours. At 10.45 p.m. the blood sugar was 82 mg%, which is within normal blood sugar levels. The blood sugar never dropped after that right up to the time of her death on 19.3.1979. The prosecution seeks to submit that the patient did not have any endogenous blood sugar problem at all."

"Now we find that Dr. de Silva having attended to the patient upon her admission and having recorded the history given by the first accused had gone for his lunch and there he had discussed this bad case that had been brought to the hospital with others. He has told this Court that during his luncheon he came to know that another patient had been brought unconscious by a bearded Anglican Priest the previous year and that patient had died. Then he returned to the ward in the afternoon and he informed Dr. (Miss) Pinto of what he had learnt."

"Now there is the evidence of Dr. (Miss) Pinto that she saw this patient for the first time at 2.30 p.m. on that day, and the first accused told her the history of the patient. She however, did not record it because it was already recorded by Dr. de Silva. She said that the first accused told her that the patient was brought to hospital unconscious and that she had been unconscious from the night of the previous day and that she had been regaining consciousness on and off intermittently and that when she was conscious he gave her something to drink if possible."

"She told us that the Senior House Officer Dr. Wickramasinghe also came there and at that time the first accused repeated the history to him also. We find there is an entry at EPGH18A made at 9 p.m. by Dr. Wickramasinghe, who was not a witness before us but the handwriting and signature has been identified to the following effect: 'Suspected poison - inform police - Hypoglycaemic agent attempted suicide/homicide.' We have the evidence that the police had been informed and they first began looking into the question of the state of health of the deceased from 5.2.1979. Evidence of the conversation that Dr. de Silva had and the information that he got was led in this case to explain the conduct of Dr. Wickramasinghe in making the minute at EPGH18A and the consequent information carried to the police. We might mention here that investigations into the death of Mrs. Peiris really started after 19.3.1979."

"It is the evidence before us, both from the oral testimony and from the documents that the deceased Mrs. Peiris lingered on unconscious until 19.3.1979 when she died at 9.30 a.m. (Vide EPGH72A). We find a minute addressed to the police post by Dr. (Miss) Pinto to the effect 'Cause of death cannot be given. Hold an inquest and a judicial post-mortem' (Vide EPGH 73A). This minute has been made, say Dr. de Silva and Dr. (Miss) Pinto, because of the possibility of induced hypoglycaemia by the administration of an anti-diabetic drug which has not been excluded by them. Thereafter, a judicial post-mortem was done and the primary cause of death was given by the JMO as is evidenced by his post-mortem report produced and marked in evidence as EPGH 41."

"In the appropriate cage the JMO has written 'Cause of death due to pneumonia in both lungs and pulmonary oedema resulting from prolonged unconsciousness due to diffuse brain damage. This could have been caused by hypoglycaemia resulting from ingestion of a hypoglycaemic agent like glibenclamide'."

"Now it is the evidence of Dr. de Silva that he made a tentative diagnosis as to the cause of permanent brain damage and unconsciousness. This tentative diagnosis actually gives two alternative causes:

1.   Either hypoglycaemic coma, or

2.   Cerebrovascular accident (Stroke)."

"He says he always gives more than one diagnosis as a practice at the outset. He also said that doctors always look for these two conditions in cases of unconscious patients brought to them. He came to this conclusion upon his examination of the patient at that time, which showed that she (a) was deeply unconscious, (b) had no external injuries, (c) her breathing was normal, (d) the pulse was low - difficult to feel, (e) blood pressure 60/40, (f) heart rhythm normal - two sounds."

"His conclusion therefore, was that the coma was either due to hypoglycaemia or stroke. The doctor proceeded to tell the Court why he clinically eliminated all other possible causes of coma within reason as being responsible for the deceased's condition. It is appropriate that we set them down here and give the reasons why he said he eliminated the possibility that those conditions afflicted the deceased."

Mr. Bandaranayake said that he eliminated the following:

Diabetic Coma:

There was no history of it. The history was that she was not a diabetic. Furthermore there was no smelling of acetone which is usually found in diabetic coma patients and also her respiration was normal. Therefore there was no dehydration as is usually found in diabetic coma. The urine test also showed no sugar in the urine.

Uraemic Coma:

This is usually due to kidney diseases. In such cases there will either be dehydration or swelling. There was neither. Again, breathing will be acidotic. Here breathing was normal and there was no acidotic smell either. He took a blood sample. Furthermore, in this type of coma, blood pressure is high. But in this case it was the opposite. In this patient there were no signs or symptoms as aforementioned.

Hepatic coma:

This was obviously not a case of hepatic coma. In such cases there is a distended stomach, a history of alcohol, jaundice, liver and spleen palpable and a bleeding tendency in the skin and vomiting blood. This patient did not have any of these signs or symptoms and no history either. She did not have flapping tremors which is a characteristic of hepatic coma. It was fairly obvious that this patient was not in hepatic coma.

Meningitis and encephalitis:

They are infections of the brain covering. Patients usually have high fever, severe vomiting, severe headaches and neck stiffness. This patient did not have any of these signs or symptoms or history.

Endocrinal dysfunctions:

They are problems of ductless glands such as the pituitary. They usually show excessive pigmentation inside the mouth, under the skin, body hair distribution abnormal, lose body hair and have a peculiar face, myxoedema, swelling of the eye lids and loss of hair on eye brows. None of these signs were there in this patient. We therefore exclude them clinically as having nothing to do with the state of coma.

Head Injuries:

There were no external injuries whatsoever, either on the head or anywhere else.

Infectious Diseases:

The deceased was not suffering from any infectious disease or fever.

Drugs:

Dr. de Silva said that he could not exclude the possibility of an anti-diabetic drug causing the state of unconsciousness and the brain damage. However, he did exclude many other poisons as possible causes. He said that usually poisoned patients come with vomiting, gastrointestinal and throat problems, have loose motions and diarrhoea. These features were not there in this patient. There was no history of her having taken a poison. Also there was no respiratory depression, and she did not have any symptoms or history of vomiting etc. Furthermore there were no signs of cyanosis. No involuntary movements of the tongue and limbs, no smell of poison, no stains of poison seen in the mouth or around it, no burning or corrosive marks anywhere on the body. So he excluded other poisons."

ANTI-DEPRESSANT DRUGS

"In regard to anti-depressant drugs Dr. de Silva had this to say. In the history of anti-depressant drug overdose, usually the patients become hyperactive before they go into coma and then they become unconscious. There was no such history. Even if the patients are in coma they have frequent involuntary movements of hands and feet and the body temperature is high. This patient did not have these features. Furthermore, such patients have fits and this patient did not have fits at that time. Dr. Sathanandan, a specialist Psychiatrist, who prescribed Tofranil, which is an anti-depressant drug to this patient on 16.1.1979, has told us that he prescribed a mild starting dose and with that dosage she could not have got into a coma."

"He said the usual symptoms of an overdose of anti-depressant drugs are:

(1) Fits before unconsciousness - there was no such history,

(2) High fever,

(3) Cardiac irregularity, which can be detected,

(4) Depressed respiration,

(5) Abnormal distension of abdomen because of urine retention,

(6) Paralysis of the gut.

This patient did not have any of these signs and symptoms. Her heart and respiration were normal. The doctor also said that thirty to forty Tofranils would constitute an overdose. The testimony of Dr. de Silva in regard to the history and signs and symptoms of the patient is supported by entries in the BHT P21. Before we pass from this subject, we would like to point out that Dr. Nagaratnam, who has testified on behalf of the prosecution confirmed the opinion of Dr. de Silva on these matters, on Dr. de Silva's findings of facts and recording of history," Mr. Bandaranayake said.

POSSIBILITY OF SUICIDE

"Dr. Sathanandan has also told the Court that in his opinion Mrs. Peiris had no suicidal tendency whatsoever when he interrogated her in the Durdans Hospital. He rules out the possibility of suicide as most unlikely as she has recovered almost completely from her depression on 20.1.1979. Dr. (Miss) Pinto who also looked after this patient in ward 47B supports the opinion and the findings of Dr. de Silva."

"Dr. Subramaniam, the JMO, who did the post-mortem examination, also confirms that there were no diseases of the liver or the kidneys or the brain. There were no infections of the brain and there was no evidence that she had suffered a stroke. He rules out the possibility of cerebrovascular accident. He also said that there were no signs of diabetes or signs of ingestion of poison. He too confirms the findings of Dr. de Silva and he also expressed the opinion eliminating all those other causes of coma. He had this patient under observation while she was alive and knew the clinical history. There is therefore, medical evidence before this Court that the cause of the brain damage and the unconsciousness of 31.1.1979 was not the result of any of the above mentioned causes except hypoglycaemia."

"Dr. de Silva now says that since he learnt of the post-mortem findings he eliminates the possibility of a stroke altogether and he confirms his opinion that the cause of unconsciousness was hypoglycaemia. That has been the clinical findings of both de Silva and Pinto and the post-mortem findings of Dr. Subramaniam and confirmatory evidence of Dr. Nagaratnam that the cause of the coma and the cause of the brain damage was hypoglycaemia."

"Now this opinion presented by the prosecution and which the prosecution must establish beyond all reasonable doubt has been contested by the defence, who have joined issue and placed evidence before the Court that there is still another probable natural way in which permanent brain damage and unconsciousness could have occurred on 31.1.1979 and that natural cause could well arise from the state of depression in which the deceased was at the relevant time. This was a matter which will receive the attention of the Court. The prosecution must necessarily eliminate beyond all reasonable doubt the possibility that the deceased died of natural causes, if they are to establish the charges. For the time being, we consider the treatment given to the patient during the time of her hospitalization and all other relevant evidence to determine whether the prosecution has established the immediate cause of her death, which we are told was double pneumonia arising out of the condition of prolonged unconsciousness."

"It was Dr. (Miss) Pinto who managed the patient with Dr. de Silva and other House Officers. We have already described the treatment Dr. de Silva gave her when he first examined the patient and how the patient was treated for several hours following. Dr. de Silva told us that the first accused kept on asking a lot of questions such as how long it would take a patient in hypoglycaemia to get permanent brain damage and he replied that it would depend on two factors:

(1) The level of blood sugar, and

(2) The period of such low blood sugar.

Thereafter, the first accused had asked him about the significance of a milky white tongue and of a chilly red tongue."

"Dr. (Miss) Pinto has also told the Court that antibiotics were started from the first day - 500 mg of ampicillin intramuscularly 6 hourly and given to prevent the onset of pneumonia to an unconscious patient as a prophylactic measure, anticipatory of infection and that this was continued right up to her death. She said the patient was generally on 50% dextrose 100 ml, normal saline, potassium chloride one vial and sodium bicarbonate 50 ml given for unconscious patients and dexamethasone/hydrocortisone 200 mg. Oxygen was also given at the early stages. Intravenous administration of glucose was discontinued on 7.2.1979 and normal foods were given as at that time irreversible brain damage had been confirmed. It was not necessary to sustain life but oral dextrose was given through the nasal tube. The patient remained on nasal feeding. All nourishments were given in liquid form and life could be sustained with ordinary foods. When there is permanent brain damage there is no way in which dextrose could help further. This patient never recovered consciousness."

"Bed sores were seen after about 7.2.1979. They could not be prevented as the patient was extremely bad. On 11.2.1979 fits were observed. From 12.2.1979 the antibiotic chloramphenicol was also given to prevent infection. Penicillin and gentamycin was also given for the bed sores. The patient developed a face swelling and fits. Lasix and mannitol were also given. An antibiotic spray was used for the bed sores. The BHT P21, the FBC and the treatment sheet were produced at the trial. Complications set in as a result of prolonged unconsciousness. Fluids were given to maintain the balance in the body. Liquid diet maintained four hourly right up to the time of death. There was therefore no dehydration. The patient was regularly turned and cleaned and the wounds dressed right up to the time of her death. Secretions from her lungs were removed regularly, sucked out every two hours to prevent suffocation. She had secretions. Later pneumonia developed despite the antibiotics. But they cannot exactly say when it first developed. The patient died on 19.3.1979."

JUDICIAL POST-MORTEM

"Thereafter, Dr. Subramaniam held the judicial post-mortem and he has told us that he found a softening of the brain cells all over but there were no infections of the brain. He also found infected bed sores on the right side of the head and other extensive bed sores. There was also swelling on both upper arms and forearms due to prolonged unconsciousness. There was pneumonia in both lungs, thrombosis of the left calf of the leg due to prolonged immobilization. Dr. Subramaniam also said that there were no signs of cerebrovascular accident, no signs of heart diseases or any other organic disease and no signs of corrosive poison. He examined all these organs during the autopsy. He said that there was a great antecedent probability that infections and complications would set in, in cases of prolonged unconsciousness. He gave the immediate cause of death as 'Pneumonia resulting from prolonged unconsciousness arising in the ordinary course of nature.' We bear in mind the cross examination and submissions of the defence on this aspect of the case."

"The treatment given to the patient in the General Hospital, the nursing and medical care has been in our view sufficient and adequate as is evidenced by the oral testimony supported by the documents. We are satisfied on the evidence before us that indeed Mrs. Peiris died of pneumonia arising out of her prolonged state of unconsciousness from 31.1.1979 to 19.3.1979 and that this condition of infection could not be prevented after she had suffered irreversible brain damage on 31.1.1979. This is the evidence that we accept in this case. We accordingly hold that the prosecution has proved beyond all reasonable doubt that the deceased died as a result of pneumonia which was a complication that arose in the ordinary course of nature from the fact of prolonged unconsciousness. It could be appropriate to mention at this point that Dr. de Silva expressed the opinion that hypoglycaemia was the cause of this coma, which he observed clinically."

Mr. Bandaranayake then discussed the initial opinion of Dr. de Silva regarding cause of coma.

"Dr. de Silva has told us that the features he saw in this patient were of hypoglycaemia and not of stroke. They were:

- history of dizziness or giddiness, plus fluctuating levels of consciousness from drowsy to coma,

- history of loss of consciousness two weeks earlier with a quick recovery,

- history that the patient never had high blood pressure,

- that the patient had no symptoms of partial paralysis or weakness of one side. In case of stroke there usually is very high blood pressure of about 200/130. Further, there was no vomiting and no neck stiffness."

"So, Dr. de Silva says the neurological state of the patient was consistent with hypoglycaemic coma. It was confirmed by the blood sugar report - EPGH16B, which showed that the blood sugar upon admission was 30 mg%. Stroke patients will not have a low pressure. Furthermore, in hypoglycaemia brain damage is diffused as it was found in the patient on autopsy. But in stroke, brain damage is localized. Again CVA is a sudden onset illness. So in all these circumstances Dr. de Silva eliminated stroke and his opinion is that the cause of the permanent brain damage and unconsciousness was definitely hypoglycaemia. This opinion is confirmed by Dr. Nagaratnam. We shall consider this opinion in greater detail in the course of this order," said Mr. Bandaranayake.

"The evidence of doctors de Silva and Pinto were criticized by the defence on the following matters:

(1) that they were influenced by the contents of P13 and of the GTT findings in P24, which suggested 'Reactive Hypoglycaemia', and that is why they make a diagnosis of hypoglycaemia, and

(2) those doctors denied this and said that was not the only reason why they came to their conclusion.

Dr. de Silva said that he mentally eliminated all other causes of coma, according to his observations, his clinical findings, signs and symptoms and the history given. On the question of the history that the patient felt bad two or three hours after meals, he said he asked the first accused whether the deceased had taken anti-diabetic pills or drugs and that the first accused said that she had not, and that she was not a diabetic."

"Dr. de Silva has made a statement to the police on 5.2.1979 and on 6.4.1979 and in those statements there were the following omissions:-

(a) that the first accused had asked him how long it would take for irredeemable brain damage to occur after hypoglycaemia, and

(b) about the colour of the tongue.

Dr. de Silva said that he may have not given these details to the police. We observe that these omissions are in regard to evidence relating to the conduct of the first accused in the ward on 31.1.1979 and that they do not touch on the question of the cause of death. At this point it is appropriate that we consider the defence in regard to the question of the cause of death of Mrs. Peiris."

"So having found that the immediate cause of death was a result of pneumonia, which was an infection arising naturally from the state of prolonged unconsciousness, and having eliminated other causes for the condition of permanent brain damage and coma observed on 31.1.1979, the prosecution must further establish to the satisfaction of the Court that the cause of irreversible and permanent brain damage and the state of unconsciousness that the deceased was found to be on 31.1.1979 at ward 47B of the General Hospital, Colombo, was induced hypoglycaemia, which is what the prosecution is seeking to establish in regard to her death."

"Upon this question, the defence has joined issue with the prosecution most vigorously and by cross examination and submission and by the evidence of a witness on its behalf supported by documents, sought to convince the Court that there is a probable natural way by which permanent brain damage and coma could have occurred and that if the Court considers the defence position probable or likely or if the Court believe the defence witness, or the evidence placed before the Court by the defence raises a reasonable doubt on the prosecution case, then the prosecution would have failed to prove that the cause of Mrs. Peiris's death was the result of a criminal act and in these circumstances the accused would be entitled to an acquittal on the charges framed concerning her death."

BURDEN OF PROOF

"This is not to say that there is any burden or duty on the defence to prove the innocence of the accused or show any circumstances suggestive of their innocence. We have repeatedly pointed out that there is no burden on the defence to prove their innocence or to tender any evidence before the Court. The burden of proof throughout this trial remains with the prosecution to establish the charge beyond all reasonable doubt. Nevertheless the defence is at liberty to point to circumstances consistent with innocence and to place evidence in support. In these circumstances the Court now proceeds to consider which the defence says is consistent with a natural condition, which resulted in brain damage and coma, and to assess whether what the defence points to is more likely on a balance of probability, or whether it raises a reasonable doubt in the prosecution case."

"It is the prosecution case that the cause of irreversible brain damage and coma was induced hypoglycaemia. The defence however at the very outset of the case with the very first witness called by the prosecution, namely Malrani Dodangoda, a daughter of the first accused, took up the position in cross examination that whilst the deceased was in the United Kingdom between May and November 1978, she was ill-treated by her daughter Mihiri and she became sad and depressed so much so that she lived in fear in an atmosphere of constant friction and tension and that she wrote letter ID1 to the first accused complaining of the atmosphere prevalent in her home in Cardiff. It was the position of the defence that ID1 was relevant as a dying deposition as it pointed to circumstances of the transaction which resulted in her death."

"In examining the evidence in regard to a probable natural cause of death, it is fitting and proper that we review and examine the deceased's statement in this connection. Statements of deceased persons if they are relevant to the cause of death maybe received in evidence whether they are tendered by the prosecution or the defence. We bear in mind that such statements are not upon oath and have not been subjected to cross-examination and the witness has not testified before us. We bear in mind that we should consider whether the deponent might have made a mistake or has a reason to falsify the statement. The defence also produced documents ID2 to ID6 which were letters written by Malrani to her father the first accused, where too the witness has referred to this atmosphere. Indeed counsel for the second accused submitted to Court that ID1 was the bedrock of the defence in regard to the charges concerning the death of Mrs. Peiris."

"So the defence put it to Malrani that the deceased state of health was low at the time she returned to Sri Lanka on 6.12.1978, that she was depressed, had gone through a hard time physically and mentally, which suggestion the witness denied. After her return to the island, the defence next pointed to the evidence that the first accused had taken the deceased for treatment to Dr. Weerasena who had indeed treated her with two drugs Stelazine and Artane given for depression with anxiety. So the defence points to the fact that Dr. Weerasena prescribed these drugs to her to support their position that the deceased was depressed upon her arrival in Sri Lanka. It was also in evidence that there was a marriage proposal in the air for Malrani, who was unmarried at the time and that the return of the deceased to Sri Lanka was mostly in view of the possibility of a marriage for Malrani. We are told that Malrani did not marry this particular gentleman who has been referred to in this case as Mr. X," Mr. Bandaranayake said.

ENDOGENOUS REACTIVE DEPRESSION

"So it was a suggestion put by the defence that was a further reason why the deceased was depressed in the weeks following her return home. The defence further pointed to the hospitalization of the deceased at the Durdans Hospital, between 15.1.1979 and 20.1.1979. She was treated by a psychiatrist Dr. Sathanandan, who diagnosed an 'Endogenous Reactive Depression' and treated her with the drug Tofranil and that she recovered almost fully and was discharged but asked to continue with the drug for a week or two."

"The defence further pointed to the evidence of Dr. E.V. Peiris who examined her on 24.1.1979 and found her untidily dressed, hair uncombed and quite a different person to the well-dressed always well groomed lady whom he knew. He ordered certain blood tests to be done, which included an Extended Glucose Tolerance Test for the purpose of finding out whether she had a blood sugar problem. He also asked her to continue taking Tofranil as prescribed by Dr. Sathanandan for another week or so."

"Upon this background, we have the added evidence that the deceased was admitted unconscious to the General Hospital on 31.1.1979 at 12.15 p.m., and that at the time her blood pressure was 100/60 just below normal but that at 12.30 p.m., when her blood pressure was again taken in the ward it was found to be 60/40 which was a sharp drop and that she was deeply unconscious. She was treated with 50% dextrose and dexamethasone. She did not regain consciousness thereafter. Her blood pressure rose gradually and settled by the next day to the normal level. This remained so until her death. A blood sugar test done at the time of admission showed a blood sugar value of 30 mg% which was hypoglycaemic. The evidence before us is that the normal blood sugar is between 60 and 100 mg%. Her blood sugar rose after the administration of dextrose to 82 mg% by 10.45 p.m. Thereafter her blood sugar remained normal throughout her illness until her death on 19.3.1979."

Commenting on Dr. Abeysuriya's evidence, Mr. Bandaranayake said, "Dr. Abeysuriya, a neurosurgeon, was invited by the physician-in-charge of ward 47B to examine the patient on 3.2.1979 which he did and found her to be semicomatose. He had expressed the view at that time as is borne out by an entry in the BHT that 'Her comatose state appears due to cerebral anoxia consequent to a sustained hypotension about 72 hours ago'. He recommended the regime of treatment to be continued and suggested some skull review. Dr. Abeysuriya was also present at the post-mortem examination in March. But he did not actually participate in the post-mortem. Dr. Abeysuriya was listed as a prosecution witness on the indictment."

"When the case for the prosecution was nearing its conclusion, the defence made an application to the Court that in the event of the prosecution not calling the witness Dr. Abeysuriya, the Court should direct the prosecution to tender the witness for cross examination. In the event of the Court not directing, the defence asked the Court to call the witness as a witness of Court and permit cross examination by the defence. The prosecution indicated to Court that they were not relying on any evidence of Dr. Abeysuriya and therefore they were not calling him. The Court refused the other application and did not summon the witness as a witness of Court."

"Thereafter upon the close of the prosecution case, the defence submitted that there was no case to answer. Both accused were called upon for their defence. At this point the defence called three witnesses Dr. Abeysuriya, Mr. Henry, Assistant Government Analyst and another witness to speak to the productions taken to the Analyst. The defence now points to the evidence given on oath by Dr. Abeysuriya and the opinion expressed by him and asked the Court to accept such opinion as probably correct and reliable and indicative therefore, of the probability of an entirely natural cause of brain damage for which no one could be held responsible. In the result, says the defence, the prosecution has failed to establish the charge of homicide in respect of the death of Mrs. Peiris and consequently all other related charges."

REACTIVE HYPOGLYCAEMIA

"The medical witness for the defence, Dr. Abeysuriya, has expressed an opinion that Mrs. Peiris probably suffered from moderate depression and that this condition of depression suppressed the function of the hypothalamus-pituitary gland complex, which occasioned a fall of blood pressure, which diminished the oxygen supply to the brain which resulted in permanent brain damage. Also associated with the suppression of the hypothalamus function was a condition of 'Reactive Hypoglycaemia', deriving from the state of depression which caused a drop in blood sugar. The witness has expressed this opinion on the history that he was given of the patient and the documentary evidence available to him and his own observations in the background of his knowledge and experience."

"He has observed a steep fall in blood pressure on 31.1.1979 at the General Hospital and a fall in blood sugar which was recorded at the hospital. If this opinion is believed or accepted by the Court or if the Court is of the view that it is probably correct and that death was probably due to natural causes or it raises a reasonable doubt in the prosecution case, then the accused would be entitled to an acquittal on those charges concerning Mrs. Peiris. Dr. Abeysuriya told the Court that surgeons required knowledge of diabetes and various other neurological conditions associated with diabetes. He said that for metabolism of brain cells sugar is necessary and therefore, a neurosurgeon should be acquainted with sugar metabolism. This is controlled by the hypothalamus and pituitary glands, which are the master endocrine glands of the body."

"He had seen the patient on 3.2.1979 at the request of Dr. Nanayakkara and she was unconscious. He went through the BHT P21 which contained a minute to him and also P13, which was a letter given by Dr. Weerasena for the purposes of admission. Besides the medication rendered, the BHT also contained the history of the illness and signs and symptoms given by the first accused, the letter of admission P13. According to the evidence of Dr. Weerasena who made it, particulars contained therein were given to him by the first accused. The minute addressed by Dr. Nanayakkara to Dr. Abeysuriya, EPGH21 also draws upon the history provided by the first accused," Mr. Bandaranayake said.

"With this information, Dr. Abeysuriya examined the patient and he gave his diagnosis, which has been referred to, that her comatose state appeared to be due to cerebral anoxia consequent to sustained hypotension suffered about seventy hours ago. It is a fact we have observed that no probable cause for the hypotension has been stated by Dr. Abeysuriya at that time. Perhaps it was not relevant. He is the only medical witness who has expressed this opinion, and no other medical witness who has testified in this case was specially cross examined as to whether acute or moderate depression could result in a stress factor, which could cause both a reactive hypoglycaemia and a suppression of the hypothalamus activities causing both a fall in the blood sugar, as well as fall in the blood pressure to an extent sufficient to cause permanent brain cell damage."

Mr. Bandaranayake said that the basis of Dr. Abeysuriya's opinion was, firstly depression.

"It would be convenient at this point to set down the particulars relating to Abeysuriya's diagnosis and his explanation as to how the blood pressure falls due to depression. He says that if one is a severely or even moderately depressed, this mental condition constitutes a stress factor. This stress factor then suppresses the function of the hypothalamus-pituitary endocrine complex. It is the hypothalamus gland, which sends chemical messages or signals to the pituitary gland to secrete its hormones, which are the ACTH and growth hormones. These hormones in turn stimulate the adrenal cortex to secrete large amounts of cortisone. When the pituitary gland secretes its hormones there is an increased demand for cortisone. But the suppression of the hypothalamus decreases pituitary function, which in turn suppresses and diminishes adrenal function causing a lack of cortisone in the blood."

"Now it is cortisone that activates the sympathetic nervous system to activate and constrict peripheral blood vessels to maintain resistance and blood pressure. Cortisone tends to boost blood pressure. These tiny blood vessels all over the body are called arterioles. The sympathetic nerves require cortisone to activate and regulate the function of the arterioles. Thus, the deficiency of cortisone leads to vascular collapse. When it is so collapsed, blood stagnates and accumulates throughout the body in the capillaries. Fluid is also lost from the blood to tissue."

"So for the proper function of arterioles, cortisone is necessary. Collapse of the peripheral vascular mechanism causes blood circulation and blood volume to diminish. It produces a shock like state - blood pressure drops leading to insufficient oxygen reaching brain cells. The vasomotor center of the brain is affected. If of sufficiently long duration, permanent brain damage can occur. The suppression of the hypothalamus also has another consequence. It affects blood sugar because when functioning normally, the pituitary gland is also releasing glucose to the blood and if the pituitaries are not activated blood sugar is also affected."

The second basis of Dr. Abeysuriya's opinion was 'Spontaneous Reactive Hypoglycaemia' Mr. Bandaranayake said.

"Now Dr. Abeysuriya's testimony is that in addition to the suppression of the hypothalamus/pituitary endocrine gland complex, severe or even moderate depression could also result in spontaneous reactive hypoglycaemia, leading to a fall in blood sugar. He supports this opinion with regard to P24 (EPGH 6), which shows the results of an extended GTT done on the deceased on 29.1.1979 at Glass House, a private laboratory situated in Colombo. He also relies upon the history of signs and symptoms of the deceased's sickness given by the first accused as embodied in P13 and found in the House Officer's entry in the BHT P21 at entry EPGH10C. It appears to the Court that basically Dr. Abeysuriya is seeking to explain by his opinion two things that have been observed by him from entries in the BHT upon her admission to the General Hospital - the collapse of blood pressure and the low blood sugar."

"In regard to blood pressure, Dr. Abeysuriya is apparently taking into account the value of 60/40 on 31.1.1979 and Dr. Weerasena's testimony before this Court that on 15.1.1979 at that Vicarage, Mrs. Peiris's blood pressure was not recordable. In regard to blood sugar, Dr. Abeysuriya is taking into account the blood sugar value of 30 mg% as seen in the BHT on 31.1.1979 and the results of extended GTT done at Glass House on 29.1.1979 together with the history recorded in P13 and in P21, i.e. that the patient felt giddy two or three hours after meals which is regarded as a symptom of reactive hypoglycaemia. It is the opinion of Dr. Abeysuriya that the combined action, moderate depression and reactive hypoglycaemia brought down the blood pressure and the blood sugar resulting in brain damage."

"He says his explanation presupposes the existence of a depression of at least moderate severity initially. Arising from this depression, the deceased was having a condition of reactive hypoglycaemia, together with the suppression of activity of the pituitary and compensatory mechanism, which may have existed later due to the suppression of the hypothalamus, which could affect blood sugar."

"Now in considering his opinion it would be convenient for the Court to consider depression resulting in the fall of the blood pressure and reactive hypoglycaemia resulting in the fall of blood sugar separately. It is essential that the Court examines the basis of Dr. Abeysuriya's opinion in the background of his knowledge and experience, in the background of the documentary evidence and in the background of testimony relating to other facts and circumstances which are relevant to this issue. It is convenient to this Court to examine his opinion evidence regarding spontaneous reactive hypoglycaemia arising out of depression in the first place," Mr. Bandaranayake said.

"The prosecution has in the course of this trial placed opinion evidence before this Court, which the Court has accepted as reliable on this question of reactive hypoglycaemia. It was the evidence of several other doctors who testified before us that rebound or reactive hypoglycaemia is also called 'post-prandial' in that after meals when there is increased blood sugar there is a reaction to this increased sugar by heightened insulin activity, resulting in a lowering of blood sugar to a level below normal fasting level, two to three hours after meals. This was well explained to us by Dr. Joseph, retired Senior Surgeon and confirmed by Dr. Nagaratnam, a Consultant Physician."

"Other doctors who testified for the prosecution have also confirmed this opinion. It is also the evidence in this case that the cause of this reaction is not known but that it is quite common and is not a condition, which results generally in unconsciousness excepting in very rare occasions when it can occur but for short periods. It is usually sufficiently treated by regulating the diet - small meals at regular intervals. Dr. Joseph also said that neuropsychiatric symptoms do not occur in this group. What is important is that the preponderance of medical opinion led in this trial is that the cause of reactive hypoglycaemia is not known."

"So now we critically examine Dr. Abeysuriya's opinion that even moderate depression causes reactive hypoglycaemia. In the course of his testimony, while being examined by the defence he made the assertion of the opinion we have set down but he did not back it up with any medical book or publication. In the course of examination, however, in response to a question put by the counsel for the prosecution, he took out a document from a file of papers he had with him and answered the question put by the counsel. This document was not produced and marked by the defence and so the prosecution marked the document as P49."

MODERATE DEPRESSION

"In the course of his testimony Dr. Abeysuriya told Court that 'I am guided by this document to express the opinion that Mrs. Peiris's case is a rare instance. I have no personal previous experience of this condition.' It is quite clear to this Court by the trend of his testimony that he depended largely or perhaps entirely on the contents of P49 to express the opinion he has expressed, namely, that the cause of the deceased's brain damage and coma was probably due to moderate depression causing reactive hypoglycaemia and also causing a fall in the blood pressure and thereby interfering with oxygen supply to the brain cells."

"He said he had known this earlier but he has not told us where or how or when he learnt this. So before we go further it would be proper to set out relevant features of P49. It is an article presented by one B. J. Corel in 1969 and published in the British Medical Journal at page 49. It concerns an experiment done in Australia on sixteen severely depressed patients in order to measure the cortisol level in their blood, to ascertain whether their level was low in their depressed state or in their recovered state."

Mr. Bandaranayake said that article does not say from where they got the sixteen severely depressed patients for their experiments.

"Looking at the question intrinsically, we think it is safe to assume that the patients were obtained from mental hospital or asylum being persons certified by qualified people to be severely depressed. We think that this minimum scientific standard must have been adopted to make the tests scientifically credible and acceptable to be published in a prestigious journal such as the British Medical Journal."

"Furthermore, such patients have to be kept under control and after the initial tests, have to be treated to enable them to recover. This treatment has been done with electrical shock and not with the use of drugs which may interfere with the experiment. So we are confident that the patients of the experiment were persons known medically to be severely depressed. Dr. Abeysuriya has agreed that the patients would have been from a mental institution. The importance of this fact cannot be over emphasized, i.e. that the subjects were indeed severely depressed persons as the article says and were not merely moderately depressed persons. The purpose of the experiment was to measure the amount of cortisol in the blood. Cortisol is normally measured in units. Five to twenty units of cortisol per 100 units of blood is considered normal. This unit of measurement is also found in Ganong's Physiology and this is the measurement used in the experiment."

Mr. Bandaranayake said that certain criteria had to be satisfied. They are,

- blood sugar is induced to fall by insulin injection below 45 mg% for the purpose of the experiment,

- the cortisol level is given a range a minimum of 5 to a maximum of 25,

- the cortisol level for the purpose of the experiment should not reach up to the lowest figure of 5. It should be below 5.

"After insulin shock has been induced and the patient is hypoglycaemic, his cortisol level is measured. Months later when the patient has recovered to a normal mental state his cortisol level is again measured and these two measurements are compared. Before the administration of insulin the mean fasting blood sugar of the patient have been taken and the figure is shown as 85mg% + or - 2.3. Now it was found that after the administration it fell to below 45 mg% also satisfying the criteria. In the other four patients, the blood sugar did not fall below 45 mg% thus, not satisfying the criteria of the experiment. After the patients recovered the mean fasting blood sugar level was again taken in the recovered patients and found to be 78 mg% + or - 3.3, giving rise to the observation in the article that in the depressed state the patients had fasting blood sugar levels significantly higher than in the recovered state."

"In regard to cortisol levels the experiment showed the following:-

After hypoglycaemia was induced on the severely depressed patients at the commencement of the experiment the following cortisol levels were found. Only four patients showed that their cortisol levels fell to below the unit of 5. These four patients satisfied the criteria of the experiment. In three more patients the cortisol level was above the unit of 5. We are not given the actual figures in these three patients."

Mr. Bandaranayake said that in the remaining nine patients, the cortisol level remained at acceptable normal levels nearer the figure 25 thus not satisfying the experiment.

"The experiment showed that even in severely depressed patients where hypoglycaemia is induced by the injection of insulin that the cortisol level remained normal in 60% of the patients. This could mean that in those 60% one would not expect a fall in the blood pressure according to the information given to this Court by Dr. Abeysuriya. It was only in four patients representing 25% that the criteria were satisfied and cortisol was found to be low. In the residuary three patients the cortisol level was seen to be above the mean mark. We would also like to point out that the initial fasting cortisol level in any of the patients before hypoglycaemia was induced is not mentioned."

"It is upon the results of the document P49, which we have enumerated that Dr. Abeysuriya has ventured upon his opinion. So in this background let us examine that part of his opinion where he says that moderate depression can result in reactive hypoglycaemia and that certain documentary evidence in this case which was available to him suggested the presence of hypoglycaemia in Mrs. Peiris on 31.1.1979."

"The question of the reliability of Dr. Abeysuriya's opinion about the presence of reactive hypoglycaemia in the deceased on 31.1.1979 must be examined in the context of the constituent parts which go to make up his opinion about reactive hypoglycaemia. Those parts, we will now enumerate as follows:

1. The reliability of Dr. Abeysuriya's opinion that moderate depression causes 'Spontaneous Reactive Hypoglycaemia.'

2. The reliability of Dr. Abeysuriya's opinion in regard to the values seen in document P24, which was the extended GTT done at Glass House on 29.1.1979."

"Now in regard to (1) above it is seen that depression is a state of mind and a degree of depression is best assessed by a psychiatrist and not by a neurosurgeon. Again we would like to point out that the experiment showed in P49 was conducted in conditions of an induced hypoglycaemia, i.e. that blood sugar was induced to fall below 45 mg% by the injection of insulin."

EXPERIMENT

"This is a key fact that should be prominently borne in mind. This experiment was not done on patients having a spontaneous natural endogenous reactive hypoglycaemia. Reactive hypoglycaemia was induced so P49 is no authority that shows depression causes spontaneous reactive hypoglycaemia. In the experiment as we have pointed out the hypoglycaemia was induced. So, Dr. Abeysuriya cannot use P49 to support his opinion that he has expressed to this Court that severe to moderate depression causes reactive hypoglycaemia and that it did so in the case of Mrs. Peiris on 31.1.1979. The article has no bearing to any theory of reactive hypoglycaemia being caused by or arising out of depression whether severe or moderate."

"Dr. Abeysuriya's opinion on this point is not supported by any medical text book or journal or publication. It is not supported by the reference to the 'Text Book on Hypoglycaemia' by Marks and Rose, second Edition 1981, which has been referred to by the defence in this case, particularly to page 202 Table 9:3, where it is shown that 'Reactive Hypoglycaemia' is seen to co-exist in conditions of 'Depressive Psychosis' which incidentally is not the same thing as 'Reactive Moderate depression'. So, Marks and Rose is no authority for Dr. Abeysuriya's preposition either. The preponderance of the medical opinion before this Court is that the cause of Spontaneous Reactive Hypoglycaemia is not known. Furthermore, his opinion is not supported by any personal experience that he may have had."

"It is apparent to this Court that his opinion is not founded on any of the disciplines of or accepted medical knowledge. It is our judgement therefore, that the opinion expressed by Dr. Abeysuriya that depression causes 'Reactive Hypoglycaemia' is unreliable, misleading and unacceptable and is not an expert opinion and is therefore irrelevant. The medical opinion that we accept is that the cause of 'Spontaneous Reactive Hypoglycaemia' is unknown."

"We next turn to the value given in P24 which the prosecution placed before this Court in order to show certain conduct by the first accused which the prosecution submits is consistent with his guilt. The blood sugar values which this document showed were also relied upon by the defence and taken into account by Dr. Abeysuriya to express the opinion that Mrs. Peiris suffered from 'Reactive Hypoglycaemia' on 29.01.1979, two days before her admission to hospital."

"Before we embark on an examination of this opinion we have to state that the taking of that extended GTT at Glass House involves the testimony of Dr. Weerasena on important particulars. Even the contents of P13, which again Dr. Abeysuriya has taken as a guide to express his opinion that on 31.01.1979 the deceased suffered from 'Reactive Hypoglycaemia' again involves the testimony of Dr. Weerasena. Before we discuss the blood sugar values shown in P24 in all the circumstances of this case, it is proper that we focus on the witness Dr. Weerasena and consider whether he has given reliable testimony in this case."

"Dr. Weerasena has spoken to many matters concerning the first accused, relevant to the first accused's conduct and concerning events relevant to this case spanning a period of nearly four years. Dr. Weerasena's name has cropped up over and over again. It is the case for the prosecution that Dr. Weerasena has been deceived by the first accused over and over again and that the first accused made use of Dr. Weerasena's professional position to mislead both him and other doctors concerning the illness of both, his wife and of Russel Ingram, in order to accomplish with the second accused a common criminal endeavour. It is proper that we tabulate briefly the several matters that have transpired in evidence connecting Dr. Weerasena with the first accused."

"We begin:-

(1) With the evidence of Dr. Weerasena that in 1979, the first accused was introduced to him as a patient to whom he prescribed the drug Euglucon as treatment of his diabetes.

(2) It is also the evidence of Dr. Weerasena that he treated Russel Ingram in 1979 for sores.

(3) It is also the evidence of Dr. Weerasena that he gave a certificate to the first accused concerning some alleged sign of stigmata claimed to be carried by the first accused some times.

(4) It was the evidence of the Ingrams, that the first accused told them that Dr. Weerasena was treating Russel Ingram who was lying seriously ill at the Vicarage.

(5) A document was produced by the defence in that case marked ID7 purporting to be a request for a serum amylase test by Dr. Weerasena in respect of the patient Russel Ingram. When that document was produced by the defence, Dr. Weerasena flatly denied making that document.

(6) Soon after the deceased Mrs. Peiris returned to Sri Lanka from the United Kingdom the first accused took her to Dr. Weerasena for treatment for puffiness of stomach and sleeplessness for which Dr. Weerasena prescribed the drug Stelazine and Artane.

(7) A few days thereafter the first accused again got Dr. Weerasena to prescribe other drugs for puffiness of stomach of the deceased

in the absence of the deceased, which Dr. Weerasena says he did.

(8) On 15.01.1979 the first accused called Dr. Weerasena to the Vicarage and Dr. Weerasena came and found Mrs. Peiris unconscious with an unrecordable blood pressure and had immediately removed her to Durdans Hospital and treated her after which treatment she recovered.

(9) During the period of hospitalization at Durdans, Dr. Weerasena had Mrs. Peiris treated by Dr. Sathananthan and Dr. Attygalle with the consent of the first accused.

(10) Upon her discharge from Durdans on 20.01.1979, Dr. Weerasena again gave a letter to the first accused to be given to Dr. E.V. Peiris to examine the deceased, which that doctor did. Thereafter the first accused asked Dr. Weerasena for a letter to have an extended four-hour GTT done saying Dr. Peiris ordered it, which letter Dr. Weerasena gave and has been produced in this case marked P11. Again on 30.01.1979, at the request of the first accused, Dr. Weerasena saw the deceased at the Vicarage.

(11) Yet again on the morning of 31.01.1979 the first accused telephoned Dr. Weerasena and got him to prepare P13, which the first accused submitted to the General Hospital, Colombo, on the admission of his wife to Hospital."

CRIMINAL PURPOSE

Mr. Bandaranayake said that in all the above circumstances it would be seen that Dr. Weerasena has been resorted to by the first accused on many matters concerning the treatment of both Russel Ingram and Mrs. Peiris.

"As we said earlier on prosecution has submitted to this Court and Dr. Weerasena is well aware of that fact that it is the case for the prosecution that the first accused improperly made use of Dr.

Weerasena to achieve his criminal purpose. In these circumstances it is fitting that this Court bears these matters in mind and that the Court views the testimony of Dr. Weerasena with circumspection and scrutinized it carefully in evaluating his testimony because as a human being, responsive to human emotion he maybe having a number of mixed motives when he comes to testify against the first accused at this trial as a prosecution witness where the first accused stands charged with double murder. We looked to see whether his evidence is objective and detached or whether it is coloured and revengeful and therefore rendered unreliable."

"Coming back to the question of P24, is Dr. Abeysuriya entitled to rely on P24 to form an opinion? That is to say, is one figure shown in P24 reliable? It was the evidence of Dr. Abeysuriya that on GTT alone he could say that Mrs. Peiris had 'Spontaneous Reactive Hypoglycaemia'. On being asked the question 'If you did not have the data, the history that two to three hours after meals the patient felt giddy would it have affected your opinion?' Answer: 'It would not have - with this GTT it is not possible to express an opinion', and he added in response to the next question 'provided the conditions were satisfied'. He was also questioned 'Do you know the conditions in which the tests were taken?' Answer: 'No'. The next question was 'You did not know the duration of the fast'. The answer is not recorded. In fact we have no evidence of the duration of the fast before the test."

"Then the prosecution showed him the results of an extended GTT done at the General Hospital on 08.02.1979 over five hours while the patient was lying unconscious. At the GTT of 08.02.1979 the fasting blood sugar level is seen as 81 mg%, which is well in to the normal blood sugar values and the blood sugar level at the end of five hours shows that it has come back to the figure 81 mg%, which was the original fasting value. During that test the blood sugar has not gone below that figure at any stage. This blood test was done at 5 a.m. on the 8th. Dr. (Miss) Pinto had ordered the test on 07.02.1979 for the following morning and had further ordered that all IV and oral fluids should be omitted after 8 p.m. But nevertheless a nurse has given her Horlicks at 10 p.m. At 5 a.m. the following day Dr.

(Miss) Pinto herself started the test and after taking 8 samples over 5 hours she took the samples herself to the laboratory. This evidence is supported by entry at EPGH80A and at entry 29B in the BHT P21. At EPGH 123 one finds the requisition for this test."

"The test itself was done by witness Oliver Fernando and a report is produced as RIGH 124. The Court is satisfied with the method used and the care taken to do the test. The cross examination of this witness does not in our view affect the results shown in report RIGH 124. On the face of it the figures do not suggest a spontaneous reactive hypoglycaemia. Dr. Abeysuriya however when questioned on this test said that the figures were probably correct, but the witness was quick to add that the test was not done under standard conditions. He said there was carbohydrate in the stomach at the start of the test as she had been given malted milk seven hours before the commencement of the test at 5 a.m. In the results, the figures were unreliable as they could be misleading and he was therefore not prepared to say that that test showed that the deceased was not having 'spontaneous reactive hypoglycaemia' on 08.02.1979."

"Now the question is this: If he probably correctly says that the result of EPGH124 cannot be taken at face value because standard conditions were not observed as is evidenced by the BHT and the FBC, how can he venture a reliable opinion on the results of P24 when there is no information before this Court as to the fasting conditions before that test was done at Glass House? Dr. Abeysuriya did not claim to know that he knew what the fasting conditions were. In the first place Dr. Abeysuriya knows that that test was done at Glass House which is a private laboratory. He knows very well that at such laboratories the onus is on the patients to comply with the pre-conditions for a reliable test. There is no laboratory control. Patients are called in from a verandah to cubicle in order to draw blood and they are returned to the verandah. It is a busy place."

"In the case even the pre-conditions were told by telephone and the appointment for the test was marked on a wall calendar hanging by the telephone operator who is the person who gives instructions about fasting. We are further told that it was the first accused who booked the test and those instructions were given to him. We have no evidence that the deceased knew anything about extended GTT. So how does Dr. Abeysuriya venture to express an opinion to the Court on such bald material? It is obvious to us that he is going only on the plain figures in P24 coupled with the statements in P13 and those in EPGH 10C. His conduct in venturing an opinion on the values on P24 is self-contradictory when viewed in his cautious attitude towards the figures in EPGH 124. He knows less about the circumstances, which preceded P24 than he knows of the circumstances of those events which preceded the start of the General Hospital blood test P254, which are tabulated in the documents before him. Yet, he ventures an opinion on the one he knows less about."

Mr. Bandaranayake then examined the evidence regarding the circumstances under which an extended GTT was done at Glass House on 29.01.1979.

"The prosecution produced these extended GTT results and let all the evidence concerning these test in order to show the conduct of the first accused, and it is the case of the prosecution that the results of the test were manipulated by the first accused to show a false 'Endogenous Spontaneous Reactive Hypoglycaemia' and upon that result he made false statements to Dr. Weerasena to induce him to write P13, and also that the first accused made a false statement to Dr. de Silva to give a false lead. We will consider these statements in due course. The defence relied upon these extended GTT results as showing that represents honestly and correctly a true state of the deceased's blood sugar position as of that date and that the first accused far from maliciously meddling with her blood sugar was actively caring for his wife in her depressive illness and trying his best to have her treated. Upon the evidence placed before Court, the circumstances under which the deceased was taken by the first accused for these tests are important.

"They are as follows: Upon her discharge from Durdans on 20.01.1979 almost fully recovered, Dr. Weerasena requested that the deceased be shown to Dr. E.V. Peiris, a consultant specialist physician, who also happened to be a family friend of the first accused. So he gave a letter to the first accused to be given to Dr. Peiris. We next find that the first accused had taken his wife to see Dr. Peiris on 24.01.1979. Dr. Peiris described what happened rather vividly. He said that the first accused did all the talking and showed him some blood reports taken at Durdans and that the first accused gave a history that the deceased had been sleeping and could not be roused on 15.01.1979 at the Vicarage before she was hospitalized at Durdans. As he was not sure how much dextrose had been given before his blood test, he ordered a four-hour extended GTT to be done and he gave the first accused a letter for this purpose and that letter has been produced and marked as exhibit P22."

"Now, according to Dr. Weerasena, the first accused met him after 24.01.1979 and told him verbally of the test that Dr. Peiris had ordered without showing him P22 or making any reference to that letter. Instead, Dr. Weerasena says that the first accused asked for a letter from him requesting a four-hour extended GTT to be done and so, Dr. Weerasena gave him a letter, which has been produced and marked at this trial as exhibit P11. When we look at this evidence intrinsically we believe Dr. Weerasena because if P22 was shown to him or the fact of its existence was disclosed, there would have been no reason for Dr. Weerasena to give yet another letter."

TESTS AT GLASS HOUSE

"With these two letters P11 and P22 what does the first accused do? The evidence is that he booked an ordinary GTT by telephoning on the 27th for the 29th morning. That is the evidence of witness Mary Ann Edna the telephonist at Glass House who noted down the booking on the wall calendar and gave instructions accordingly. So we begin with only an ordinary GTT, which is done over two and a half hours generally on diabetic patients. That was all that was booked. No diary or book entry has been made in this connection. No payment was done at the time. The telephonist informed the laboratory of the booking."

"It is a fact that the blood test was done on Mrs. Peiris on 29.01.1979. Nimal Soysa was the receptionist at Glass House that morning. According to him, the first accused came with the deceased. Witness knew of the appointment. He called the first accused into the Reception Room. The first accused stated that he wanted a GTT, an ESR and a full blood count done for his wife. He did not show any letters from a doctor. He did not show him P11 or P22. The witness stated that he saw P11 and P22 for the first time, when they were produced in Court. The witness stated that once the test started, after sometime the first accused made a request for an extended GTT over four hours. So he charged him an extra forty rupees and amended the bill. This witness produced a receipt P23, which is a receipt from the Glass House for the money received and which shows an amendment to the price – an increase of forty rupees. This witness further told Court that if a patient knows what test he wants done, they do that without a doctor's letter. If a doctor's letter is shown, they will write on their report "At the request of Dr. ...." The witness stated that he charged half-rate as the first accused was a priest."

"The conditions under which these tests are done at Glass House are also relevant in this case. After the blood is drawn, the patient is asked to sit in the lobby or verandah for a while until it is time for next sample of blood to be drawn."

"We have the evidence of witness Harridge who was the lab technician on that day. He said that there was an appointment for a GTT for a lady named Eunice Peiris. Witness got to know of it that morning from the Reception. Witness came downstairs to the cubicle and found the working sheet, looked at it and called the patient who came in from the Reception area with the first accused. The witness was shown the working sheet P24, which he identified as a document made by him. It contains details of the blood sugar test that was done. The witness further stated that he had seen the first accused before as he had earlier worked at the Cardiology Unit of the General Hospital, Colombo, next to which is situated the St. Paul's Church, Kynsey Road. Thereafter, either a doctor or one of the supervisors drew the blood from the deceased. When the first sample was taken at 8.30 a.m., the witness marked that fact on P24. He labeled the bottle with that sample. That was the fasting blood sample drawn. Thereafter, he administered glucose to the patient. Witness stated that the first accused was helping the patient. The first accused was playing the more prominent role asking questions from the witness and telling the lady what to do. He did all the talking. She appeared weak and sick and hardly spoke," Mr. Bandaranayake said.

"Witness stated that when he called out her name, she walked into the cubicle with the first accused from the verandah about ten yards away. She went to the toilet room and gave specimens of urine. After the initial fasting blood sample was drawn and glucose was Administered, the patient was asked to sit in the verandah until next sample was drawn. The test began at 8.30 am and ended 12.30 p.m. During the test, after the first hour, but before two and a half hours, the first accused told the witness that he had given a call to his doctor Dr. Weerasena and that Dr. Weerasena wanted an extended GTT done over four hours. So the witness spoke to the doctor-in-charge who charged an additional fee and the witness proceeded to take blood samples over four hours. The witness denied that he was ever shown P11 or P22. The witness said that if the first accused had shown him those letters or had shown them to the Reception at the beginning, they would have ordered an extended GTT over four hours. This the first accused did not do."

"Under cross examination, it was suggested by the defence to this witness that what the first accused told him during the test was that it was a mistake to have ordered an ordinary GTT. The witness denied this suggestion and said that if that were so there would have been no necessity for the first accused to have told him that Dr. Weerasena had stated so over the telephone. Then the defence suggested to the witness that what might have actually happened was that the first accused just stated that what Dr. Weerasena wanted was an extended GTT over four hours, but by some mistake he (the first accused) ordered an ordinary GTT and therefore when he realized his mistake he wanted it extended. The defence position was that the witness was speaking from memory and that he could be making a mistake in regard to his testimony. This too the witness denied, although he granted a possibility of error. But his position appeared to be that what he was telling us was most probably the correct position."

CHANGE IN THE DURATION OF THE TEST

Continuing, Mr. Bandaranayake said, "The witness supported this by informing Court that the first accused knew a lot about GTT and even showed him two blood reports during the test. In the re-examination, he stated that if the first accused had these two letters all be needed to have done was to have shown them to the Reception. This he has failed to do. This fact is proved by reason of the alteration of the receipt P23, which has been made contemporaneously. The two documents P11 and P22 were recovered by the police in the course of the investigations from the Vicarage on 03.04.1979. In the circumstances, we accept the evidence that the first accused asked for a change in the duration of the test sometime after it was taken. This he need not have done because he had the two letters. There is no explanation whatsoever for this conduct."

"We reject the defence submission that it might have been a mistake. It is our finding that that conduct was intentional. One cannot just pass it off as a mistake. One has to make a booking. In this case it is the evidence that he booked this test two days earlier and even on that day he had the two letters. Both these letters request an extended four-hour GTT. The first accused must have known that what was being done at Glass House at the start was an ordinary test for him to have requested and 'extended' one half-way through. Dr. Weerasena has flatly denied that he gave any telephone instructions about this test. We believe Dr. Weerasena because in the face of P11 there was no need for him to give any telephone instructions on the subject," Mr. Bandaranayake said.

"So the question arises as to why the first accused ordered an ordinary test in the face of P11 and P22. Taking into account all these matters, we have no reasonable doubt whatsoever that the conduct of the first accused in regard to this matter was intentional."

Mr. Bandaranayake said that the result of the tests showed a fasting blood sugar level of 73 mg%.

"Then after three hours it falls down to 65 mg% and at the fourth hour it is at 51 mg% and there showing that from two and a half to three hours after the administration of 50 grams of glucose at 8.30 a.m. the blood sugar fell below the fasting level of 73 mg% - suggesting 'reactive hypoglycaemia'. Neither the prosecution nor the defence has complained of the diagnosis and the methods used in testing the blood or of the knowledge or experience of the persons who did it. All that evidence is before us and we are satisfied that the test was properly done. Both sides rely on the figures for their respective positions. The normal value of blood sugar recognized at this laboratory is from 60 to 100 mg% and they use the Somogyi method for the test."

CONSISTENCY OF THE EVIDENCE

"We accept the evidence of witness Harridge and it is supported by the receipt P23. This evidence bears on the conduct of the first accused. We have examined the evidence intrinsically and with reference to the documents that have been produced. We know the consistency of the evidence amongst the Glass House witnesses. The cross examination of these witnesses has not raised any reasonable doubt in our minds about their veracity and about the accuracy of their testimony."

"The figure of this extended GTT shows a reactive hypoglycaemic curve at face value. This fact is confirmed by Dr. Nagaratnam. It was the evidence of Dr. Abeysuriya that on the face of it, values are consistent with three situations:-

1. A spontaneous hypoglycaemia caused by insulinoma or pancreatic tumours;

2. A spontaneous hypoglycaemia caused by 'Rebound or Reactive Hypoglycaemia';

3. Induced 'Factitious Hypoglycaemia' caused by the administration of insulin or an anti-diabetic drug."

"Dr. Abeysuriya however chooses the second situation, namely that of 'spontaneous hypoglycaemia', because he accepts these figures at face value. He has not told Court of any other material he had of the circumstances surrounding the test. All we know is that the first accused brought the deceased from the Vicarage on the 29th morning. We do not know how long she fasted before the test. We do not know whether she consumed anything during the test. Now it is not enough to accept figures at the face value and express opinion. No responsible opinion can be expressed in this way."

"So, let us now examine the proved circumstances from the point of time of the discharge of the deceased from the Durdans Hospital up to the morning when she was presented at the Glass House. We find the accused had two letters from doctors Weerasena and Peiris requesting a four-hour extended GTT, but he booked an ordinary test on 27.01.1979 and he does not show or produce those letters at the Glass House before the test began at 8.30 a.m. If he had produced them, we have no doubt, an extended GTT would have been commenced and he would have been charged the full amount at the very outset. Why did he not do this? Further the evidence is that the first accused accompanied the deceased for this test, and he played a rather prominent role. If he had the best interest of his wife at heart, why did he not take the letters with him and show them? Is it possible, we ask ourselves, that the showing of these letters could make no difference to the test? That is to say if he had produced the letters and committed himself to a four hour test from the very outset, would that have made a difference?"

"In considering the prosecution position, we think that it could make a difference for a person waiting for an opportunity, looking for a chance to do some harm secretly. The prosecution has raised the conduct of the first accused as an issue in this case. The prosecution submits that these acts of omission and commission were deliberate. In these circumstances, it is legitimate for the Court to ask the question as to why an ordinary test was booked in the first instance on the 27th and why those letters were withheld on the 29th or why the first accused did not ask for a four-hour extended test at the very outset. The evidence, which we believe, is that the deceased herself had nothing to do with the telephone booking or any of the events concerning the duration of the test. All she did was to give her blood and her urine upon request," Mr. Bandaranayake said.

"During the test, he suddenly changes the test to an extended one. He does this before the end of two and a half hours. He tells the technician that he was so advised by Dr. Weerasena over the telephone. Dr. Weerasena denies that he ever gave the first accused any such instructions, but he only gave the letter. These documents have been taken from the possession of the first accused. So the conduct of the first accused becomes suspicious. The defence position that the change of the test, after it began was because of a mistake, is in our opinion, quite improbable and untenable and intrinsically very weak. If any instruction has to be given by doctor he would give it directly to the lab and not via first accused," Mr. Bandaranayake said.

"We are firmly convinced that Dr. Weerasena is speaking the truth on this matter. So in the results, the first accused's conduct in changing the duration of the test on the pretext that it was in consequence of telephone instruction of Dr. Weerasena or on the pretext that he had forgotten the instruction originally given is mendacious. We also view his conduct of patient being left out in the verandah to go anywhere they wish in the interval between the takings of blood samples. In these circumstances, the possibility of manipulating the blood sugar is ever present."

"We also have it in evidence that the first accused did not show the report containing the results which he had collected from the Glass House that very evening of 29.01.1979 to either Dr. Weerasena or Dr. Peiris. Dr. Peiris says that he expected the first accused to return to him in three or four days, but he did not do so. Dr. Weerasena says that he visited the Vicarage at 3 p.m. on 30.01.1979 in response to a call by the first accused, but he was not shown the blood report. We believe both these doctors on this matter. Their testimony has a consistence in regard to the first accused's conduct. Furthermore, both these doctors state that the first accused telephoned them early in the morning of 31.01.1979 and told them of the figures, which contain in the reports. So we see a consistency against the testimony of the two doctors," Mr. Bandaranayake said.

"The honesty and integrity of Dr. Peiris, who is a senior consultant physician with the highest qualifications in his field, has not been attacked by the defence. We believe both the doctors when the say that the first accused did not show them the reports at any time. So the question arises 'Why not?' The purpose of taking a test is defeated if the report is not shown to the doctors who ordered it or to any other doctor for that matter. This report has never been shown by the first accused to any doctor, but it has been found by the police in his Vicarage. But we see this significant fact, although he had the report on the evening of the 29th he waited till the morning of the 31st, until a few hours before she was admitted to hospital critically ill, to inform the doctor of the contents of the report. This conduct of the first accused, in the context of his other conduct concerning this blood test, becomes quite suspicious."

DISHONEST

"We have no evidence that fasting conditions required of an extended GTT were observed. In conclusion, the defence says that the conduct of the first accused on 29.01.1979 concerning this blood test can be explained on the basis of a mistake and that Dr. Weerasena has not stated the truth and the memory of the Glass House witnesses cannot be trusted. We have given our minds to these submissions. We have examined the evidence intrinsically and by the application of common sense test of credibility. We believe that the Glass House witnesses and Dr. Peiris and Dr. Weerasena upon all matters relevant to the question that we are discussing. We accept their evidence as reliable and truthful and we find that the conduct of the of the first accused relating to the taking of the extended GTT – the results of which are produced by the prosecution as P24 - as dishonest, secretive and not straight forward, forthright or reliable."

"We have no evidence before us of the fasting conditions before the GTT. So in the back drop of the first accused's unsatisfactory and suspicious conduct whilst playing a prominent role in presenting his wife for the blood sugar test, and his suspicious conduct in waiting until the last moment before admitting his wife unconscious to the hospital, to rattle off figures from the reports over the telephones to the doctors who had ordered the test and in the absence of any evidence

458

regarding fasting conditions before the test on the 29th, we have a real and substantial doubt as to the reliability of the figures shown in the Glass House report. Although the figures themselves maybe correct, we think in fact they truthfully and correctly represent a true uninduced, spontaneous fall in blood sugar after three hours of the administration of glucose at the outset of the test. Dr. Nagaratnam has told this Court that the fall of this blood sugar on this day can be induced by the administration of an antibiotic drug."

"We know that an anti-diabetic pill will be effective after about fifteen minutes. That was the evidence of both Professor Jayasena and Dr. Nagaratnam. Dr. Abeysuriya has submitted that it is a possibility. In the results we cannot and do not accept this figures shown in P24 at face value. It is our finding that in this background, these figures are not credible or reliable as definitely representing the spontaneous fasting blood sugar level of the deceased on 29.01.1979. It is our finding that no positive, affirmative and reliable medical operation of spontaneous reactive hypoglycaemia can possibly be made on these figures in these circumstances. In the background of the first accused's conduct anything could have happened. The medical opinion so expressed must, in our view be treated as completely unreliable and untrustworthy and of no value in these proceedings."

"We now turn to the contents of P13 and the House Officer's note EPGH10c, which are two more criteria upon which Dr. Abeysuriya formed an opinion, together with GTT P24, that the deceased probably had a 'spontaneous reactive hypoglycaemia' arising out of her depression. The feature that is relevant to our personal consideration is the reference to 'feeling giddy two to three hours after meals', which is a sign of reactive hypoglycaemia."

DYING DEPOSITION

"In P13, which is the admission letter given by Dr. Weerasena to the first accused, the words 'a four-hour GTT' show that there is hypoglycaemia after four hours and she also says that she feels giddy when she takes sugar after a lapse of about two to three hours. In the BHT entry at EPGH10, the following words found in page two thereof 'Later she felt giddy two to three hours after meals'. Let us now consider whether what it is written in these documents truly represent what the deceased felt during this relevant period. It is not a dying deposition made to either of the witnesses. Both doctors say that the statements were made to them by the first accused. So let us consider the evidence of the circumstances under which each of these witnesses say the first accused made the statement to him. Taking P13 first, it is the evidence of Dr. Weerasena that on the 31st morning at about 7.30 a.m., just before he left home for his clinic, the first accused telephoned him and told him – (a) the results of the extended GTT, and (b) on the 30th the previous day, the patient felt giddy two to three hours after meals."

"Acting on this information, he wrote P13. That is to say that the blood sugar level last read out to him showed a hypoglycaemia and that the statement of the first accused that the deceased felt giddy after meals also suggested 'reactive hypoglycaemia' and so he wrote 'There is a hypoglycaemia etc.' It was suggested to Dr. Weerasena by the defence that this evidence is untrue and that P13 represents his own findings after the examination of the deceased and upon the history he also knew of her condition and upon a consideration of the Glass House report."

"We will consider the circumstances intrinsically:

(a) Dr. Weerasena said that the first accused telephoned him in the morning. So does Dr. Peiris, Rev. Edison Mendis and Myrtle Mendis. They also say that the first accused telephoned them early that same morning. So here we have several witnesses speaking almost with one voice and saying the same thing. So we have an opportunity of comparison by the abundance and the range of evidence provided to the Court. We believe all these witnesses on this fact. Rev. Mendis says that he was asked to collect a letter from Dr. Weerasena from the Clinic which he did at about 10.30 a.m. So this means that the first accused did not go to Dr. Weerasena's house or the Clinic to obtain this letter himself. This makes it highly probable that the request for the letter P13 was over the telephone.

(b) Dr. Weerasena says that he was not shown the report, but the figures were phoned to him. Dr. Peiris says the same thing that the first accused phoned him that morning before breakfast and rattled off some GTT figures. We have no hesitation whatsoever in believing Dr. Peiris. We trust his memory on this matter. He testified having his notes before him. So we observed his conduct that morning when the first accused telephones different people while his wife was at the Vicarage. From these circumstances the evidence of Dr. Weerasena on this point is also rendered most reliable when he says that the first accused telephoned him and gave the GTT figures over the telephone and that is why he came to write what is found in P13. Dr. Weerasena and Dr. Peiris cannot give exactly the same evidence about this conduct unless it happened in that way. It is not even remotely suggested that they conspired with each other to say exactly the same thing on this point only. We also observe in P13 that Dr. Weerasena has made a mistake in saying that there was hypoglycaemia after four hours. He was cross examined on this. He stated that he should have written 'after three hours'. This mistake is also consistent with his not having the document before him. It is also seen that in P24 the blood sugar value goes below the fasting value after three hours.

(c) Dr. Weerasena says that even though he went to the Vicarage at about 9 a.m. on 31.01.1979, he was not shown the report. Dr. Peiris says that even though he ordered the extended GTT on P22, he too was never shown the report although the first accused was well known to him and had officiated at his daughter's wedding some years previously. Here too we observe the conduct of the first accused consistent with his deliberately not showing the report to the doctors before his wife's admission to hospital. He in fact never showed this report to anybody. We accept Dr. Weerasena's evidence that the first accused did not show him the report of the blood test done at the Glass House.

(d) Now we come to the reference to 'feeling giddy when she takes sugar after a lapse of two to three hours'. In the first place, 'feeling giddy' is a symptom and not a sign. It is something felt by the patient and generally should be so mentioned by the patient who can faint or lie down or hold his head, which is a sign that can be observed by others. Such a sign can be for several reasons. But the signs of giddiness can be identified as such by the patient. So intrinsically this is not something that could have been observed by Dr. Weerasena. Even if it were to be observed by a person such as a doctor, it must be so observed two to three hours after meals and Dr. Weerasena wanted to know when she had her last meal, unless she has been in hospital and everything is monitored. So it is safe for the Court to conclude that such a thing was told to Dr. Weerasena by someone. If so, by whom? Was it by the deceased herself? Dr. Weerasena has seen the deceased once in December, twice on the 20th of January and once on the 30th of January. We know that on none of these occasions has the deceased told him that she was feeling giddy so many hours after meals. We believe Dr. Weerasena when he says that she was feeling giddy so many hours after meals. We believe Dr. Weerasena when he says that she never said such symptoms. It is not in the BHT at the hospital. Dr. E.V. Peiris does not say that such a history was given to him on the 24th. So in these circumstances, we are confident that Dr. Weerasena is speaking the truth on this matter. For another thing, when the evidence placed before the Court about the deceased Mrs. Peiris, we have no material whatsoever upon which we can infer that Mrs. Peiris would have known the significance of feeling giddy in relation to meals that she has had."

Continuing, Mr. Bandaranayake said, "Ordinarily a patient would not know the time factor with regard to meals and the feeling of giddiness as relevant unless a doctor probes such a matter, and we know that none of the doctors who saw her up to the 30th of January questioned her in this regard. Now we know that from Dr. Weerasena that in 1979 when he prescribed Euglucon to the first accused for his diabetic condition he had told him that if he feels giddy after the tablets to take some sugar. When we examine this statement intrinsically we consider it quite normal and proper for a doctor prescribing a drug to tell his patient what to do if there are side effects from that drug. We accept Dr. Weerasena's evidence. We also have the evidence of many witnesses who have testified before us in this case namely, Dr. P.A.P. Joseph, Dr. Dayasiri Fernando, the Glass House technician. Dr. E.V. Peiris said that he knew a lot about 'hypoglycaemia'. We also have the evidence that he had the book P40. The prosecution has placed in evidence extracts from that book marked P40A-P40N. These extracts show that there is plenty of information about 'hypoglycaemia'. We also have the evidence of Dr. Wijesiriwardena that in July 1978, the first accused produced before him several blood sugar reports in respect of the blood sugar position of Russel. We have the evidence of Dr. E.V. Peiris that the first accused produced the blood sugar reports in respect of his wife on 24.01.1979. So, Dr. Weerasena has told Court that it was the first accused who gave him the information that his wife was feeling giddy two to three hours after taking sugar on the telephone on the morning of 31.01.1979. Dr. Weerasena says that this symptom is consistent with a 'Reactive Hypoglycaemia' and in the context of the figures of the GTT that he gave over the telephone. Dr. Weerasena says that he prepared P13."

REACTIVE HYPOGLYCAEMIA

Mr. Bandaranayake said that in all these circumstances, upon an intrinsic examination of this evidence the Court accepts Dr. Weerasena's testimony that the first accused gave him this information.

"We also find we have that evidence tending to confirm what Dr. Weerasena has stated on this central question of the symptoms of 'Reactive Hypoglycaemia'. That is the evidence of Dr. Terrence Rajah de Silva the House Officer at Ward 47B that at 12.30 p.m., the same day when he was at the bed side of Mrs. Peiris soon after her admission to the ward the first accused gave him the history of the patient's illness and we find that part of what the first accused told Dr. Silva is identical with what Dr. Weerasena says the first accused told him. Dr. de Silva had never seen or known the first accused. He was only getting a history from the husband of the patient and he wrote it down immediately. In BHT P21, which is seen at pages two and three at entry marked EPGH 10c, 'History from the husband Rev. Father Mathew Peiris - marked thirst, loss of appetite, later she felt giddy two to three hours after meals'. There is yet another entry note P21 at EPGH 11. 'The patient had been given glucose at a GTT and she became very drowsy after the test', also at EPGH11B at page 2 it is stated, 'Yesterday she had slurring of speech – she took some sugar, but she became very drowsy according to her husband'. Dr. de Silva says that he found this report quite strange, so he made a special note of that saying that this is what the husband says. We accept this contemporaneous note made by the House Officer at the time of admission as true and accurate and representing fairly what was said by the first accused to him. We have no doubt whatsoever that the House Officer is speaking the truth. His testimony has not been rendered unsafe by any cross examination. We see in these entries ample support for what Dr. Weerasena says that the first accused told him."

"There is reference to two things in both P13 and P21. They are, (a) giddiness two to three hours after meals and, (b) that she became ill after taking sugar. Looking at the defence documents in this background, it surely is inconsistent with the suggestion that there was continuing disunity and disharmony in this family between the mother and the children leading to disappointment, sorrow and associated reactive mental depression suffered by the deceased. We accept Malrani's evidence on this matter. It is an accepted fact that Mihiri was in Sri Lanka during this period, but that she stayed with her in-laws but visiting her home and spending the night in the company of her parents, which intrinsically is quite a natural course of conduct of behaviour. So we believe Malrani that this in fact took place. We do not agree with the inference that the defence wishes us to draw as probable in the circumstances."

"In the case of the marriage proposal, the uncontradicted evidence in the case is that there was a suggestion made about this by the first accused in October and the mother and the daughter came to Sri Lanka to investigate it and to ascertain its suitability and then if both parties are agreed, it might have resulted in marriage. That was the evidence of Malrani. It is a very common occurrence in Sri

Lankan culture where the parents investigate the suitability of their daughter's marriage partners. As it was turned down, Malrani was not questioned by the other side as to why the marriage did not take place. But, Dr. Abeysuriya has told this Court that part of the history given to him before testifying for the defence was that the deceased had not agreed to the marriage. Dr. Abeysuriya has used this circumstance as true and as one of the circumstances upon which he inferred that the deceased was moderately depressed as to suffer a hypothalamic function collapse," Mr. Bandaranayake said.

CONVENIENT INFERENCE

"We do not agree with Dr. Abeysuriya that is a necessary inference that the deceased was moderately depressed even if what he told us was true. If that were true, it is consistent with a proper exercise of parental functions whilst being in full possession of her mental faculties in the best interests of her children. It shows that the deceased has approached this question with great circumspection. In the circumstances the inference drawn by Dr. Abeysuriya is open to serious objection. If it were untrue, then Dr. Abeysuriya is not entitled to draw any inference and if he unknowingly did so his opinion is rendered unreliable. We do not agree with the inference placed by Dr. Abeysuriya on this material is a necessary inference or a probable inference. It maybe a convenient inference for the purpose of expressing the opinion that he did."

"The next aspect of the case, which we consider are the events at the Vicarage after the return of the deceased to Sri Lanka on 6.12.1978, which have bearing on the matter raised by the defence. This evidence we divide into two phases. The first phase is from 6.12.1978 to the day on which the deceased was taken by the first accused to Dr. Weerasena who prescribed Stelazine. That day appears to be around 10.12.1978, because we have before us a document produced by the prosecution, namely a drug purchase receipt, where the first accused has purchased the drugs prescribed by Dr. Weerasena on 11.12.1978."

"We refer now to the evidence of Malrani, who again plays a central part as a witness for the prosecution regarding evidence during this period. She was living at the Vicarage until 2.1.1979 with her parents. She had the opportunity of being a witness to certain events, which she has described and are of significance to the cause of death. The prosecution has submitted that the chain of events culminating in the admission of the deceased to the General Hospital started the very night that the deceased returned home to the Vicarage and to the consortium of her husband. On 6.12.1978, says Malrani, the first accused allegedly got into a trance while she and the deceased were lying on their bed. After the trance, the first accused explained that the angel had told him that the deceased had some stomach ailment and that the angel said that the deceased should be shown to Dr. Weerasena. The first accused asked the deceased whether she had any pain and the deceased said that she had no pain."

"The prosecution relied upon the statements made by the deceased as circumstances of the transaction which led to her death. If they are believed after a proper consideration, then they could well form circumstances relating to the case. We bear in mind that such statements have been made by a person not before Court, that the statement is not on oath and that statement has not been tested by cross examination. We have to bear in mind the possibilities that the respondent may have some reason to say something false. We also have to consider whether the person who testifies before us regarding such a statement is a reliable witness."

"Malrani stated that the deceased was puzzled about this pronouncement. She also believed the first accused. Malrani stated the deceased questioned the first accused and asked him what all this was about. Malrani also stated that for the whole of that month of December, no doctor came to the Vicarage and treated her mother although there were several occasions when her mother appeared unwell, looking drowsy, sleeping a lot, unable to attend parties but sometimes well, walking about, not drowsy."

"It is also the evidence of Rev. and Mrs. Mendis that the deceased visited them on 7.12.1978 the day after her return to see her grandchild who was with them. On that occasion the deceased appeared very well and cheerful and happy. Eardley Mendis speaks of the deceased attending Thursday evening services on 7.12.1978. This evidence, if believed, suggests that the deceased was behaving quite normally and trying to adjust herself to normal family life at the Vicarage as quickly as possible," Mr. Bandaranayake said.

SEVERE DEPRESSION

"In this background we have the fact that the first accused took the deceased to Dr. Weerasena who diagnosed anxiety upon the history told to him by the first accused and prescribed an anti-depressive drug called Stelazine. The evidence shows that would have been just two or three days after the return of the deceased to the Island. The defence cross examined Dr. Weerasena on the footing that Stelazine is a major tranquilizer and not a mere anti-depressant. The defence referred to the book 'Clinical Pharmacology' by Laurence and Bennet, which is a physicians' standard text book and the defence suggested that Mrs. Peiris suffered a severe depression. Dr. Weerasena said that Stelazine was not a major tranquilizer as suggested by the defence, that in any event he used it in very mild doses to help her to get over a state of anxiety. This opinion was confirmed by Dr. Sathanandan, that indeed the dosage prescribed was very mild and that it would not even cause drowsiness by itself."

"The defence says that it is probable that the condition of anxiety she suffered as evidenced by the letters was aggravated by the failure of the marriage proposal. For one thing, we do not know whether the marriage proposal failed before 9.12.1978 or thereabouts. In any event we do not have sufficient evidence to come to a conclusion as to when the proposal was abandoned and we are not in agreement that the inference drawn by Dr. Abeysuriya is a necessary inference. So we observe the first accused's conduct in rushing the deceased to Dr. Weerasena once between 6.12.1978 and 11.12.1978."

"On a latter occasion without the presence of the deceased also within this time, Dr. Weerasena says that the prescribed Maxalon and Festal for puffiness of the stomach which the first accused claimed the deceased suffered from and he also sought treatment for himself for a high blood a pressure condition for which Dr. Weerasena prescribed Declinax, which brings down blood pressure. These drugs have been bought on 11.12.1978 by the first accused from the New City Chemists, Maradana."

"In regard to the conditions which prevail in the United Kingdom, we have come to a conclusion that it is not material upon which this Court can say that there was a continuing state of strained relations between the deceased and her daughter leading to depression. Upon the evidence before us, it is our considered decision that the inference, which the defence wishes us to draw, is improbable. We believe Malrani in regard to her evidence of a trance and the conduct of the first accused. She had an opportunity to witness this. The first accused was known to indulge in activities of this nature. We see no merit in the defence suggestion, denied by the witness, that she was been put up by the Mendises to falsely testify against her father."

"Taking all these facts into consideration, it is our view that the evidence does not point to anything concerning the children for the deceased to be anxious about, if indeed she was anxious. If at all, the evidence points to the conduct of the first accused as confusing the deceased. Upon this question of trances, the Court has to decide issues upon evidence concerning things of this world. There is no possibility for the Court to come to any finding upon things super-natural. There is no evidence that the first accused indeed had any connection in fact either with the divinity or the demon. Such things depend on questions of faith. This Court cannot decide upon such matters. This Court can decide only on the facts before us deposed to by the witnesses. The first accused claimed that he was communicating with the super-natural and that he uttered certain words. Our function is to see whether that is true or not."

Mr. Bandaranayake then considered the evidence of events at the Vicarage after the return of Mrs. Peiris to Sri Lanka and the evidence after Dr. Weerasena treated Mrs. Peiris in mid-December.

CHURCH RIVALRIES

"As regards this period, we have evidence from witnesses Malrani, Rev. Mendis, Mrs. Mendis and Eardley Mendis. We bear in mind the submission made by the defence in the cross-examination of these witnesses on the footing that as Rev. Mendis in particular, was not well disposed towards the first accused owing to Church rivalries, he influenced the children and roused them against the second accused and against their father the first accused, and that their evidence is therefore coloured because of prejudice. Bearing this submission in mind, we examine their testimony."

"It was the evidence of Myrtle Mendis that shortly after the deceased visited her on 7.12.1978, she returned that visit by going to the Vicarage but that the deceased was not cheerful like on her visit to Dehiwela. Myrtle states that on another visit to the Vicarage on 29.12.1978 to invite the deceased for a family lunch on the New Year's Eve that was on 31.12.1978 she says the deceased told her 'I am not sure that I can come as I am feeling dizzy'. At a visit between Christmas and the 29th, Mrs. Peiris had told her that she does not feel well, off and on and then she is alright. On 31.12.1979, Mrs. Peiris did not come for lunch. The first accused telephoned and said they were not coming rather abruptly, but he did not give a reason. They assumed that Mrs. Peiris was unwell. On 2.1.1978 when Myrtle went to the Vicarage to see Malrani off, Mrs. Peiris was not well and she did not go to the airport to see Malrani off. Myrtle questioned Mrs. Peiris, who stated that she was feeling drowsy, dizzy and weak, but sometimes she is all right," Mr. Bandaranayake said.

"Rev. Mendis has told us that he visited the Vicarage on the 10th or 11th of December after her visit to Dehiwela and he found her dull, slow speaking and feeling drowsy. On another visit, between Christmas and the New Year, she found Mrs. Peiris disinterested in things. Upon questioning her, she said she was depressed and that the first accused had her treated by Dr. Weerasena. Upon this the first accused said, that she was unwell but that he did not say what was wrong."

"Witness Eardley Mendis has also told us that he had dinner with the deceased on the night she returned from abroad and that on the following day she attended the Thursday Service, but that after sometime he found his sister's health had deteriorated around Christmas time and that the first accused told him that she was unhappy about the children being abroad. We know that both Malrani and Mihiri were in Sri Lanka during this same period. We bear in mind the criticisms that have been made by the defence in relation to the testimony of these witnesses. They are speaking to observations that they claimed to have made themselves, in relation to the conduct of the first accused and symptoms and signs of sickness of Mrs. Peiris. All of these circumstances and suggested culpability of the accused, only depending on other proved circumstances regarding the cause of death."

"When we look at this body of evidence intrinsically, we do not see any substantial reason why we should doubt their evidence. The suggestion that Rev. Mendis has influenced the children is unacceptable to us. The misconduct of a parent could well prejudice children, but to say that intentionally and falsely such allegations were made in order to prejudice the children is another matter."

"We have seen and heard these witnesses who have testified before us on oath. We have had the opportunity of observing their demeanour. We are satisfied that they have been objective in their testimony and simply speaking to incident that took place such as for example, that Mrs. Peiris did not attend their party or to observations that they have made with regard to the drowsy state of the Mrs. Peiris, which by itself is consistent with any interpretation. So we are confident that the witnesses are not exaggerating suppressing facts and are reliable. So we accept their testimony relating to the above matters as reliable. So upon this evidence, which we accept, it is clear that Mrs. Peiris was ill after her return. None of the witnesses have ventured to give a reason for her state of health. They speak in relation to fixed events such as the Christmas day, Malrani's party on the 29th and Edison's party on the 31st."

LYING UNCONSCIOUS

"The following day Malrani left for England. So in this sense, there are fixed events regarding which the witnesses are asked to speak. So they speak to the conduct in relation to that event, so that they have a good reason to remember these events and soon thereafter Mrs. Peiris was lying unconscious in hospital for nearly seven weeks. So that there is a continuing chain of events, proximate to each other which would help the witnesses to recollect the chain culminating in the death of their sister and we find that they made their statements to the police fairly soon after."

"Now the fact that Mrs. Peiris did not attend Rev. Mendis's party and the fact that she could not go to see Malrani off at the airport stands uncontradicted. In fact her state of ill-health on the 3rd December 1978, is confirmed by an admission made by the first accused to Dr. E. V. Peiris. So, the probabilities are that the deceased was in fact ill considering this period, but we also observe a peculiar feature and that is that at that time the first accused did not disclose that his wife had been unconscious on 31.1.1979 to his wife's relations or to his younger daughter."

"Another matter which is highly significant in this connection is that Dr. Weerasena has not been called in during this period to examine or treat Mrs. Peiris. On 15.1.1979, Dr. Weerasena says that upon an urgent call by first accused he left his patients at the clinic and rushed to the Vicarage where he found the deceased in a state of unconsciousness. The first accused and the second accused were present with her. We say that it is significant that Dr. Weerasena was not called in on 31.1.1979 because, it is to him that the first accused has turned on so many occasions concerning her health after her return. Nor is there any evidence that any other doctor has attended to her."

"So we find the conduct of the first accused strange. We are satisfied that Mrs. Peiris was not well on 31.12.1978, because if she had been well we have no doubt that she would have gone for the party. So in this context we examine the conduct of the first accused. He rushes to Dr. Weerasena no sooner she arrives in the country at a time when all the witnesses who had any connection with her saw in unison that she looked well, happy, cheerful and visiting relations etc. But a few days later, when she was observed to be ill by all these same witnesses drowsy, distracted, complaining that she does not know what is wrong with her, unable to attend family functions and unable to see her daughter off at the airport, what does the first accused do? He keeps her at home up to a point of time in the middle of January. Two days after Mihiri left Sri Lanka, Mrs. Peiris was found unconscious at the Vicarage with an unrecordable blood pressure."

"This must have been sudden because on 14.1.1979, she has written a lengthy letter to her children in Wales which has been produced in this case marked 2D1. It has not been pointed out to this Court that anything in that letter is incoherent or confused indicating thereby that the deceased's mental state was not sound. As a matter of fact, a passage from that letter is relied upon accepted and adopted by the defence as correct, reliable, truthful, gave a correct picture of the state of things at that time. But on the next day by 5 p.m. she is flat on her bed, unconscious with no pulse and with her blood pressure that was inaudible even through a stethoscope. We have the admission of the first accused to Dr. E.V. Peiris that Mrs. Peiris had blackouts twice in December on the 17th and on the 29th and that she was in a collapsed state. So we see that this must have been after Myrtle Mendis visited her on that day because Myrtle Mendis had been speaking to her and she had stated that she had been feeling dizzy. This admission itself supports the evidence of Rev. and Mrs. Mendis, Malrani and Eardley that Mrs. Peiris was unwell from about mid-December."

"But what is most significant is that according to Malrani, Mrs. Peiris stated that the first accused was giving her pills and that she thought that those pills were making her drowsy. Malrani has also told this Court, and we accept her evidence, that her father used to give tablets to her mother and that after taking those tablets mother used to sleep and sleep. Malrani also told Court that Mrs. Peiris never took tablets on her own, but that they were always given to her by the first accused. This evidence is supported and confirmed by an admission made by the first accused to Dr. Sathanandan at the Durdans Hospital."

"We have scrutinized the evidence of Malrani with great care bearing in mind all the criticisms made of her evidence and the submissions of the defence. However, it is our finding that Malrani has been an objective and fair witness who has not falsely testified in this case. We accept her evidence as truthful. Now in the background of proved facts, we ask ourselves whether there is any merit in the defence suggestion that Mrs. Peiris suffered from an endogenous natural mental illness. If she was depressed and she took Stelazine she should have recovered because we see that when she was depressed at Durdans when she was treated, she recovered fully in 3 or 4 days. If as the defence says Stelazine is a major psychiatric drug, then we can see no reason whatsoever why she should have remained in a poor state of health if the cause of her poor state of health was an endogenous mental ailment."

NO MENTAL ILLNESS

"In the result, these contradictions arise when examining the defence suggestions and the proved conduct of the first accused. The evidence points unerringly to an overwhelming probability that she was not suffering from any endogenous mental illness and that her physical state was not due to any natural causes. According to Myrtle, he went out of his way to help people when they were sick by calling in the best doctors. If they were due to natural causes, then we would expect the first accused would have had no hesitation in doing the same for his wife. The fact that he kept the collapse of his wife with black-outs a secret, lends credibility to an inference that these blackouts had something to do with the pills proved to have been administered by him to his wife."

"In dealing with his aspect of the case, we must first mention an important matter. It was the evidence of Dr. Abeysuriya in cross examination that he was given data concerning the history of Mrs. Peiris's depression and possible cause of it and that before he gave evidence for the defence he was informed that there were some family problems that worried Mrs. Peiris and that also there was a question of the abandonment of a marriage proposal for her daughter and also that her children were abroad and also that there was a question concerning another lady at the Vicarage, whom Mrs. Peiris did not like."

"All these were factors which he took together along with the information that Mrs. Peiris had been examined and treated for depression by a psychiatrist. In this connection, we must point out at once that the defence produced a document in evidence marked as exhibit 2D1, which is a letter written by the deceased to her daughter in England dated 14.1.1979."

Mr. Bandaranayake said this date achieves significance for two reasons. (a) Because it has the date after her daughter Mihiri returned to the United Kingdom, and, (b) Because it was the day before she became unconscious and was admitted to Durdans.

He said that a passage relied upon by the defence as relevant to the cause of death tended to contradict a previous statement that the deceased has made in December, concerning the second accused.

"The defence pointed out that Mrs. Peiris had written 'Fortunately Dalrene looks to the marketing'. The reference to Dalrene there is reference to the second accused. At the time it was produced, Counsel for defence submitted that the purpose of marking it was for two reasons. (a) That it provided substantive evidence of a statement made by Mrs. Peiris, which related to the circumstances that led to her death, and (b) That it contradicted the testimony of Malrani that Mrs. Peiris objected to the second accused visiting the Vicarage."

"Counsel for the second accused submitted that this document proves that Mrs. Peiris did not object to the second accused's presence at the Vicarage and that therefore Malrani's testimony is unreliable. This matter needs consideration. We go back to the evidence of Malrani. She says that her mother told her father that it was not nice for the second accused to be visiting the Vicarage so often, to which the first accused replied that it was the angel's guidance and that the angel had asked him to look after this family, and that Mrs. Peiris accepted what the first accused said as she believed in angels and she believed in the first accused and trusted him."

"So we have the fact that Mrs. Peiris accepted what the first accused stated and also 2D1, which is what she wrote, which clearly shows then that by the 14th January 1979, she had accepted the presence of the second accused at the Vicarage and was thankful to her for being helpful around the house. In these circumstances, we hold that the fact of the second accused's presence at the Vicarage was not a fact which could reasonably have contributed to depression. 2D1 clearly eliminates any possibility that Mrs. Peiris became unconscious by the following day because of sorrow resulting from the second accused's presence. So we find that this factor, which Dr. Abeysuriya took into account as true to base an opinion did not probably exist. So two of the factors which Dr. Abeysuriya took into account, namely, the abandonment of the marriage proposal and the presence of a woman at the Vicarage could not have contributed to her depression because they were probably non-existent."

"We have also expressed the reasons for our opinion about the matter of the marriage proposal. As for the children who were abroad, it is true they were abroad but all of them doing well. All of them were employed. Two of them were married and the grandchild was in Sri Lanka all of which ordinarily are things which comfort parents and do not disturb them."

DURDANS HOSPITAL EVIDENCE

"Dr. Weerasena has told us that the first accused telephoned him in the evening of 15.1.1979 and asked him to come urgently to the Vicarage as the deceased was unconscious. He said he went there immediately leaving behind two of his patients and found the first accused and second accused in the Vicarage and Mrs. Peiris lying senseless on a bed. The first accused told him that Mrs. Peiris had been drowsy and suddenly got unconscious."

"Upon examination he found that she responded sluggishly to painful stimuli. Her blood pressure was unrecordable in that it could not be heard even with a stethoscope. Her pulse could not be felt. Dr. Weerasena realized it was an emergency. He phoned for an ambulance, he phoned Durdans Hospital and alerted them to this patient and gave them instructions as to what to do as soon as she was brought there, viz. to administer 10% dextrose drip and dexamethasone, one to elevate blood sugar and the other to elevate blood pressure. He himself saw the patient off in the ambulance and went to his clinic in Kollupitiya and attended to his patients, but whilst doing so he phoned Durdans and was told that the patient had recovered."

"We now examine the questions, (a) Are the matters deposed in evidence by Dr. Weerasena supported in any way?, and (b) Is there any evidence oral or documentary, tending to show that what Dr. Weerasena says is accurate?"

"The entry at page 1 of the BHT, marked in evidence as exhibit P10, is not in Dr. Weerasena's handwriting. There is reference to the fact that he is the doctor in attendance. The very first entry at the top right hand corner is to the effect that 10% dextrose and dexamethasone are to be administered. Thereafter, there is a writing giving a history of the patient and thereafter the observations of the House Officer who examined her. These are all the entries on the first side of the BHT page 1."

"There is nothing there to indicate that Dr. Weerasena had been present at Durdans at the time Mrs. Peiris was admitted. All entries on that page are by the office staff that registered the patient, a nurse about the first aid given and observations and comments by the House Officer Dr. (Mrs.) Panditharatne, who testified before us in the case. These facts arising out of the document that has been contemporaneously made at the time of her admission incontrovertibly support Dr. Weerasena's testimony before this Court as to the circumstances just narrated under which Mrs. Peiris came to be hospitalized that evening."

Mr. Bandaranayake said that there was further support for Dr. Weerasena's testimony coming from Rev. and Mrs. Myrtle Mendis, who said that the first accused telephoned them and informed them that Mrs. Peiris had been unconscious and admitted to Durdans whereupon they immediately took a bus and came to Kollupitiya from Dehiwala, and saw Mrs. Peiris by 6.30 p.m., recovered and conscious and able to speak at that time.

"So Myrtle Mendis says that she was surprised because the telephone message from the first accused said that Mrs. Peiris was unconscious, but when she came to Durdans within a very short time she found her conscious. It will be seen therefore, that there is a satisfactory body of evidence independently supporting Dr. Weerasena on material parts concerning this incident. We have a further factor that might be mentioned in this connection, i.e. when the first accused took Mrs. Peiris on 24.1.1979 to Dr. E. V. Peiris, he gave him a history that Mrs. Peiris has had a blackout and fallen on the ground at the Vicarage on 15.1.1979. Taking all this evidence together, we have no hesitation in believing Dr. Weerasena that he has spoken the truth before us in regard to the circumstances under which he got Mrs. Peiris removed to hospital and saved her life on that day, because he says if she had not been given this emergency treatment she would have died. This fact too we accept," Mr. Bandaranayake said.

"Now when we pursue this BHT P10, we find that it was the first accused who has given the history to the House Officer at Durdans who has recorded it, because it was the first and the second accused who accompanied Mrs. Peiris from the Vicarage in the ambulance to Durdans. The history given is as follows: 'Treated for acute depression with Artane and Stelazine. Was drowsy since yesterday.' Dr. (Mrs.) Panditharatne has seen this patient after she recovered consciousness. This doctor has noted, 'Drowsy, responds to stimuli, does not talk but obeys commands and blood pressure 150/90.' On the next page are entries, 'Abdomen soft, conscious, no neck stiffness, and plantar reflexes down. 10% dextrose and dexamethasone to be continued'."

"Upon the medical evidence that has been placed before us, it would appear that there were no signs of stroke in this patient and that the blood pressure had picked up but, that the patient was drowsy. Dr. Weerasena says that he visited Durdans and saw Mrs. Peiris at about 9 p.m. that night and that she was seated up and talked with him and then he wrote a minute to Dr. Attygalle to see the patient. In that minute he has mentioned that her blood pressure was unrecordable that day and that the patient had been depressed for some time and had been very drowsy since that morning. So, one can see that certain particulars in that entry must have been from the history given to him by the first accused. The contemporaneous note also supports his oral testimony that her blood pressure was unrecordable at the Vicarage. Dr. Weerasena has not been there at that time. He makes entries for the first time at the bottom of page 2, which supports his evidence that from the Vicarage that he returned to his clinic and came to the Durdans only at about 9 p.m."

"So it is entered that the first accused who has given the history concerning his wife and what is significant is this:

(1) that he has not stated that the patient was unconscious or in a senseless condition in which she was brought to hospital, but he has merely stated that the patient was drowsy since yesterday, and,

(2) that he has stated that the patient had been treated for acute depression. He has not mentioned that the patient had a blackout and fallen down, which is the history he gave Dr. E. V. Peiris."

"Now as far as the above is concerned, we believe Dr. Weerasena for the reasons we have already given that the first accused telephoned in the evening and said that his wife was lying unconscious at the Vicarage and that he rushed there leaving some of his bad patients behind and found Mrs. Peiris unconscious on a bed breathing rapidly. Dr. Weerasena has said that he could not feel her pulse, nor did she obey commands, she responded only sluggishly to painful stimuli, her blood pressure could not be heard through the stethoscope and that it was therefore unrecordable and she needed immediate attention without which she would have died. He said that the first accused had told him that Mrs. Peiris had been drowsy and suddenly got unconscious."

"At this point we would like to compare Dr. Weerasena's evidence with that of Dr. E. V. Peiris, who has told us that the first accused told him that on 15.1.1979 his wife had complained of severe thirst twice the previous night and in the morning had a blackout and fell down. So we see that the first accused gives a different history of Mrs. Peiris's illness to the two doctors. We also find that he has withheld this history of blacking out or unconsciousness in giving the history of the patient to the Durdans Hospital where he has only said that she had been drowsy."

"In these circumstances we see Dr. (Mrs.) Panditharatne examined the patient at Durdans after she recovered consciousness, having had dextrose and dexamethasone, which Dr. Weerasena had ordered. So when Dr. (Mrs.) Panditharatne examined the patient she obeyed commands and responded to stimuli and clearly shows that she is recovering consciousness. Mendis confirmed this when she said that by 6.30 p.m. when she went the deceased was conscious and talking."

"So we find that is the history that the first accused gave of drowsiness only which is recorded in P10 which Dr. Sathanandan took as data for his diagnosis. Dr. Sathanandan has told us that he was quite unaware of the fact that Mrs. Peiris had been unconscious and brought to hospital. It is apparent to us that even Dr. Weerasena has not realized this that the fact of unconsciousness was not recorded in the BHT at that time. That is entirely consistent with Dr. Weerasena not realizing the significance of this at that time."

"Upon the evidence of Dr. Weerasena and the evidence of Dr. E. V. Peiris to the effect of the first accused's admission to him about his wife fainting and falling on the ground having earlier complained twice of severe thirst, we hold it proved beyond reasonable doubt and that we are satisfied that is the correct position, that Mrs. Peiris had been unconscious in the Vicarage on 15.1.1979. This is the fact that we hold established in this case. We also observe that upon the medical opinions that we have in this case the symptoms of severe thirst referred to by the first accused is a symptom of hypoglycaemia, which is another symptom which Dr. Sathanandan was not aware of."

"Dr. Weerasena has told us that Mrs. Peiris did not suffer from acute depression when he saw her in early December but that she was anxious and that he prescribed mild doses of a drug Stelazine. The dosage of Stelazine prescribed is confirmed as being mild by Dr. Sathanandan. In these circumstances we find that the first accused has given a history to the Durdans Hospital that his wife was having acute depression. This in our view is a significant fact. We see that Dr.

Weerasena has in a minute to Dr. Attygalle (page 2 of P2) only said that Mrs. Peiris was depressed for some time. He has not said that she was acutely depressed."

"We have the further fact that Dr. Weerasena prescribed only sufficient pills of Stelazine with Artane to prevent side effects for about 10 days up to about second January. So that in any event, there was no necessity for Mrs. Peiris to be given Stelazine beyond that period. It is a fact that around that time the first accused had neither met Dr. Weerasena concerning Mrs. Peiris nor brought her to him. So, one could assume that there was no necessity to consult him on this question of depression. On the other hand, if she had been depressed and the first accused had on his own continued with Stelazine then there should be no question of a mental condition causing her drowsiness and depression because she was on the drug which would elevate her mood. We are satisfied that the first accused did not consult Dr. Weerasena for the period of one month between about the 12th of December and the 15th of January. Dr. Weerasena says he was not consulted; Malrani says that no doctor came to the Vicarage and there has been no cross examination suggesting this either. So, we are confident that Dr. Weerasena is speaking the truth that during this period of one month between mid-December and mid-January he had no occasion whatsoever to treat Mrs. Peiris."

"But yet, we have the admission of the first accused himself to Dr. E.V. Peiris that she had blackouts and collapsed sweating on 17.12.1979 and on 31.12.1979. But when no medical attention is given to her we have the evidence that on 31.12.1979 the second accused visited the Vicarage and we also know that on that day Mrs. Peiris could not attend the New Year Eve party at her brother's house," Mr. Bandaranayake said.

ATTACKS OF DROWSINESS

"We can look at this question in another way. If the first accused was continuing with Stelazine in January there was no reason for Mrs. Peiris to have collapsed unconscious at the Vicarage on 15.1.1979. We find that after her admission to Durdans on the drug Tofranil, which is also an anti-depressant drug, she recovered fully in the space of four days. If he had discontinued Stelazine and she had all these attacks of drowsiness on the 17th and 31st as admitted by and confirmed by prosecution witnesses Malrani and the Mendises, that she was drowsy at the Vicarage during this period, we can see no reason why the first accused did not get medical help for her, if he felt it was necessary to rush her to a doctor no sooner than she returned to Sri Lanka."

"We find his conduct is self-contradictory and suspicious. This whole question of an ordinary natural cause of depression is therefore cast in suspicion and substantial doubt, as to whether there was any natural endogenous cause whatsoever which resulted in this condition. In these circumstances we find that the data given to Dr. Abeysuriya is most unreliable and unsafe and no reasonable, proper and reliable inference could be drawn to support an expert medical opinion."

"Dr. Sathanandan told us that infections such as meningitis and encephalitis were irrelevant because if they are present the patient would have been much more ill. Dr. Sathanandan says he definitely eliminated stroke as the cause of the illness. She looked depressed and he had been aware that she had been unconscious and that she recovered consciousness upon the administration of dextrose and dexamethasone. It would have influenced his diagnosis because then he would have looked for some physical cause for her depression. He said that if he had been aware of the fact of unconsciousness he would have thought about the matter more before coming to a diagnosis of a mental cause to the exclusion of a physical cause. He says there are physical illnesses that cause depression. Depression can be associated with many physical disease or illnesses. Hypoglycaemia is one of the conditions which could cause a depressive feeling. So in the absence of that information that on 15.1.1979 she had been admitted unconscious to Durdans, which is the evidence that we believe and accept," Mr. Bandaranayake said.

"Dr. Sathanandan has made a diagnosis of 'endogenous reactive depression', which he said afflicts older people after forty years caused by a precipitation like a family bereavement, failing of an examination, on a broken love affair to mention some of the situations. This condition, he said was eminently curable and this is what he set about doing and succeeded in doing within four days. He prescribed the drug Tofranil 25 mg three times a day together with a sleeping draft nitrazepam. The trade name of the latter is Mogadon and the dosage 10 mg, in the night. He said that these drugs have no effect on a person not suffering from depression. The dosage he prescribed was the smallest beginning dosage of these drugs and if it is insufficient he would have increased the dose. He said this drug elevates the mood of the person."

"He also stopped the drug earlier prescribed by Dr. Weerasena namely Stelazine and Artane. He could well have been misled into thinking that she was not recovering on those drugs. So in these circumstances we are convinced that the first accused would have been aware of the fact that Stelazine and Artane had been stopped. For Dr. Sathanandan to say this, it must mean that he was under the impression that Stelazine was being given right up to the time of Durdans admission."

"We counteract this evidence with the testimony of Dr. Weerasena, which we believe that he prescribed Stelazine for a maximum of about ten days about the 9th or 10th of December, so that this prescription should have been over by about the second of January. It was the duty of the first accused to have informed Dr. Sathanandan of the true facts. If in fact Mrs. Peiris had been taking Stelazine right up to the 15th of January, we see no reason whatsoever for her to become unconscious as a result of the condition of mental depression caused by a mental disease. In the result we observe a maze of contradictory conduct on the part of the first accused, in relation to his wife's sickness."

"Dr. Sathanandan has also spoken of a conversation he had with the first accused and the deceased. During that conversation he says he asked them whether there is a possibility of her having taken an overdose of the drugs Dr. Weerasena had ordered, and the first accused had said that it was not possible because it was he who gave the drugs. We believe Dr. Sathanandan. This is also confirmed by statements made by the deceased to Malrani and Rev. and Mrs. Mendis that the first accused was giving her drugs. We find that all these witnesses support each other on this matter."

NO SUICIDAL TENDENCIES

"Further, as a psychiatrist, Dr. Sathanandan definitely excludes possibility of Mrs. Peiris having any suicidal tendencies. He was exhaustively examined on this question by counsel in this case and he has categorically stated his opinion that Mrs. Peiris was not at all likely to have ever contemplated suicide. Upon these circumstances, we believe the evidence before us that it was the first accused who was giving her the drugs whatever they were. We accept the evidence of Dr. Sathanandan as expert testimony before us upon these matters. He also has told us that Mrs. Peiris has recovered very well to almost 100% from her depression and that she was discharged from hospital on 20.1.1978. We observe that for ourselves from the document P10."

"So, we have the evidence that the diagnosis of Dr. Sathanandan that Mrs. Peiris suffered from 'Endogenous Reactive Depression' on 16.1.1979 is open to considerable doubt upon the admission of the specialist who made the diagnosis. His factual observation that Mrs. Peiris looked depressed may well be correct and reliable. But, the opinion as to the cause he says might have been different had he known the full history and had he known that she had been unconscious at the time she was admitted to hospital."

Mr. Bandaranayake said that this is a clinical fact, which the Court has held to be established in this case and it was not known to Dr. Sathanandan at the time he made his diagnosis.

"Dr. Sathanandan has further told us that if he had known that she had been admitted unconscious and regained consciousness upon the administration of dextrose then her depression would have been consistent with a physical cause and not a mental cause. So we see upon this discussion that the three factors Dr. Abeysuriya took into his reckoning for arriving at an opinion of the presence of a moderate depression on account of a mental condition are:

(1) The objection of Mrs. Peiris for the presence of a woman at the Vicarage,

(2) The feeling of sadness at the breakdown of a proposal of a possible marriage for Malrani, and

(3) The diagnosis of 'Endogenous Mental Depression' by Dr. Sathanandan.

They are all without substance. We have already expressed our views."

Continuing, Mr. Bandaranayake said, "Upon the reasons we gave that far from objecting to the presence of the second accused, Mrs. Peiris was thankful to her presence in January 1979 as is evidenced by 2D1. We also have the evidence that upon the explanation given by the first accused that the angel had asked him to look after the second accused and family, Mrs. Peiris accepted that position. We have also expressed our views and given our reasons as to why we hold that abandonment of the marriage proposal for Malrani could reasonably not have caused a depression in Mrs. Peiris because Dr. Abeysuriya says it was Mrs. Peiris herself who was responsible for that abandonment."

"Now we see that Dr. Sathanandan's diagnosis is open to considerable doubt. The history that the first accused has given to Dr. Abeysuriya on all these matters has influenced Dr. Abeysuriya to his decision and opinion. So if that data is non-existent or unreliable or open to real and substantial doubt that must affect the reliability of the opinion of Dr. Abeysuriya. In such circumstances an opinion of the probable presence of a moderate depression causing a fall in the deceased's blood pressure at the hospital on 31.1.1979, thus depriving Mrs. Peiris's brain cells of oxygen and causing anoxia is most unreliable."

"What we see is that the opinion that the fall in the blood pressure was due to an endogenous mental condition suppressing the hypothalamus is unreliable. The data concerning the actual presence of an endogenous mental condition in our opinion is totally unreliable. On this evidence before us there is a distinct probability that her depression was due to a physical cause and not a mental cause. In the circumstances we hold that Dr. Abeysuriya had no reliable material before him upon which he could have come to a reliable opinion regarding Mrs. Peiris's illness. In the result his opinion that Mrs. Peiris was probably depressed on 31.1.1979, which in itself is a long jump from 15.1.1979 because he has no data about depression in the intervening period, causing damage to brain cells as described by him is unsatisfactory and not based on any acceptable foundation."

Mr. Bandaranayake said that on 20.1.1979, Mrs. Peiris was fully recovered and Dr. Abeysuriya did not say how he could just come to a conclusion that she was depressed on 31.1.1979, and that he based his opinions mostly on the contents of P49, in which in one experiment it was stated that in a small minority of cases of severe depression, low cortisol level was observed upon insulin shock being induced in those patients.

"There is no evidence whatsoever that Mrs. Peiris was severely depressed. The only evidence is that she suffered from 'Reactive Depression'; for whatever it is worth that opinion too is doubtful. It could have been a depression arising out of her physical condition. The medical journal Dr. Abeysuriya used in support of his theory that moderate depression causes suppressed hypothalamus activity, does not support that opinion in fact. In the most, it supports a theory that severe depression is seen to really cause a depressed cortical activity only to 25% of cases investigated. The vast majority had not suffered such a result."

MODERATE DEPRESSION

"So it is seen that in itself is acridity. Again we have earlier in this order rejected Dr. Abeysuriya's opinion that moderate depression causes spontaneous 'Reactive Hypoglycaemia'. That opinion also is not supported by the very document he relied upon because in the experiment the hypoglycaemia was induced by insulin injection. Furthermore, we observe the further very important fact that on 15.1.1979 despite an unrecordable blood pressure, Mrs. Peiris did not suffer brain damage which fact by itself makes Dr. Abeysuriya's opinion improbable, unlikely and unreliable."

"In this context we also like to remind ourselves that on 31.1.1979 on admission to the General Hospital Mrs. Peiris's blood pressure was 100/60, which is only just below normal. So that if she was unconscious as Rev. Mendis says at 11 a.m. when he went to the Vicarage, which is evidence that we believe and accept, her blood pressure had not fallen. It might even be safe for us to conclude that at that time her blood pressure was higher than 100/60 which would mean that it was normal."

"We also bear in mind Dr. Abeysuriya's own testimony that in a state of unconsciousness the stress factor of mental depression is inoperative. We also bear in mind the admission made by the first accused to Dr. Terrence de Silva that Mrs. Peiris had been drowsy to unconscious for the previous eighteen hours with a fluctuating level of consciousness. In this context it is difficult for us to accept that there was a criterion of a depressive stress factor causing a sudden fall of blood pressure between 12.15 p.m. and 12.30 p.m. We have given our reasons for holding that the data upon which Dr. Abeysuriya came in his finding about 'Reactive Hypoglycaemia', namely P24, P13, and P21, highly suspicious; or emanated from the first accused whose conduct concerning GTT of 29.1.1979 we have held to be mendacious and more unreliable. Therefore, the data Dr. Abeysuriya needs to testify about Reactive Hypoglycaemia is itself unsafe and unreliable and unacceptable to this Court."

Mr. Bandaranayake said that the result is that the opinion that Dr. Abeysuriya expressed before this Court that in all the circumstances he was made aware of, that there is a great probability that Mrs. Peiris suffered a moderate depression on 31.1.1979 due naturally to an endogenous mental condition resulting in spontaneous 'Reactive Hypoglycaemia', and also resulting in a suppression of the hypothalamus with a resultant fall in blood pressure and a resultant deprivation of oxygen to brain cells causing an anoxia, which explain the condition of permanent brain damage, is unreliable, incredible and unacceptable.

Mr. Bandaranayake said that the unconsciousness seen on 31.1.1979 is,

- not supported by any acceptable and proper scientific or medical knowledge,

- not supported by any other medical opinion from among a plethora of doctors who have testified before Court, and

- not based on any true, correct, acceptable and convincing data, is self-contradictory and speculative.

"We place no reliance on his opinion whatsoever. In the result his evidence does not amount to expert testimony placed before this Court. We reject it as irrelevant to these proceedings. In the result it is our judgement that the defence submission that permanent brain damage and the state of unconsciousness which Mrs. Peiris suffered on 31.1.1979 was due to natural mental disorder is not supported by any credible evidence. The facts and circumstances pointed out by the defence and the opinion evidence they have led at this trial does not in our view cast a reasonable doubt on the prosecution case. We do not think that the defence position is at all likely and that is our finding."

"But this is not all. We also observe the conduct of the first accused in March 1978, upon the evidence given before this Court by Dr. J. G. C. Peiris, who is a visitor in this island on holiday from the United Kingdom. He had made a trip to Sri Lanka to witness the Centenary Royal-Thomian Cricket Match played in March. He says the first accused met him and he discussed the deceased's case history and had asked him what he thought of it and Dr. Peiris said he replied saying that it appears that the deceased was in a hypoglycaemic coma. Then the first accused had asked him how that would have happened and he had replied that it is possible by one of two ways. Either Mrs. Peiris would have taken an anti-diabetic drug or somebody would have given it to her and also told him that it would be difficult to prove she had taken it herself or whether it had been administered to her by someone. Dr. Peiris says that at that stage the first accused made him a request to give him a certificate on an affidavit to the effect that the deceased was a highly depressed person and was a hypochondriac taken to treating herself with drugs for imaginary diseases."

"The first accused had told him that he will get the document drafted by a lawyer and bring it for him for signature. Dr. Peiris says that he was not prepared to give the first accused such a false document and that he avoided the first accused from that time until he returned to the United Kingdom. The question of the credibility of Dr. J.G.C. Peiris will be more fully dealt with in another part of this order but sufficient to say that the Court believes Dr. Peiris as a truthful witness who can be relied upon to speak the truth. The Court has had the opportunity of observing the manner in which this witness gave evidence. This witness has been the family doctor of the first accused for several years from the 1960s up to 1974 when he left the country. Dr. Peiris is presently resident in England. He has no reason as far as we can see to speak a falsehood concerning this priest. He had been a trustee or a helper of the first accused's church while he was in Sri Lanka."

"The defence suggested to Dr. Peiris that what the first accused said to him was that he was advised by his lawyers to get this certificate. Dr. Peiris categorically denied this. We have no hesitation in accepting the testimony of Dr. Peiris. The testimony of Dr. Peiris was that the first accused sought to falsely create a document which would support a position that Mrs. Peiris was indeed mentally ill and took drugs. Dr. Peiris says that she was a perfectly normal person in all the years that he knew her and that she did not suffer from cancer and that the biopsy done on the growth in the breast was shown to be non-cancerous and that he had been present at that operation. This fact is supported fully by the post-mortem examination which also showed that Mrs. Peiris did not suffer from cancer of any organ. The question arises therefore as to why the first accused wanted such a false document medically certified. This conduct of his has to be contrasted with his having given a history to Dr. Terrence de Silva as is shown in P21 that Mrs. Peiris could not have taken an overdose of an anti-depressive drug. We have contrasted his conduct on yet another occasion and that is during the hospitalization of his wife."

"Dr. Weerasena has told us one day he met him on the corridor near ward 47B and they had a conversation and Dr. Weerasena had asked the first accused whether it is possible that the deceased could have taken anti-diabetic drugs and the first accused had looked surprised and said that he must go home and check it. We also have to consider his conduct as evidenced by the testimony of Dr. Peiris in the back drop of the defence document 1D1 and the position taken up by the defence in that regard is that the deceased suffered from a mental condition which could explain all the facts of her illness. In all these circumstances we are of the opinion that the defence suggestion in respect of the death of Mrs. Peiris is without any foundation, utterly unreliable. We reject the defence opinion offered before this Court upon the evidence of Dr. Abeysuriya and all the documents produced on behalf of the defence and other proved facts and circumstances. The opinion of Dr. Abeysuriya, we hold to be irrelevant in these proceedings. The totality of the evidence pointed out by the defence and the submissions made by the defence do not create a reasonable doubt in regard to the prosecution case."

CAUSE OF PERMANENT IRREVERSIBLE BRAIN DAMAGE

"It is our judgement that we reject the evidence as to the cause of irreversible brain damage and coma suffered by Mrs. Peiris tendered by the defence through their witness Dr. Abeysuriya. We consider Dr. Abeysuriya's evidence irrelevant in these proceedings. We also hold that the facts and circumstances placed before this Court does not show that she suffered irreversible brain damage due to natural causes, resulting from a mental sickness. In the circumstances it becomes necessary for the Court to examine the evidence to see if there is satisfactory cogent evidence before this Court establishing the cause of the irreversible brain damage and resultant unconsciousness, which led without doubt to pneumonia in the ordinary course of nature and consequent death despite all the medical care she received. In the proved circumstances of this case the prosecution must place satisfactory evidence before the Court to prove the cause of the brain damage and the coma on 31.1.1979 to prove that a crime had been committed."

Proceeding to evaluate the evidence before the Court in this respect, Mr. Bandaranayake said that it is a fact established in this case that Mrs. Peiris did in fact suffer irreversible brain damage on 31.1.1979.

"There is no contest about that and there is sufficient evidence led by the prosecution to prove it. With this proved fact as a fixed point in this case it is necessary for the party that brings the charge to eliminate all their possible causes for this condition except one that must be established beyond reasonable doubt. The prosecution has set about this task first with the evidence of Dr. Terrence de Silva. We have already recited his evidence where he had enumerated a number of possible causes of coma with damage being caused to brain cells. He spoke of cardiovascular coma, encephalitis coma, endocrine disorder coma, head injuries, poison, overdose of anti-depressant drugs, alcoholic coma, coma caused by infectious decease, a long list. He eliminated all of them but one, namely, hypoglycaemia and he gave his reasons for doing so."

"We next find that Dr. Subramaniam who had MBBS, MRCP (Forensic Medicine, UK) and Diploma in Medical Jurisprudence, twenty years' experience as a JMO and who has given evidence in a number of cases, and who was the JMO Colombo, held a judicial post-mortem examination and has examined all the glands and organs and vessels and tissues and cells in the human body and all things related to the above conditions and has told this Court that he confirms the evidence of Dr. de Silva in that he did not find any signs of symptoms of diseases. We are confident that they have spoken the truth and that they have no reason, no prejudice and no pride to mislead the Court. We accept their evidence as reliable opinion evidence and we come to the finding of fact that all these other possible physical conditions in the human body enumerated by Dr. de Silva, which might sometime be responsible for coma and brain damage in a person, have been satisfactorily eliminated by the evidence led by the prosecution and that it is established and proved in this case beyond reasonable doubt."

"We are left with the question of hypoglycaemia as the cause of the brain damage and coma. That was the opinion of Dr. de Silva based on his clinical observation of the patient, which he says is now confirmed beyond all doubt by the post-mortem findings. It is therefore, the duty of the Court to examine his evidence with a view to forming an opinion of its reliability. Dr. de Silva had before him the history given by the first accused as well as documents available with the BHT and his own observations of the patient and his clinical findings and the course of her illness and her responses to treatment, e.g., entry at EPGH 14A, that at 1 p.m. the patient has not recovered consciousness after dextrose. We bear in mind the cross examination of this witness that he was greatly influenced informing his opinion by the contents of P13 and P21, but denied by him."

"Dr. de Silva had the results of the blood sugar test, which was done upon admission, which showed a very low blood sugar namely 30 mg%, which entry is at EPGH 16B at page 5 of P21, based on the pathology report EPGH 92, which was available to him at 3.50 p.m. He also had the fact of unconsciousness plus the position that normally when an unconscious man is brought they routinely check out the question of hypoglycaemic coma/diabetic coma which we see in the case of Dr. Weerasena too. Then, looking at the question intrinsically, the blood sugar test is done to check sugar as a routine. Now in the report EPGH92, we find the time 12.30 written which means, that sample has been sent upon admission. We also have evidence that a certain suspicion too had arisen about this patient. Rightly or wrongly the suspicion was that the hypoglycaemia had been induced," Mr. Bandaranayake said.

"In these circumstances we do not see much force in the defence contention that the contents of P13 and P21 had much to do in the forming of his opinion. On the contrary, there was a sufficient body of independent data from observation and tests done at the hospital and responses to treatment from which Dr. de Silva could have reached his conclusion of hypoglycaemia on 31.1.1979. The fact of the matter is that they suspected the first accused and ordered that he not be permitted to bring prepared foods for the patient and ordered that visitors be not allowed near the patient and brought the patient close to the nurses table so that he could be under observation as they suspected that the hypoglycaemia was induced."

SUGAR WAS BAD

"We find that despite the patently confusing statement by the first accused that sugar was bad for the patient that Dr. de Silva had in fact administered dextrose which we have no doubt saved her life that day. Dr. de Silva has also asked the first accused whether Mrs. Peiris had taken anti-diabetic pills, which the first accused denied and which history is recorded in P21. We do not accept that the Dr. de Silva made a diagnosis on merely the contents of P13 and the history given."

"It is a fact in this case that the patient was treated for hypoglycaemia at the initial stages and that she lived on normal food given in liquid form through a nasal tube and that she so lived for the whole of the month of February and for three weeks in March. She died of infection arising actually from prolonged coma complicated by bed sores and causing pneumonia. She has been treated appropriately for the secondary infection. She has not been treated for any endogenous diseases but she continued to live with normal fluid diet. So this picture we have of this patient, confirms the inference that there was nothing organically wrong with her. This is a picture we can observe for ourselves upon the oral testimonies of Dr. de Silva and Dr. Pinto and the evidence in the BHT and FBC, and treatment chart. Now in this background we examine the evidence of Dr. Subramaniam which is that there was no organic cause of the brain damage because all the organs he examined showed no signs of disease. We are satisfied with his knowledge and experience. He says that there were a number of doctors present at the autopsy. This patient appears to have had special relevance to the doctors as everyone was curious to know what was wrong with her. The police had been alerted."

"Dr. Subramaniam had himself seen the patient in early February and kept her under close observation so that he knew her medical picture and treatment and responses to treatment at first hand from his own observation. So this was a special case where attention had been focused for some time. It is in these circumstances that Dr. Subramaniam came to do the post-mortem so that we feel confident that it was one with care."

Mr. Bandaranayake said that the Court has a preponderance of medical opinion, including the testimony of Dr. Subramaniam, who actually did an autopsy on all relevant organs of Mrs. Peiris and found that there was no physical disease condition of the brain and no disease condition of any of the organs either that could possibly lead to brain damage.

"He did histology on some organs. He had also visited this patient on 5.2.1979 while she was in the ward, had examined her, and knew her case history as reflected in the BHT and FBC etc. He confirmed the clinical findings of Dr. de Silva, who had Mrs. Peiris under his care and visited and treated her almost on every other day of her hospitalization. We have the further evidence of Dr. Nagaratnam, who has had the benefit of knowing the post-mortem findings and the clinical findings of Dr. Subramaniam and confirm the findings of Dr. de Silva and Dr. Subramaniam. In this way we are confident that these opinions have been expressed by skilled and experienced experts in their fields who have sufficient knowledge and experience to offer a valuable and reliable opinion to the Court on satisfactory data comprising their own observations of the patient of the course of the sickness, the personal examination of the organs of the body, the responses to a line of treatment in the background of their skill and experience in treating physical disease," Mr. Bandaranayake said.

"We accept his evidence that there was no organic disorder, no cardiovascular disease, no liver or kidney disease, no diabetes, no endocrine disorders, no large hungry tumours to reduce blood sugar to 30 mg% upon admission. The histology he did on the pancreas and surrounds show no signs of pancreatic disease, no hyperplasia, no adenomatosis, no nesidioblastosis and no insulinomas or tumours of any sort. All these disease conditions can produce excessive amounts of insulin, which could bring down blood sugar levels. They were not found at histology."

PERMANENT BRAIN DAMAGE

"Furthermore, the medical picture one gets from the period of hospitalization according to the medical opinion before us completely rules out the possibility of the presence of any of these insulin producing endogenous conditions. She was never known to suffer any of these diseases in her fifty nine years. She suddenly falls ill since 6.12.1979 and she is unconscious with permanent brain damage on 31.1.1979. She was on a normal diet whilst being unconscious and her blood pressure and blood sugar remained normal. That is completely contradictory of an insulin secreting disease. She had no history or symptoms of any of the organic disorders mentioned. Her blood sugar, once it picked up on the same day with the infusion of dextrose, never fell again. No prepared foods brought from outside were given to her."

Mr. Bandaranayake said that the fact of living for seven weeks without medicines just on normal diet makes the probability overwhelming that she did not have any endogenous organic disorders.

"We are convinced that Dr. Subramaniam's opinion is correct. It naturally follows that we focus on the condition of the brain. Dr. Subramaniam says that the only abnormality was in the brain cells. There was generalized damage more marked on the frontal lobes of the brain. But there was no sign of infection, no meningitis or encephalitis. We have referred to these conditions in detail in another part of this judgement explaining what they mean and repetition would serve no purpose. There were no signs of cerebrovascular accident."

"So upon the examination of the brain, which is relevant to this question of irreversible brain damage we find that, (a) there was no infection of the brain, and, (b) no cerebrovascular accident. But, there was generalized softening of the brain cells. He said that once softening occurred cells die. This brain damage was ante-mortem," Mr. Bandaranayake said.

"Looking at the cells under a microscope merely confirmed his macroscopic observation. He described the histology he did. He took representative parts and examined the slides he made. He explained the process. We accept it as satisfactory. It is the same process as employed by Dr. (Mrs.) Balasubramaniam and practised the world over. He said he found most of the damage to cells in the cortex. Such damage was consistent with hypoglycaemia. He said the generalized damage he found is fully consistent with having been caused by hypoglycaemia. Upon being asked by the prosecution whether if her condition was diagnosed as hypoglycaemia whether he would contradict it, he answered 'No'," Mr. Bandaranayake said.

"It is the position of Dr. Subramaniam that there was no demonstrable cause for a hypoglycaemic condition, no organic cause for it. There was no other cause also to show a reason for unconsciousness, e.g. no stroke or heart condition. He has expressed the opinion that the brain damage could have been caused by hypoglycaemia resulting from a factitious agency, an outside agency, namely the ingestion of a hypoglycaemic agent like glibenclamide. That is in his report as well. We have the evidence of Professor Jayasena and Dr. Nagaratnam that glibenclamide acts on functioning cells in the pancreas and makes them secrete more insulin. It is sold in Sri Lanka under the trade name Euglucon. Under cross examination, Dr. Subramaniam said that the softening of the brain cells was seen all over. There was no localized damage. He also said that one could not distinguish between brain cell damage due to anoxia and due to hypoglycaemia, i.e. lack of oxygen and lack of glucose. Sugar produces energy for the cell and lack of energy results is cell death. Similarly lack of oxygen could also result is cell death."

NO NATURAL CAUSE

Continuing Mr. Bandaranayake said, "In the opinion of Dr. Subramaniam, he found no natural cause whatsoever for brain cell damage. Therefore, he said brain cell damage was caused by hypoglycaemia, which was induced by the administration of an anti-diabetic drug. He has taken into account the low blood sugar value at admission. Dr. Nagaratnam agreed with Dr. de Silva's exclusion of all conditions leading to coma which we have particularized earlier. Dr. Nagaratnam agreed with the diagnosis of hypoglycaemia causing brain damaged made by doctors de Silva and Subramaniam, and approved entirely the treatment given to this patient. He said he definitely eliminated cerebrovascular accident with the information he now had after the post-mortem findings and he gave his reasons."

"Dr. Nagaratnam said that hypoglycaemia has been demonstrated in this patient. He said all signs and symptoms and the sugar tests demonstrated its presence. He said that prolonged hypoglycaemia for about five hours would deprive the brain of sugar and oxygen but damage need not be permanent. Prolonged does not mean days. It can happen in a few hours. He said prolonged hypoglycaemia for about twelve hours would affect the vasomotor centres of the brain, which would cause the blood pressure to drop as in this case. That would produce a shock state by the lack of oxygen causing a metabolic disturbance at cellular level. Blood flow is reduced and oxygen is reduced and one gets into shock. In these circumstances the brain damage is entirely consistent with hypoglycaemia."

"In other words", Mr. Bandaranayake said, "Hypoglycaemic shock resulting from a lack of glucose affects vital centres of the brain. We know that hypoglycaemia begins when blood sugar drops from the normal 60-100 mg% range to 50 mg% or 40 mg% depending on the age and condition of the person. Mrs. Peiris was fifty nine years old and frail and weak. That was the evidence before this Court. Dr. E.V. Peiris said she looked frail on 24.1.1979. Her blood sugar on admission had dropped to 30 mg%. Rev. Mendis said she was unconscious at about 11 a.m. The first accused has told many people from early morning that she was sleeping and in deep sleep. At about 7.30 a.m. that day he has asked Dr. Weerasena for a letter of admission to hospital and has told Dr. E. V. Peiris also early in the morning that he was admitting her to hospital. There must be some reason that he has himself observed early in the morning for him to decide that she needed hospitalization. We must view all circumstances connected with this admission in its proper setting."

"The first accused has also told Dr. de Silva as part of the history he gave on admission that Mrs. Peiris had been having fluctuating levels of consciousness from drowsy to deep coma for the previous eighteen hours. The language appears to be straight out of the book P40. How would he know about deep coma? The conduct of the first accused in seeing this need to admit his wife to hospital from early morning and the history he has given coupled with the observation of Rev. Mendis that she was unconscious at the Vicarage at 11 a.m., points to one single inference, and that is that she has been unconscious for several hours before 11 a.m."

DROWSINESS

"Dr. Weerasena saw her at the Vicarage at about 9 p.m. the previous night and she looked drowsy but not in need of hospitalization. Drowsiness is a symptom of hypoglycaemia. It happens when sugar begins dropping. Now we place all of these circumstances against the evidence that prolonged hypoglycaemia for about twelve hours could result in hypoglycaemic shock where the vasomotor centre of the brain is affected resulting in a drop in blood pressure thus causing reduced oxygen and reduced blood sugar reaching brain cells, causing permanent and irreversible brain damage and unconsciousness. We are satisfied that upon the entire picture of events that is what happened. We are satisfied that the conduct of the accused making arrangements to transfer the deceased from the Vicarage to the hospital from early that morning is consistent only with the inference that she was unconscious at that time and had been so for some time before. None of the deceased's relations had been at the Vicarage that morning to see Mrs. Peiris."

"But, the inference upon all of these proved circumstances is clear and that is that Mrs. Peiris was unconscious at the time the first accused was telephoning people and informing them that the deceased was sleeping but that he was hospitalizing her. That is an irresistible inference that we draw. So, we find this weak lady in a hypoglycaemic condition for several hours since early morning at the latest that day, before her admission. That is the only inference that we can draw. The proved facts are entirely consistent with the opinion evidence that this situation caused permanent brain damage. The opinion evidence rendered is reliable in the proved factual setting. If she had been unconscious for many hours since early morning, there can be no question of a mental state causing a sudden drop in blood pressure between 12.15 p.m. and 12.30 p.m., as in unconsciousness, the mental state becomes irrelevant," Mr. Bandaranayake said.

"We are satisfied beyond all reasonable doubt that it was hypoglycaemia that caused the irreversible brain damage on 31.1.1979. The opinion of Dr. Subramaniam and Dr. Nagaratnam is rendered perfectly safe and reliable in the factual setting. We adopt that opinion without reservation. All the surrounding facts do not admit of any other inference. These facts render hypoglycaemia being the cause of the brain damage as the only deducible inference in this case. We accordingly find this fact proved. In coming to this finding we have borne in mind all the submissions of counsel for the defence and the defence placed before this Court."

"We hold that the cause of the brain damage is a physical cause namely hypoglycaemia. Even Dr. Abeysuriya agreed that it is a possible cause and he was giving only a probable contrary opinion, which we have held to be unreliable as a scientific opinion and therefore irrelevant in this case. The defence led the evidence of Mr. Henry, the Assistant Government Analyst, who is a qualified chemist and has a Master's degree in chemistry, who said that anti-diabetic drugs can be identified in urine up to two days, in faeces up to five days and in blood up to three days, if one is looking especially for it. The defence complains that no effort was made by the hospital authorities on 31.1.1979 or on the next following days to take a sample of the blood, faeces and urine of Mrs. Peiris and have it analyzed for an anti-diabetic drug."

"Defence says, if the prosecution says that the cause of hypoglycaemia was induced by the administration of anti-diabetic drugs, they could have and they should have tested for it. Mr. Henry has told us that glibenclamides such as Euglucon are not accumulated in tissues, so that one does not find it in muscles because it does not accumulate in proteins but traces of it can be found in the laboratory in urine etc."

"So the defence asks, if that is so, why did not the prosecution do it? If a test had been done and glibenclamide had been identified in a sample, then that could amount to clear proof of that fact. So the defence says that the absence of such proof is a circumstance which should be considered in favour of the defence. The defence says that this is particularly so, because of the entry on the BHT at 9 p.m., which the prosecution relies upon and proved in evidence as EPGH 18A. If they have suspected it, the proper thing for them to have done was to have looked into it."

Mr. Bandaranayake said, "The prosecution has submitted that it is the evidence of the doctors, that according to their knowledge, they did not think that it was possible to do such a test in this country. Indeed it was the evidence of one of the prosecution medical witnesses that it involves special procedures not available in this country. That was the evidence of Dr. E.V. Peiris. He was presented as a witness to facts and not on opinion. It is also the position of the prosecution that a minute had been made conveying the suspicion of the information to the police post and thereafter it would be the duty of the appropriate investigation branch of the government to have taken meaningful steps in this matter. Their position is that the JMO, if at all, should have taken such steps. We know that the police started questioning people on 5.2.1979 and that in fact no steps had been taken in the first 3 days in this direction."

"It would appear that the possibility of identifying these things in this country at the present time is known to the experts in the Government Analyst's Department. It is our considered view that the prosecution has placed sufficient material before this Court in order to draw a reliable inference."

Mr. Bandaranayake said that in all these circumstances, the Court is left with considering the question of a factitious induced hypoglycaemia.

CAUSE OF HYPOGLYCAEMIA IN MRS. PEIRIS

"The evidence is that Mrs. Peiris was not a diabetic. So that she was not under treatment for diabetes either with insulin or with an anti-diabetic drug. In the circumstances, there is no question that she suffered brain damage because of the accidental consumption of medicines prescribed to her. We turn to the question that arises upon our finding that hypoglycaemia caused irreversible brain damage and unconsciousness, which in the ordinary course resulted in her death from complications arising out of the prolonged unconsciousness. The question is 'What caused the hypoglycaemia?' 'Was it an endogenous spontaneous hypoglycaemia arising out of a natural disease condition or was factitious and induced by the administration of a blood sugar reducing agent?' It is necessary for the prosecution to establish an induced hypoglycaemia, induced by the first accused in view of counts three, four and five of the indictment."

"We have in an early part of this judgment considered in detail the possible known causes of endogenous spontaneous hypoglycaemia. It is not necessary in our opinion, nor is it appropriate that we go over on that ground in detail once again. To summarize it, spontaneous hypoglycaemia can be caused by a disease of the endocrine ductless glands, such as the pituitary and adrenal; diseases of the thyroid glands; disease of the liver and the kidneys; acute alcoholism; large benign hungry tumours; cancerous tumours, which are all diseases of non-pancreatic deep areas of the body."

"There are also diseases of the pancreatic tissue areas such as the pancreas itself or its ectopic tissue situated in parts of the body where it should not be found, secreting excessive amounts of insulin which could result in hypoglycaemia. The diseases of pancreatic tissue known to cause hypoglycaemia are hyperplasia, microadenomatosis and nesidioblastosis. The last, according to the medical evidence is not very relevant in adults but has been seen in infants up to six months of age. Nevertheless, we include it for the purpose of our discussion. Lastly there are the tumours of pancreatic tissue, namely, the insulinoma, which could either benign or malignant and which we have been told is a very very rare condition. Such tumours can be as small as 5 millimeter and they could be difficult to find because they could be deep seated and occult, hidden in the tissue," Mr. Bandaranayake said.

EVIDENCE DOES NOT SUPPORT PRESENCE OF NATURAL DISEASE

"On this question of spontaneous hypoglycaemia, we have also exhaustively dealt with the medical evidence before the Court, namely, the opinion evidence of Dr. Nagaratnam, Dr. Dayasiri Fernando, Dr. Joseph and Dr. Sheriffdeen, as to its causes signs and symptoms means of identification, course of illness and behavioural patterns. We have given our minds to all these conditions. The evidence of doctors de Silva, Pinto and Subramaniam is that neither clinically nor at judicial autopsy or at histology, macroscopically or microscopically either any such disease condition was found. The histology was done only on the pancreas and the surrounding tissues. The endocrine organs, the liver, kidneys etc. were examined macroscopically and at the post-mortem they showed no disease conditions whatsoever. There were no hungry tumours which are known to be so large that they weight from 1 to 20 lbs. and can be felt externally. They did not exist."

"Dr. Subramaniam says that there were no signs of cancer whatsoever in this patient. He confirms Dr. J.G.C. Peiris's evidence that the growth removed from Mrs. Peiris when she had her breast removed in 1968 showed after biopsy that it was not cancer. We see that all the post-mortem findings support the clinical findings that there was no disease from which Mrs. Peiris suffered. That is obvious to us when we view the documents maintained at the hospital containing contemporaneous entries of everything that was done during the period of her hospitalization. We see that on the very first day after the administration of glucose her blood sugar level reached upwards to very high levels and then stabilized within the normal range for the rest of her life which lasted another seven weeks in the hospital. So also her blood pressure, which stabilized on the following day, and remained within the normal limits for the rest of her life."

"The infusion of dextrose by drip into her was discontinued on 7.2.1979, as there was no necessity for such an infusion to maintain or sustain life. Some glucose had been administered orally with the rest of the normal liquids and feeds that she was getting. So, from this picture we see that this lady lived for seven weeks on normal food and antibiotics were given merely as prophylactics to prevent infection, as she had bedsores caused by prolonged unconsciousness and unavoidable in these circumstances."

"The defence cross examined the JMO on the basis that the histology was confined to the pancreas and its immediate surroundings. We remember the evidence of Dr. Dayasiri Fernando about all the possible sites of insulinoma. The defence also pointed out that no histology was done on the endocrine glands, but we also observe and it is a fact, which is significant that clinically there were no signs whatsoever of insulinoma, or any other natural endogenous spontaneous and producing causes. There was no history of endocrine glands malfunctioning. There was no history of pituitary or adrenal malfunctioning. There were no signs or symptoms of such conditions either," Mr. Bandaranayake said.

"Dr. de Silva has told us the signs and symptoms of this condition and his evidence has been corroborated by Dr. Nagaratnam. There were no clinical signs of liver or kidney disease and the autopsy showed that they were normal. Dr. Joseph has told us that there could be hypoglycaemic conditions in cases of acute kidney diseases. Such an event could easily be seen at an autopsy. The question of alcoholism hardly arises in the case of Mrs. Peiris. There is no evidence whatsoever that she was a drunkard or that she took any kind of alcohol at any time of her life. The histology done on the pancreas eliminated any possibility of hyperplasia, adenomatosis, nesidioblastosis or insulinoma."

"The evidence before us is that sufficient number of slides had been made on representative sections of ectopic tissue and that in the circumstances the opinion is rendered reliable. It is supported by Dr. (Mrs.) Balasubramaniam who has also testified before Court about what is medically accepted with regard to histological opinions. These two pathologists are consistent in their testimony."

"We also remind ourselves, as we stated earlier, that Dr. Subramaniam saw this patient on 5.2.1979 and he followed her sickness, and he was fully aware of the clinical history and the cause of her illness and her response to treatment when he approached the autopsy that he did on 20.3.1979. The evidence does not support any inference whatsoever of the presence of a blood sugar reducing spontaneous natural disease. Upon the evidence we have before us, we eliminate the existence of such a disease in Mrs. Peiris with confidence. This opinion we have reached upon our own observations with regard to the cause of her illness at the General Hospital, the treatment she was given, the fact of life for seven weeks on normal food and the opinions both clinical and after post-mortem of the doctors supported by the specialist physician Dr. Nagaratnam. Their testimony is not contradicted by any other medical opinion."

"We also bear in mind that the defence led evidence in this case to suggest that Mrs. Peiris had no physical cause for her illness, but that it was occasioned by a spontaneous mental disease which constituted a trigger factor which caused a fall in blood pressure and resulting anoxia and permanent brain damage. We have ruled out the defence evidence as to the cause of death led before this Court as irrelevant in these proceedings," Mr. Bandaranayake said.

SUICIDE

"We now consider the question of suicide. We are assisted by the opinion of the psychiatrist Dr. Sathanandan, who had this patient under his care between 16.1.1979 and 20.1.1979 just before she suffered permanent brain damage. Dr. Sathanandan expressed the opinion that Mrs. Peiris showed no signs whatsoever of any tendencies towards suicide. He was examined and cross examined at length on this subject and his testimony is before us. So we have reliable evidence here of a psychiatrist that her personality was not that of a suicide. We take this as a factor in our consideration. We take it as evidence of a person specially learned in these matters that Mrs. Peiris did not have a mental frame of mind nor was she the type to commit suicide. We have also the admission by the first accused contained in the history he has given to Dr. de Silva that his wife would not have taken an overdose of anti-diabetic drugs. We also have the evidence of the dying deposition of Mrs. Peiris made at Durdans Hospital that she did not take any drugs but, that the tablets were always given to her by her husband."

"That testimony is supported by the testimony of Malrani Dodangoda and by the evidence of Rev. Mendis. Dr. Sathanandan has told us that the first accused admitted to him at the Durdans Hospital that it was he who gave the deceased her tablets. We have the further fact the she was in good health for most of her life. We also determined in all probability she was not suffering from any kind of mental depression but drowsiness can be explained in another way. There has also been no recent calamity in her life, such as the death of a relation. She had a home, a family, sufficient funds, and children doing well and in good health, grand children, all the requisites of contentment. In the circumstances, when we examine the evidence intrinsically we are confident that we can rule out the possibility of suicide as fanciful. It is our judgement that her death was not the result of suicide."

ACCIDENT

"As far as accident is concerned, we bear in mind that twice in January Mrs. Peiris was hospitalized in a state of unconsciousness, removed to hospital from the Vicarage. The first accused was continuing to stay at the Vicarage at that period of time. The evidence is that the second accused was living in an annexe in Nugegoda and was working at Colonial Motors, Union Place, Colombo. It is also in evidence that the first accused owned a motor car which Chandrakanthi has told us, was a Renault Dauphine. Then the second accused's work is over in the evening. The police were having both the accused under surveillance. The surveillance officers have testified about the association of the accused. The prosecution has placed evidence before the Court," Mr. Bandaranayake said.

"The following instances of association of the accused were testified to by Inspector Lambert Perera. On the 9th May 1979 at about 5.30 p.m., the first accused had parked his car at Alexandra Place and waited. Then the second accused came and got into the car and both of them drove away. This shows that she had come from Colonial Motors by bus and then got into second accused's car in Alexandra Place. We have evidence in this case that the first accused used to take lunch for the second accused on his bicycle. So the prosecution says, what is the cause that the first accused has tried to disguise his association with the second accused, by not coming to Colonial Motors to pick her up? It also suggests that it takes place by prior arrangement. Having picked her up the evidence is that they went to Nugegoda and he dropped her at home."

"On the 14th May 1979, he picked up the second accused's son at Albert Perera Mawatha and had come to Nugegoda and picked up the second accused and her child. They had parked their car in Manel Hotel, Maharagama and had dinner. On the 15th May 1979, he picked up the second accused and her child and parked his car outside Raheema Hotel at Thurstan Road. The police were unable to keep track of them. According to the evidence of Inspector Crusz, on 3rd May 1979, the second accused came out of Colonial Motors at about 5 o'clock in a Fiat car, which drove off to Cinnamon Gardens. The second accused got out from her car and got into the Renault car of the first accused parked inside Osusala. Police followed the car, which went to Albert Perera Mawatha, where the second accused got off."

"The evidence about this continuing association shows that a great attachment had developed between the first and second accused. The second accused voluntarily goes to the first accused after prior arrangement and that the fact the second accused was meeting the first accused was not open in the sense that the first accused did not openly go to her work place and take her. This suggests that they did not wish their relationship to be known," said Mr. Bandaranayake.

"Upon the foregoing we will now set out our conclusions in regard to count number 3 of the Indictment. The gist of the offence of conspiracy is the agreement between two or more people to commit a crime, which means that there should be a plot or a plan be known to each of the accused on that there was agreement between them to give effect to it. Conspiracy is generally proved by circumstantial evidence. We shall examine the evidence against each accused to ascertain if there was indeed a plot to kill Mrs. Peiris and whether each knew of the plot and agreed between themselves to commit her murder."

Mr. Bandaranayake said that the transaction or criminal conduct in pursuance of a conspiracy as the Court said before would be:

- The formation of intent,

- Communication and acceptance of intent,

- The commission of overt acts or supporting acts in furtherance of such agreement.

"We divide the evidence under the following heads for convenience:

- Association between accused and the accused and the deceased,

- Motive - is there evidence of motive against each of these accused? and,

- Opportunity - For conspiring and agreeing to murder the first accused's spouse.

- Agreement on the method of killing.

If so, arising out of the method of killing and agreement or building up the infrastructure to facilitate the commission of the offence so that it will go unobserved, undetected and unpunished."

"We have referred at length to the evidence regarding association between the accused and the relationship that grew between them from September 1976 to March 1979. We find there is ample evidence from which the Court can safely infer that the association between the accused was very close by December 1978. The first accused was the husband of Mrs. Peiris and she was living at material times in the house of the first accused. The second accused frequently visited the home of Mrs. Peiris, who knew her well and was quite friendly with her," Mr. Bandaranayake said.

"We have accepted as a proved fact that the first accused put a ring on the second accused's finger on 10.08.1978 on the date of the second accused's husband's death. We have also decided it as a proved fact that the second accused did not protest or take the ring out of her finger at that time. In these circumstances we draw the inference that she accepted that ring. We therefore draw the inference that this was a promise of things to come. That conduct is very significant to this case and that has been proved beyond reasonable doubt. We remember that the first accused was not free to marry at that time and that is why we take this circumstance as something amounting to a promise to marry the woman when he is able to and that is the inference we draw from the words he has uttered at the time that soon he will also be like her."

"As far back as April 1978, whilst in Wales he had predicted that there was something wrong with her when in fact there was nothing wrong with her. To our minds, this is clear evidence that the first accused was contemplating something connected with the health of his wife. In these circumstances we relate his conduct in placing a ring on the second accused's finger and her accepting that and the statement he made that very soon he will be like her from which we draw the inference that it was tantamount to a promise to make himself free for the two of them to be united at some time in the future. The fact that the second accused did not object to what happened at the funeral house of her husband clearly shows that she was in agreement with what the first accused was doing and that there was consensus between the two of them. So in these circumstances the proclamation made by the first accused in Wales attaches to the second accused as well."

EXECUTED A WILL

"Thereafter, we find upon the first accused's return to Sri Lanka that the association between the couple grows stronger. We know that the second accused was living in the Vicarage for a continuous period from February 1978 to the middle of August 1978. We also know that the association between the accused has continued because we have the fact that in November 1978 the second accused executed a Will with the help of the first accused. We have the further fact that the accused opened a joint bank account. We see no reason whatsoever for the first accused to open a joint bank account with a woman who is not his wife or his ward. Each of the accused must necessarily be aware of these facts and they have done it voluntarily and jointly."

"Thereafter, we have the evidence that the second accused continued to visit the Vicarage in December at a time when we have reliable evidence that the deceased was showing symptoms of hypoglycaemia. We hold it to be proved beyond reasonable doubt that all those signs and symptoms of hypoglycaemia, which were observed by the relations of the first accused in the Vicarage, must also have been observed by the second accused for the reason that it has been proved that she could recognize those signs. We refer specially to the fact that she had read the book, which was the counterpart of P40. P40 contains information regarding diabetes and the opposite of diabetes, which is hypoglycaemia, information regarding the signs and symptoms of hypoglycaemia and what causes it, and that a sufficient steep fall of the blood sugar could result in drowsiness, unconsciousness and death. The book also contains information of the fact that drugs have been developed to control diabetes in that they have the effect of bringing the blood sugar level down so that if that is administered to a normal person, his normal blood sugar level will come down to hypoglycaemic levels."

"It is a proved fact that the second accused was at the Vicarage on 31.12.1978 along with the first accused and Mrs. Peiris and that Mrs. Peiris was too sick even to attend a party and that the first accused has admitted to Dr. E.V. Peiris that she had a collapse and that she collapsed sweating. We are confident that at least the second accused would have known about it by visiting that house that day. We also have the proved fact that the accused were together at the Vicarage on 15.01.1979 when Mrs. Peiris was unconscious with an unrecordable blood pressure and they took her and admitted her to Durdans," Mr. Bandaranayake said.

"We have evidence through 2D1 that the second accused was visiting the Vicarage during this period. We have the further evidence, which we accept as a proved fact, that the second accused spoke an untruth to the deceased and misled her as to why she was unconscious in the Vicarage by telling her that she had fever when in fact she had no fever. Looking at the conduct in the background of the association between the two accused, we think it is fair to draw an inference that she gave the false information deliberately in order to disguise the reason for her state of unconsciousness. We have already decided that state of unconsciousness was caused by the first accused by administering an anti-diabetic drug to her. The second accused was at the Vicarage that day."

"We have the further evidence of a continuing association between the accused while the deceased was lying unconscious in hospital and even after her death, that the accused met obviously by prior arrangement and agreement and that the first accused was giving lifts to the second accused in his car. There is evidence that the first accused had parked his car and wanted for the second accused to come and get into the car. That could only happen by prior arrangement."

"All the evidence point to the first accused having administered an anti-diabetic drug to his wife. He has made several statements to witnesses displaying his knowledge of hypoglycaemia and he also had the book P40, which was returned to him in September 1978. We also have the fact that the first accused has bought Euglucon tablets several times between September and December 1978. We accept the evidence that Euglucon was a drug that he was using to bring his blood sugar down as he was a diabetic and that he knew how to use the drug and he knew its effects," said Mr. Bandaranayake.

"We have the fact that Mrs. Peiris was unconscious twice in the Vicarage that she was taken to hospital twice in the month of January within weeks of her returning home. We accept it as a proved fact that the first accused administered anti-diabetic drugs to his wife, which caused permanent brain damage and unconsciousness and that she died of pneumonia from her prolonged state of unconsciousness. All these circumstances in our opinion when viewed in its totality are not consistent with any reasonable hypothesis of the innocence of the accused. All of these circumstances taken together point unerringly to the existence of an agreement between the two accused to cause the death of Mrs. Peiris."

Mr. Bandaranayake said that in one continuing transaction from July 1977 up to the date of her death, the known amorous relationship between the two accused points to their having wanted to get Mrs. Peiris out of the way in order to be free to have each other for themselves.

"This is the only reasonable and compelling inference, which we can draw from all of these proved facts. They are inconsistent with innocence. It is shown beyond all reasonable doubt that arising out of this association and the motive that there was agreement between the two of them to administer anti-diabetic drugs to the deceased, which the first accused did, as is evidenced by the symptoms of hypoglycaemia Mrs. Peiris had in December in the Vicarage, and we find a supporting role played by the second accused as evidenced by the falsehood she uttered on 15.01.1979 at Durdans and also her presence at the Vicarage on 15.01.1979, when Mrs. Peiris had collapsed with a hypoglycaemic attack."

SECOND ACCUSED AIDED AND ABETTED THE FIRST ACCUSED

"This is something the second accused would easily have recognized. She has in fact recognized something on Mrs. Peiris on 31.01.1979 at ward 47B which compelled her to say, 'She is just like Russel'. What was it that she saw in Mrs. Peiris that was just like Russel when Mrs. Peiris is lying deeply unconscious? Is it not a reference to the fact of lying unconscious? So if she recognized it then how can it be argued that she would not have recognized this on the 31st of December 1978 or that she did not recognize this on the 15th of January 1979? We find in the evidence before us that in regard to this same thing she must, we hold necessarily have come to know about it on 31.12.1978. She has kept it a secret. She has maintained a silence about it."

"We next see that on the 15th of January 1979, she had another opportunity of seeing the same thing and that on that occasion in the circumstances, we see that she has uttered a deliberate falsehood to Mrs. Peiris that she had high fever and she was in delirium. In the context of these circumstances, we hold that it is a deliberate act on her part playing a supportive role; seeking to help the first accused to give a false picture of the deceased and her relations and thus allay suspicions. It is in evidence that when she uttered this falsehood to Mrs. Peiris, the first accused was present and he maintained silence. The conduct of two of them in this context shows an agreement to collaboration between the two to give a false picture as to the reason for her unconsciousness. Why did she not tell Mrs. Peiris or the relations at that time at Durdans that she had been just like Russel?" asked Mr. Bandaranayake.

"We also have the evidence of Dr. Weerasena, which we believe, that Mrs. Peiris was unconscious with an unrecordable blood pressure at Durdans and the second accused was present at that time but the second accused when she saw this same thing on the 31st of December says nothing and does nothing to assist Mrs. Peiris to secure treatment for her. We observe that when the first accused does something about it, and that something is when Mrs. Peiris is at death's door, admitted to hospital thereby casting the responsibility of caring for her upon the hospital authorities, upon doctors who have to react immediately with correct emergency treatment to save her health and save her life, which they have done on two occasions on the 15th of January and the 31st January."

"On both these occasions we observe that the second accused is present near Mrs. Peiris but on 31.12.1978, when the first accused chooses to keep his wife's unconsciousness a secret the second accused also keeps it a secret. In this setting upon the evidence that we have, which we accept, that the second accused had access to a lot of information about the state of hypoglycaemia from the book which is we find quite understandable by laymen; written in layman's language where the salient features of the fall in blood sugar in people and a state of drowsiness and unconsciousness are explained."

"The second accused is an educated secretary, typist, a telephone operator who seeks position for payment and who has found employment in such a position. She says she has read the book that Dharmadasa lost. The contents of the book was so clear to Dharmadasa that she even wrote an article to the newspaper upon the subject of blood sugar, which she thought would be of general interest to the reading public. So in this background we consider it safe to infer that the second accused read and understood the book that blood sugar is sometimes lowered and when elevated as in diabetes, it can be lowered by the use of anti-diabetic drugs, and if lowered too much can be elevated again by the simple administration of sugar or ice cream or a meal. By reason of her close association with the first accused, we think it is reasonable for us to infer that she knew that the first accused was taking Euglucon. Euglucon, a drug prescribed to him to lower blood sugar prescribed to him by Dr. Weerasena, whose name the second accused would have been most familiar with. This is our inference from the evidence of their association."

"It is therefore, our conclusion upon all of these circumstances there is one irresistible conclusion that we can draw from these proved circumstances, i.e. that the second accused knew that the blood sugar of a normal person also can be lowered by the administration of an anti-diabetic drug and that it can be elevated by the administration of sugar or substances containing sugar such as ice cream or carbohydrate. Not only that, the blood sugar of a normal person can be induced to fluctuate by the intermittent administration of an anti-diabetic drug."

"Now it is apparent upon the evidence that the first accused adopted just this method, causing fluctuating levels of blood sugar – sometimes causing stuporose condition, sometimes feeling well according to the blood sugar level in the body in order to achieve a very significant result. This has to be viewed in the context of the method he has used to commit the murder of his wife, in administration of a poison to go undetected. Now in order to achieve this, he has chosen a way, which shows one of sickness which could be observed by people. So when a person is sick it is quite legitimate to have the person treated with medicines. The opportunity thus created to give medicine, gives him the opportunity of administering the poison," said Mr. Bandaranayake.

"In other words, he stimulates the condition of illness which gives him that opportunity of administering the poison without raising suspicion, because this state of the illness, which in fact he himself has engineered, is being innocently treated as a true natural illness. In the circumstances, this picture of illness will deceive the victim and the relatives into accepting natural cause and this paves the way for the patient's admission to hospital. Now a disease causing low blood sugar is not an instant killer. That is also known to the first accused. The disease, if present it gradually develops with increasing ferocity. So in that knowledge, a medical man would find it that a gradual onset of the disease as to be consistent with a natural cause."

METHOD OF MURDER

"So the Court has to look at the conduct of the second accused in the context of the method of murder chosen by the first accused, that is to say a method, which could disguise his criminal conduct and pass off death as due to a natural cause. So when one looks at the conduct of the second accused in this setting, the proved instances where she has helped the first accused to create conditions where he could continue manipulating his wife's state of health, shows a clear agreement between the accused to assist each other and help each other by preventing suspicion by creating an atmosphere, where the intended victim would voluntarily consume the poison unknowingly. The second accused's silence about Mrs. Peiris's hypoglycaemic attacks on 31st of December is therefore very significant. It is the only inference that we can draw that she was supporting the first accused in his acts by keeping it a secret."

"We have next the episode of hypoglycaemia on 15.01.1979 in the Vicarage. On that occasion too the second accused was present. The signs would have been obvious to her. The deceased recovered quickly after dextrose and at that point she uttered a falsehood. The first accused confirmed her falsehood by his silence. In the circumstances it is an irresistible inference and the Court concludes that this conduct on the part of the two accused points unerringly to a plot, a plan with full knowledge of what is going on, on the part of the both of them to interfere with Mrs. Peiris's state of health stealthily and by her conduct, the second accused supports and helps the first accused to continue to administer poison without arousing suspicion."

"Here is a repetition of their conduct on 31.12.1978. The picture is unmistakable. A gradual intermittent administration of an anti-diabetic drug resulting in signs of a disease, thus simulating a natural illness, so that no suspicion is raised. The presence of the second accused at both episodes cannot in our opinion be explained – say on the basis of coincidence. The similarity between the two episodes is uncanny. How is she present with the first accused in the Vicarage each time the deceased suffers a bout of induced hypoglycaemic attacks? It is a proved fact which we have discussed earlier that the first accused induced the hypoglycaemic attacks."

"But in the midst of the two attacks we have a further fact and that is the document 2D1. The document assists the Court to reach a conclusion. It is indeed a statement made by the deceased in the course of the transaction which resulted in her death. It shows that the second accused had won the confidence of Mrs. Peiris and had access to her, was accepted in the Vicarage and created the opportunity for the first accused to commit the crime without raising suspicion. So we see the conduct of the second accused in returning to the Vicarage over and over again voluntarily to the company of the first accused."

"We have the further evidence, which is significant, that on 31.01.1979, the first accused telephoned from Colonial Motors and spoke to Eardley Mendis and told him that Mrs. Peiris was groaning and sleeping and he asked to speak to the second accused. He gave the telephone to the second accused who then spoke with the first accused. Later at about 10 a.m., the first accused had given Eardley another call to say that he was removing Mrs. Peiris to hospital and Eardley says that when he went at lunch time he found his sister unconscious and frothing at the mouth. This he found to be very strange because this same sister had led him to the door the previous night after his visit to her. It is also the fact that the second accused visited Mrs. Peiris that day in the evening. She could have known her hospitalization only from the first accused. We see that even on the day Mrs. Peiris suffered irreversible brain damage the first accused was in contact with the second accused so that there is unremitting connection between the two of them."

FOUND ANNEXE

"There is further evidence of continuing association between the accused during the period of hospitalization and even after the death of Mrs. Peiris. There is the fact which we hold proved that the first accused found annexe accommodation for her in Nugegoda and paid three months' rent in advance for her. That was done on 26.01.1979."

"We have the further fact that the second accused had been seen together several times, after the death of Mrs. Peiris upon the evidence of the police surveillance squad. That evidence points directly to the two accused meeting each other after the second accused's work is over for the day at a point far away from her work place. The evidence shows without doubt that the second accused met on those occasions by prior arrangement. The evidence also shows that on each of those occasions the second accused voluntarily went and met the first accused and got into his car and was taken home," Mr. Bandaranayake said.

"We consider all these proved circumstances inference and that is that the second accused intentionally assisted the first accused and abetted the commission of the offence we are considering. Having considered all the matters raised by the defence, the submissions that they made and cross examinations and all matters arising upon the evidence it is our opinion that all the proved facts and circumstances are inconsistent with an innocent association between the accused or that the second accused did not know what was going on or that the second accused was misled or was an innocent bystander. The proved circumstances taken together are inconsistent with a reasonable theory that her visits to the Vicarage on the days that Mrs. Peiris was ill, was mere co-incidences. It is the judgement of this Court that on a consideration of relevant facts and circumstances that one and only inference to which the Court can come and which is an irresistible inference upon all the circumstances and which is incapable of explanation consistent with the innocence of the second accused or consistent with any reasonable theory of her innocence that the second accused aided and abetted the first accused in the murder of his wife."

PROVED BEYOND ALL REASONABLE DOUBT

"We hold that the prosecution has proved this fact beyond all reasonable doubt. It is our conclusion that she is guilty of the offence of abetment recited in count 5 of the Indictment. We have in the course of our deliberations borne in mind that the defence contested this case in the first instance as to proof of the cause of death of the two deceased persons. In both instances the defence suggested that the deceased died of natural causes."

Mr. Bandaranayake said that the defence has also pointed out that statements of prosecution witnesses were belated and therefore that they had an opportunity to prepare their evidence, that there were omissions in their statements to the police on material matters when compared to their testimony, which opened the possibility of falsehood.

"The defence also attacked the credibility of Dr. Weerasena and Mrs. Peiris's brothers and children on the footing that they were interested witnesses. The Ingrams and Jacksons too were attacked on this basis. We have considered all of the positions taken up by the defence and have applied other tests of credibility as well, in arriving at our verdict, bearing in mind that the burden of proof in a criminal case is throughout on the prosecution to establish it beyond all reasonable doubt."

"We have been unanimous on all decisions with regard to facts as well as on the law," Mr. Bandaranayake said.

"Through many months of long and absorbing trial, this Court always received the utmost courtesy from counsel on both sides. We draw attention to the fairness and the impartiality and the thoroughness with which counsel for the prosecution presented their case and likewise, to the industry, responsibility and dedication to the cause of their clients shown by the counsel for the defence. Having regard to the nature and the extent of the evidence it was not found possible to record and publish the reasons for our verdict within ten days of the taking of the evidence and the submissions of counsel."

VERDICT

Mr. Bandaranayake said, "By our unanimous verdict we convict the first accused on counts 1, 2, 3 and 4 of the indictment and the second accused on the counts 1, 2, 3 and 5 of the indictment."

Mr. Bandaranayake then asked the accused whether they had anything to say why death sentence should not be passed on them.

Rev. Peiris said in a loud and clear voice, "I would like to say as I was maintaining from the outset that I am not guilty."

He thanked the Senior Counsel Mr. R.I. Obeysekera and Mr. Cecil Goonewardena for their efforts.

Mr. Bandaranayake asked, "Anything else?"

"My faith in God," Rev. Peiris replied.

Speaking in a faint voice from the same dock, Mrs. Dalrene Ingram also pleaded her innocence and thanked the defence lawyers.

While the fateful moment for the two accused drew near, a tense silence gripped the courtroom.

Mr. Bandaranayake ordered that the fans in the courtroom be stopped. The whirling fans of the Court came to a grinding halt and there was pin drop silence.

Mr. Bandaranayake then read out the verdict that the first accused Rev. Mathew Peiris be taken to Welikada and hanged until he was dead. Rev. Peiris acknowledged the pronouncement with a slight smile and responded by making a sign of the Cross. The verdict on him was delivered and the file closed.

Mr. Bandaranayake then opened the second file and read out the same sentence against the second accused. Pale looking Ms. Ingram remained silent, but kept on wiping her eyes and face.

After the verdict was delivered Mr. Bandaranayake adjourned the Court.

The Court room was dead silent. Breaking the silence the Judges retired to their chambers.

Moments later chaos and disorder prevailed with all inside the packed court room rushing towards the dock to have a closer look at Rev. Peiris and Mrs. Ingram, now condemned to death.

As Rev. Peiris was stepping out of the dock one of his sisters hugged him weeping bitterly. The priest soon tried to console her saying "Don't worry, God is there." Mr. Mark Peiris, a younger brother of the priest was seen conversing with him, when the Court officials shut the doors to prevent the crowds surging into the courtroom.

Nearly half an hour later when the two prisoners were lead out both waved at the crowds waiting outside.

An Anglican Priest shielded the two accused from the crowd.

"We will be here" Rev. Peiris said.

CHAPTER 11

THE APPEAL

Rev. Mathew Peiris and Mrs. Dalrene Ingram appealed against the convictions and death sentences passed on them by the High Court Trial-at-Bar for the murder of their spouses.

The Appeal was heard before a Bench comprising Justices Justin Abeywardene, N. R. M. Dheeraratne and A. S. Wijetunga. Mr. R.I. Obeysekera, (now a President's Counsel) with Messrs. Anil Obeysekera, A. W. Yusuf, Jayantha Weerasinghe, Upali Senaratne, C. Padmasekera, T. C. Rajaratnam and Shanaka de Livera appeared for Rev. Peiris. Mr. Cecil Goonewardena with Messrs U. C. B. Ratnayaka, M. L. Z. Jawfer, M. S. M. Suhair, Mr. Asoka Somaratne and Kalinga Ediriwickrema appeared for Dalrene Ingram. Deputy Solicitor General Mr. Tilak Marapana, Additional Solicitor General Mr. Sunil de Silva, with Deputy Solicitor General Upawansa Yapa, Senior State Counsel C. R. de Silva and State Counsel Gamini Ameratunge appeared for the Attorney General.

Mr. R.I. Obeysekera making submissions said, "The question was, whether the prosecution successfully discharged the burden of showing that Russel's death was not the result of a natural cause. The State, having failed to show positive evidence, stating that Rev. Peiris used a stethoscope on Russel with the authority of a doctor and the fuss made, because Rev. Peiris had extra-marital relations with Dalrene, were all factors purposely stated to show that Rev. Peiris had complete control over the situation. All these statements made by Alexander Parker Ingram showed that he and his wife Cora Ingram, and in-laws, the Jacksons, had put their heads together to give it a sinister twist in order to help the case for the prosecution, because none of these statements had been made by them to the police before the trial."

"When Russel's father was leaving the Vicarage for his home, Rev. Peiris invited him to come back. There is no suggestion that Rev. Peiris was trying to keep Russel's parents away from him. Rev. Peiris had every opportunity of slipping pills in their absence if he wanted to. But what they were trying to show was that he was doing so in their presence," Mr. Obeysekera said.

Referring to the evidence of Dr. Dayasiri Fernando that Rev. Peiris was anxious to have Russel admitted to the General Hospital, Mr. Obeysekera said, "A Gastroenterology unit was opened at the Colombo South Hospital and Rev. Peiris was anxious to see that Dr. Fernando, who was an expert, saw Russel and that too not for a mere cursory examination."

Justice Dheeraratne commented, "The prosecution case was that this was a show-off to show that death was natural up to a point."

Mr. Obeysekera replied, "One can see Parker Ingram falling in line with the State's case. He had not mentioned any of these things to the police. The police investigations were conducted under the personal supervision of ASP Hema Weerasinghe. A special team had been formed."

Justice Dheeraratne queried, "When did the investigations commence?"

"In March 1979. This was under the direction of Mr. Tyrrell Goonatilleke. Mr. Hema Weerasinghe gave evidence. Even after 8 months after Russel's death and three months of investigation, these things are coming out in 1983. What is the check we could have on a witness?" asked Mr. Obeysekera.

He argued that in a criminal case it was important that a complaint should be prompt. Delays could result in complaints being fabricated.

"These witnesses did not come out with these things to the police despite several opportunities they had. These investigations were not simply rushed through. When it comes out for the first time at the trial, what is the value that could be attached to them? The evidence of Parker Ingram and Mrs. Jackson showed that there was a sinister twist to bolster up the State's case," said Mr. Obeysekera.

"The State's purpose in making Jackson, a brother-in-law of Dalrene, to speak of events at the Vicarage on a night that Russel was supposed to be critically sick, was to make out that there was something 'unholy' going on in the Vicarage. Jackson's evidence was that when he wanted to see Russel that night he found the room closed. Then he knocked at the door for about ten minutes. Later, Rev. Peiris opened the door. Rev. Peiris was dressed in a pair of khaki shorts at that time and Dalrene and her children were with him in the same room. What was Jackson trying to say? Is it not that something unholy was going on inside a Vicarage room that night?" Mr. Obeysekera asked.

Mr. Obeysekera submitted that the judges of the High Court had failed to consider several factors relevant to the credibility of Jackson and his wife, and Russel's father and mother.

"There were numerous flaws, omissions and infirmities in their evidence. The evidence that Russel was unconscious for two days at the Vicarage after he was administered four to five pills of Euglucon was highly unlikely in view of the medical evidence. According to medical evidence such a dosage of Euglucon on a non-diabetic person would have drastic effects," he said.

Referring to the prosecution evidence that Rev. Peiris placed a ring on a finger of Dalrene soon after Russel's death, and that he told Dalrene, "Do not worry I shall soon be like you", Mr. Obeysekera said, "That was a narration related in Court for the first time four years later. Police statements did not bear out such a talk being attributed to the priest by anyone of those witnesses."

Quoting evidence of Jackson, he said, "The witness had admitted as important that his wife's claim that she had seen Rev. Peiris giving pills to Russel, but he had not mentioned that in his statement to the police. When Jackson was questioned in Court why he did not tell that to the police, he replied that was because he considered it as hearsay."

Mr. Obeysekera said the dosage, the variety and colour of the tablets alleged to have been given to Russel by Rev. Peiris differed from witness to witness.

"No credibility whatever could be attached to their evidence. No inference could be drawn against Rev. Peiris that he gave misleading information about Russel to the doctor when Russel was admitted to General Hospital," he said.

Mr. Obeysekera, referring to the hospital admission of Russel, said that according to Russel's father, Parker Ingram, Russel was admitted at 2.30 p.m. on 26th June 1978.

"Dr. P.A.P. Joseph had given a letter dated 26th June to the admitting officer. The letter was collected, according to Parker Ingram, from the residence of Dr. Joseph. He had just retired as a senior surgeon and that letter would have carried weight in admitting the patient. Parker Ingram also says that Dr. Joseph told him, 'I know Rev. Peiris. Your son is in safe hands.' Dr. Joseph's evidence was that he went to the Vicarage to see Russel on the morning of 26th but was told by Rev. Peiris that Russel could not be seen as he was fast asleep."

Having regard to the friendship Dr. Joseph says he had with Rev. Peiris, he did not see the patient but went back and sent the letter and that was the first time he issued a letter without seeing a patient. This was flatly contradicted by Parker Ingram on two points, one of which was that Dr. Joseph could not have come to the Vicarage that morning."

Mr. Obeysekera said that one cannot reconcile the evidence of these two witnesses.

"The least one could say is that Dr. Joseph was not speaking the truth when he says he had not seen the patient. He had seen the patient at least six days earlier and discussed Russel's illness with the father and the need for an operation."

Justice Dheeraratne asked, "So do you want us to believe Parker Ingram that Dr. Joseph did not come to the Vicarage on the 26th?"

"My submission is that when the prosecution led evidence they should have led evidence of a consistent story," said Mr. Obeysekera.

Justice Wijetunga queried, "Why do you say that Dr. Joseph could not have come to the Vicarage?"

"Because of the sequence of events spoken to by Parker Ingram, he says that he had gone and collected the letter at about 10 a.m. and Dr. Joseph says he got a telephone call around 12 noon whilst having lunch and went to see him. He returned and issued the letter. We are left in a state of doubt what evidence to accept."

Mr. Obeysekera read out Dr. Joseph's letter to the admitting officer and said Dr. Joseph had stated in the letter that Russel's symptoms were suggestive of an islet cell tumour of the pancreas. He has told Parker Ingram the same thing.

Dealing with the evidence relating to the admission of Russel, Mr. Obeysekera said, "The wrong inference had been made that Rev. Peiris gave the case history. On the contrary, all the evidence pointed to the history having been given by Russel's father to the admitting officer. Dr. (Miss) Ruwanpathirana had said that the history was given by a relative. No doctor can have an undisputed memory years later in regard to the admission to a busy hospital when thousands of patients are admitted. The admitting doctor could give evidence only from the official record."

He requested the Court to consider the case of Russel separately from the case of Mrs. Peiris.

"When each case is considered separately there is a total inadequacy of proof. If your Lordships were to ask the question how Mrs. Peiris too died under similar circumstance that of Russel, the very thought would show that was a misjoinder of charges. If there is an inadequacy in respect of Russel the gap can never be filled. Where the death of Mrs. Peiris is concerned there is lapse on the part of the hospital authorities in not testing the blood or any samples of food given to Mrs. Peiris for the presence of an anti-diabetic drug. There is not a scrap of evidence that the drug was ever traced to the system of Russel's and Mrs. Peiris's," Mr. Obeysekera claimed.

Dealing with the evidence of nurses Manawadu and Ranaweera, Mr. Obeysekera claimed that the prosecution has failed in proving that Russel was poisoned through the feeds brought by Rev. Peiris during Russel's period of hospitalization.

"The prosecution contended that meals were brought from outside. But they failed to identify the feeds brought from outside from those feeds, which were given by the hospital because the nurses had not distinguished the different feeds when making entries in the fluid balance chart or the diet chart. The prosecution therefore, attempted to say that certain feeds could have originated from the hospital in as much as feed were not prescribed by the hospital."

"This effort of the prosecution failed in view of the conflicting evidence of nurses Lasantha Fernando and Sugathapala, who categorically stated in their evidence that milk was available in the ward and that it could be given any time the doctors prescribed it. They also stated that passion fruit and eggs were given by the hospital and that nurse Lasantha Fernando had herself mixed the passion fruit and eggs."

Thus, Mr. Obeysekera submitted that the prosecution had failed to prove the characteristics of the feeds given to Russel coming from outside the hospital either by reference to the fluid balance chart or to the diet chart or to any other document.

"On the totality of the evidence, although Rev. Peiris had taken food to Russel the prosecution was unable to connect any one of the feeds on the Fluid Balance Chart or the Diet Chart to that of the feeds given by Rev. Peiris. The prosecution contended that Russel had hypoglycaemic attacks in hospital by pointing to entries where glucose had been administered to Russel."

Mr. Obeysekera pointed out that nowhere had the nurses made entries of the symptoms noticed by them such as sweating, rapid pulse etc.

"This evidence of the nurses was an afterthought in the light of the medical evidence in regard to the symptoms of hypoglycaemia," Mr. Obeysekera alleged.

When Russel was noticed to be sweating especially after food that was brought from outside was administered to him, Mr. Obeysekera complained that no blood sugar tests were taken to prove medically and technically that the sweating was due to a lowered blood sugar level.

"This is a very unfortunate omission on the part of the hospital authorities. If the feeds were connected to the episodes of sweating, why wasn't Russel's blood tested for the sugar level and indeed why were the feeds not tested to see whether the feeds contained any hypoglycaemic agent?" Mr. Obeysekera asked.

"The prosecution has not been able to connect the feeds to the so called attacks of hypoglycaemia. Nothing can fill this gap now. Instead the prosecution was turning to speculation and prejudice to overcome this gap," he claimed.

Mr. Obeysekera said that the joinder of two conspiracies in one trial caused grave prejudice to the accused.

"The defence had thus been denied the substance of a fair trial. Although, the state maintained they were not relying on system evidence, they had achieved that result indirectly when they posed the question: How did two people die in similar circumstances with similar symptoms? This was an indirect way of saying that two deaths cannot be accounted for, except on the basis that they were intentionally caused by induced hypoglycaemia, but the State said they were not relying on system."

"The decisions of the Supreme Court state that if prejudice is likely to be caused to the accused if trials are joined, then the trial should be separated but not if the state is unduly hampered in the presentation of its case. In this instance, the two cases can be conveniently separated. The witnesses - both medical and other can be distinct in the case of each death. There was no overlapping at all. The state has used joinder of trials as a device to achieve an objective which they cannot achieve legally. The defence had been thus deprived the substance of a fair trial."

Dealing with the evidence in respect of the state's case that Mrs. Peiris's death too was caused by induced hypoglycaemia, Mr. Obeysekera said, "Although the Senior House Officer had made an endorsement in the BHT on 31st January 1979, the date of admission, querying the possibility of induced hypoglycaemia, no tests were done to detect the presence of a drug. This would have been the best proof of the presence of the drug."

"Dr. Abeysuriya, a highly qualified and experienced neurosurgeon, who was the visiting neurosurgeon, at the Colombo General Hospital had seen Mrs. Peiris on 3rd February 1979, and in his opinion Mrs. Peiris's condition was due to cerebral anoxia due to 'sustained hypotension'. In other words, Mrs. Peiris's unconsciousness was due to her very low blood pressure, which prevented blood from reaching the brain and resulting in unconsciousness. He had made an endorsement to this effect on the BHT. He was also present at the post-mortem. He was on the list of witnesses for the State. The State did not call him."

"The defence made an application towards the close of the prosecution case that Dr. Abeysuriya be tendered for cross examination or that the Court should call him in the interest of justice. Both applications were refused. Then the defence called him after interviewing him. The defence had access to him only at that stage. The judges have criticized the defence for not cross examining doctors who gave evidence for the prosecution on Dr. Abeysuriya's opinion. This was an unfair criticism, as the doctors gave evidence long before the defence had access to Dr. Abeysuriya. Indeed in this case, the prosecution should have recalled the doctors or moved to call other medical opinion to contradict Dr. Abeysuriya's opinion."

"As it is, Dr. Abeysuriya's evidence stands uncontradicted. His evidence is of a highly specialized nature and if the state was challenging his expert opinion they should have called their own experts on this aspect of the case. This they have failed to do. The judges could have rejected his evidence only if there was medical opinion, which was contrary to the evidence of Dr. Abeysuriya."

"The expert opinion of Dr. Abeysuriya was that in view of the depressed state in which Mrs. Peiris was, the function of the hypothalamus-pituitary gland complex was suppressed. This resulted in the fall of the blood pressure which in turn diminished the blood supply to the brain which resulted in permanent brain damage. Also associated with it, was a condition of reactive hypoglycaemia resulting from her depression, which caused a drop in her blood sugar. There was ample evidence that Mrs. Peiris was in a state of depression and both Dr. Weerasena and Dr. Sathanandan treated her for this condition. The test taken on 29th January at the Glass House showed that Mrs. Peiris was having a reactive hypoglycaemia as her blood sugar level dropped to 51 mg. Thus, Dr. Abeysuriya was justified in coming to the conclusion that Mrs. Peiris was depressed and also that she had a reactive hypoglycaemia."

Mr. Asoka Somaratne marked his appearance for Mrs. Dalrene Ingram and addressed Court on certain aspects of circumstantial evidence.

Mr. Cecil Goonewardena, who appeared for Mrs. Dalrene Ingram, addressing the Court said the charges of conspiracy to murder Mrs. Peiris had been based in a complete misdirection and the judges coming to wrong conclusions that Dalrene had read the book "Body, Mind and Sugar", which Rev. Peiris had given.

"The other items of evidence relied on was that, after the death of Mrs. Peiris, Rev. Peiris and Dalrene associated with each other, relying on the police surveillance evidence, which only meant that they were seen in a car and that Rev. Peiris used to drop Dalrene at her residence. And on the other two occasions, Rev. Peiris has taken the children with Dalrene and given them feeds at Maharagama and Colombo," Mr. Goonewardena said.

"The trial judges had put the letter sent by Mrs. Peiris to her daughter in England dated 14th January 1979 to adverse uses against Dalrene and ignored what was favourable to her including the fact that Mrs. Peiris appreciated what she was doing," he said.

Mr. Tilak Marapana making his submissions said, "Mrs. Peiris falling into a coma had nothing to do with a depressed condition in her. On the contrary it pointed to anti-diabetic drugs being administered. The trial judges had ample material to disregard Dr. Abeysuriya's evidence in regard to both Mrs. Peiris having reactive hypoglycaemia as well as suffering from a depression capable of suppressing hypothalamic activity. Dr. Sathananthan, the only psychiatrist who had ever examined Mrs. Peiris was of opinion that she was only mildly depressed. Dr. Abeysuriya when informed of this matter stated that though Dr. Sathananthan was unaware of it he (Dr. Abeysuriya) knew in addition that Mrs. Peiris was troubled due to the presence of Dalrene at the Vicarage. Mr. Marapana asked if it was an additional factor, was it the cause that aggravated Mrs. Peiris's depression. How was it that Mrs. Peiris came to be more depressed despite Dalrene, leaving the Vicarage for good, because Mrs. Peiris fell unconscious only on 31st January 1979? All these point to the cause of the coma having nothing to do with depression, but pointing to an anti-diabetic drug being administered."

"Dalrene Ingram was well aware that her husband Russel's condition had been induced by an anti-diabetic drug," he said.

Mr. Marapana referring to the evidence of Alex Ingram and Bridget Jackson said, "If one were to look at the position in the reverse order, one would find that Russel died on 10th August 1978 of a hypoglycaemic coma and the medical evidence had excluded any natural causes for the coma. Russel was admitted to the General Hospital on 18th July, also in the same coma. Russel came to be in this condition immediately after the pills were administered to him at the Vicarage on 16th July. According to Bridget Jackson, these pills were given by Rev. Peiris with the full knowledge of Dalrene. According to Alex Ingram, both accused had made out that Russel was being treated by Dr. Weerasena and that these pills were Dr. Weerasena's pills. It was not the case for the prosecution that Russel was having some ailment, and due to the inactivity of the two accused in not having him properly treated, the condition was aggravated. The prosecution did not say that this inactivity was wilful neglect, but rather the prosecution case was that this inactivity confirmed the fact that Russel came to be in this condition due to an anti-diabetic drug having been administered to him by both these accused."

"They wanted Russel to continue in the hypoglycaemic state until some permanent brain damage had occurred arising from his hypoglycaemia. And that indeed was what happened to Russel when he was eventually admitted to the hospital on 18th July. He had suffered irreversible brain damage by then. With Russel's death, part of the transaction was complete, and the curtain had fallen on Act 1. But the audience had left thinking that that was the end of the drama."

"The Act 2 begins with the arrival of Mrs. Peiris. It was an entirely new audience now present, and when she felt drowsy, sleepy, giddy and dizzy, that represented the background music, which the new audience was unable to recognize as being the opening bar of the theme song, hypoglycaemia. Alex Ingram who had left after Act 1, suddenly walked in towards end of Act 2, when Mrs. Peiris was in hospital in an unconscious state. He immediately recognized the music and was suspicious and ran to the police. The only two people who were present right through Act 1 and Act 2 were these two accused."

"What did Dalrene do when she recognized the theme song? She was going about having hopper feeds with Rev. Peiris! There lay the difference between her and Alex Ingram. So how could it be contended that she was an innocent victim?"

"Although, the counsel for Dalrene submitted in this Court that his client may well have been told by Rev. Peiris that Russel was being treated by Dr. Weerasena and that she may well have believed it, no such submission was made by the counsel at the trial. Having run with the hare to the trial, it appeared that now she was trying to hunt with the hounds," Mr. Marapana said.

Replying to the legal issues that had been raised by the defence, Mr. Marapana said, "The facts accepted by the trial judges justified their conclusion. I do not propose to cite further cases than those already cited by counsel for Dalrene, Mr. Cecil Goonewardena."

He submitted that he too strongly relied on these authorities as to how circumstantial evidence was to be evaluated. Nor did he propose to cite authority on how a Court should consider the defence. It is his submission that in the consideration of the defence by the trial judges, they too had had these cases in mind and given adequate consideration to any possible defence reasonably arising from the evidence.

"A new theory relating to the 'pooling of evidence' was sought to be advanced by counsel for Dalrene relying on some old authorities. None of those authorities supported the proposition that evidence led in support of one charge on the indictment could not be utilized in the consideration of any other charge in the same indictment if such evidence was relevant to the second charge. The governing matter was the relevancy of the evidence to the charge under consideration. That evidence may have already been led in support of another charge contained in the same indictment. The joinder of charges was controlled by certain rules of procedure and merely because such rules of procedure permitted their joinder in one indictment, it would not hamper any evidence relevant to another charge."

In regard to the function of the Court of Appeal, in reviewing a judgment an original Court, Mr. Marapana submitted that there were guidelines made by the authorities emanating right down from the House of Lords.

"Those guidelines were in no way to be regarded as abrogating the power vested in the Court of Appeal. The Court of Appeal always has the power, as it should, of setting right any error of whatsoever kind omitted by a trial Court. But these guidelines would enable this Court to determine whether in fact the trial Court was in error. The advantage a trial Court enjoyed in seeing and hearing witnesses and getting a feel of the case is deprived to the Court of Appeal also because, the printed evidence before it cannot record all the 'evidence' led before the trial judges. It is for this reason that an Appeal Court should be very reluctant to disturb the findings of fact by a trial judge."

Mr. Marapana said that the trial judges in this case having seen and heard Alex Ingram, Bridget Jackson and Mrs. Peiris's relations, were satisfied that they were truthful witnesses and had concluded that several facts were established on their evidence. The conclusion, which they had proceeded to draw from those facts were reasonable in the circumstances and the Appeal Court should not disturb them, even if the judges of the Court of Appeal were inclined to a different conclusion upon those proven facts.

Mr. Marapana said that instead of warning Mrs. Peiris's relations of the dangerous condition of Mrs. Peiris, Dalrene misled them by uttering falsehoods.

"The trial judges had quite rightly concluded that the evidence was unmistakably pointing to Rev. Peiris having administered the anti-diabetic drugs to Mrs. Peiris. The case against Dalrene had to be viewed in the background of the evidence dating from July 1977, which was the opening date of the conspiracy. The motive alleged in regard to the murder of Russel was a desire of these accused to get together, having eliminated each other's spouses. With the murder of Russel having been accomplished, they had achieved part of their ambition. But their enterprise would be fruitful only with the doing away of Mrs. Peiris. It was inconceivable that they would agree to commit the murder of Russel, without at the same time, having agreed also to murder Mrs. Peiris."

"In those circumstances, once Russel's murder had been proved and the second accused found to have agreed and participated in that murder, the charge of conspiracy to murder Mrs. Peiris would also appear to have been proved. The motive of this relationship, which culminated with Rev. Peiris placing a ring on Dalrene's ring finger on the day of Russel's funeral, was seemed to have developed further in the following months. By December they had even entered into legal transactions binding each other. The opening of a joint account, the executing of a Will by Dalrene, appointing Rev. Peiris as the executor and the guardian of the children, showed that they were now for all purposes husband and wife without a formal registration."

"There was the evidence of several witnesses who had testified to Mrs. Peiris being ill, showing signs of drowsiness, sleepiness, giddiness, weakness, lethargy, no sooner she returned to the country, and throughout the months of December and January."

"Dalrene was in and out of the Vicarage during this period. She must necessarily have observed these signs of Mrs. Peiris's condition. Having regard to the condition of Russel just six months before, she must have necessarily known that this was but the beginning of the end for Mrs. Peiris. From dizziness and giddiness she would soon fall into stupor and end up unconscious. And this was exactly what happened to Mrs. Peiris in January, when Dr. Weerasena was summoned to the Vicarage. He found her unconscious with an unrecordable blood pressure. If not for Dr. Weerasena's prompt action in dispatching her to Durdans Hospital and giving her dextrose infusion, she would definitely have died that day."

"Dalrene was present at the Vicarage when all this happened. When at Durdans Mrs. Peiris regained consciousness and made inquiries from her relations as to how she had come to be in that condition, what did Dalrene do? Instead of apprising them of the gravity of Mrs. Peiris's condition, and impressing upon them the seriousness of her ailment, she attempted to mislead them by saying that Mrs. Peiris had high fever, was delirious and had to be brought to hospital! The trial judges were justified in concluding that it was a deliberate act on her part, amounting to a supportive role played by her," said Mr. Marapana.

Continuing he said, "It was also relevant to note that during this crucial period, Dalrene had continued to remain in the Vicarage. When all Mrs. Peiris' relations were suspicious that these happenings were indeed strange, Dalrene was forced to leave the Vicarage. Munilal had telephoned from England and threatened his father that if Dalrene was not sent away from the Vicarage he would fly down to Colombo and kick her out himself. It was only then that she moved out to an annexe at Nugegoda, which Rev. Peiris had found for her in December."

On 12th February, Justices Justin Abeywardene (President), R. N. M. Dheeraratne and A. S. Wijetunge delivering a 58-page judgement, affirmed the conviction of Rev. Mathew Peiris for the murder of Russel Ingram and Mrs. Eunice Lois Peiris, but cleared him of the accompanying conspiracy charge. Mrs. Dalrene Ingram was acquitted of all counts. The Court convicted Rev. Peiris on counts two and four - (namely, of murdering Russel Ingram and Mrs. Eunice Peiris) and acquitted him on the charge of conspiring to murder them.

Dalrene Ingram was acquitted on all charges.

Mr. Justin Abeywardene read out the order.

The Court held that the evidence unerringly disclosed that Dalrene had reduced to being nothing but an innocent tool in the hands of Rev. Mathew Peiris.

In the course of their judgment the judges said, "Rev. Peiris possessed a genial and domineering personality. He was artful in winning the confidence of unsuspecting Russel and his relatives, and to cap it all he was found to be a glib actor, the cassock giving him credibility, veneration and authority."

"If implicit faith and confidence in Rev. Peiris lulled Russel and his relatives - Alex, Cora and others into a state of complacency regarding Russel's illness, it is equally probable that Dalrene, was also in the same boat. The proved amatory connection of Rev. Peiris with Dalrene alone makes us hesitate to think that her position was different in the absence of any unequivocal and cogent evidence to the contrary."

The judges held that they were of the opinion that the prosecution proved beyond reasonable doubt that the hypoglycaemic attacks suffered by Russel did not result from a natural cause and they affirmed the finding arrived at by the High Court at Bar through a process of elimination, which excluded the possibility of Russel introducing any anti-diabetic drug into his system accidentally.

"He was not suffering from diabetes at any time and never used any anti-diabetic drugs. Nor was he using any other drugs. So it could not be assumed that he had mistakenly taken them. There were no suicidal tendencies whatsoever in Russel. He had a steady employment at the time he fell ill and had no mental worries to speak about," the Court held.

"Thereby, the Court eliminated the possibility of Russel attempting to commit suicide by taking an anti-diabetic drug. The Court also overruled the possibility of Russel having suffered from a pancreatic tumour in the ectopic areas, as suggested by the defence, by relying on the medical evidence of Dr. A. H. Sheriffdeen, Dr. Nagaratnam, Dr. Anula Wijesundera and Dr. Dayasiri Fernando."

The Court therefore, affirmed the finding of the Trial-at-Bar that Russel's death was not the result of self-induced hypoglycaemia, or an accident or an attempt to commit suicide.

Referring to the charge of the murder of Mrs. Eunice Peiris, the Court held that the finding of the High Court that her death was not due to natural causes was tenable.

"The finding that the cause of death was hypoglycaemia followed by a coma, leading to permanent brain damage resulting in pneumonia and death was a finding proved beyond reasonable doubt," the Court held.

The Court also affirmed the finding by the High Court that the evidence led has proved beyond reasonable doubt that her death has been caused by hypoglycaemia, induced by an anti-diabetic drug.

Dealing with the case against Dalrene, the Court in considering the circumstantial evidence against her was of the view that taking each one of the items individually or all the evidence collectively that a reasonable inference could be drawn of her innocence.

"We are therefore, unable to agree with the finding of the High Court that the irresistible inference that can be arrived at was the guilt of Dalrene."

The Court of Appeal held that, whilst the evidence established a very close amatory relationship between the accused, it provided sufficient proof of a motive to commit the offence only against Rev. Peiris. In the absence of a special overt act by Dalrene, the circumstantial evidence was equivocal on the existence of a common intention on her part, that the evidence is consistent with Dalrene having been an innocent tool in the hands of Rev. Peiris.

The evidence of Dalrene's conduct relied upon by the prosecution to establish that Dalrene agreed with the Rev. Peiris and facilitated the commission of the offence is consistent with her innocence. In the result, the charge of murder against Dalrene, based on common intention and the charges of conspiracy and abetment against her failed. The conviction of Rev. Peiris for conspiracy to commit murder was set aside but, his conviction and sentence for the murder of Russel Ingram and Mrs. Eunice Peiris were affirmed.

The Court then proceeded to affirm the conviction and sentence of Rev. Peiris on counts 2 and 4 regarding the murder of Russel Ingram and Mrs. Peiris, but the Court set aside the conviction and sentence of Rev. Peiris on counts 1 and 2 charging him with conspiracy, and allowed the appeal on these counts.

The Court acquitted Dalrene Ingram and allowed her appeal on all counts.

After the judgement was delivered, counsel for Rev. Peiris, Mr. R.I. Obeysekera sought the permission of the Court to appeal against the conviction and sentence of his client to the Supreme Court on two points of law.

Justice Abeywardene (with the other two Judges agreeing) allowed the application.

Mrs. Ingram, in a white sari showed no visible signs of emotion when the judgement clearing her was delivered. Her son sat by her side in the Court room. Many people present in the Court room crowded round Mrs. Ingram after the judges had left the bench, and congratulated her.

When leaving the Court, Rev. Peiris in his cassock with a metal crucifix hanging from his neck, reacted to the verdict against him by saying reporters following him, "Will the press please make a note that I have been allowed an appeal to the Supreme Court?"

CHAPTER 12

THE SUPREME COURT DECISION

Rev. Mathew Peiris appealed to the Supreme Court against his conviction and the appeal was heard on 17th and 19th June, 23rd, 24th, 29th, 30th and 31st July, and 20th, 21st and 22nd August 1991, before Supreme Court judges K.M.M.B. Kulatunga, S.W.B. Wadugodapitiya, and P.R.P. Perera.

Mr. R. I. Obeysekera, President's counsel with Messrs. Anil Obeysekera, A. W. Yusuf, Jayantha Weerasinghe, Upali Senaratne, Champani Padmasekera, Ramya Chandra Gunasekera, Deepal Wijeratne and D. Akurugoda appeared for Rev. Peiris.

Mr. Tilak Marapana, the Solicitor General with Mr. C.R. de Silva, Deputy Solicitor General, appeared for the Attorney General.

The judges held that:

(1) The prosecution case was that the incidents complained of were committed in the course of the same transaction and the evidence was not adduced on the basis of system evidence. Father Peiris was not denied a fair trial on account of prejudice caused by the pooling of evidence led in respect of two murders at the joint trial of the accused, after the refusal by the trial judges of an application for separation of trials.

(2) The evidence supported the finding in respect of both the deceased persons that the cause of irreversible brain damage and unconsciousness leading to pneumonia and death was hypoglycaemia induced by drugs and not a natural cause.

I have reproduced here a few paragraphs from the judgement read by Justice Kulatunga.

"The facts justified as proved beyond reasonable doubt that, both deaths were the result of murders and not accidents or suicide or natural causes. The facts also justified as proved beyond reasonable doubt that the murders were committed by the Father Peiris. Where the final decision is reached, as is the case here, on the basis of antecedent determinations of act on several issues, a Court of final appeal should be slow to interfere with the findings of the trial Court."

"I have examined the case for the Father Peiris in considerable detail in deference to the strenuous submissions made by the learned President's Counsel who appeared for Father Peiris and for the reason that some aspects of the case do not appear to have been examined at length by the Court below. Having considered every issue very carefully, I see no merit in the complaint that the Court of Appeal erred in confirming the finding of the trial judges."

"It was submitted to us that the trial judges erred in their finding in respect of the extended GTT done at the Glass House, inter alia, in view of the possibility that the receptionist who took the booking for the test on the phone (and who did not testify at the trial) made a mistake in recording the booking as for a normal GTT; if so the adverse inferences made against the Father Peiris for changing the test are unwarranted. I cannot agree. That booking was on the 27th. But the evidence of Nimal Soysa another receptionist is that on the 29th when the Father Peiris came in, he asked for a GTT; the witness was not shown the letters P11 and P22 which the doctors had issued specifying the test; and that sometime after the test started, Father Peiris requested for an extended GTT for four hours. The High Court has considered the evidence and reached certain findings of facts and I see no justification to interfere with those findings."

"In the earlier part of this judgment, I have considered in detail, all the other points made on behalf of Father Peiris and agreed with the findings of the High Court. Those findings have been affirmed by the Court below. Finally, I have to consider the complaint of the Father Peiris that he has been denied a fair trial on account of prejudice caused by the pooling of evidence. I hold that as in the case of the conviction under count 2 of the indictment, here too no such prejudice has been caused; there is ample evidence to warrant Father Peiris's conviction for the murder of Mrs. Peiris; and Father Peiris has not been denied a fair trial on account of prejudice caused by the pooling of evidence. Accordingly, I affirm the judgment of the Court of Appeal in respect of count 4 of the indictment."

On 3rd February 1992, Justice Kulatunga with Judges Wadugodapitiya and P. R. P. Perera agreeing dismissed the appeal of Rev. Peiris on counts 2 and 4 of the indictment.

The full judgement is available at: http://www.lawnet.lk/docs/case_law/slr/HTML/1992SLR2V372.htm

CHAPTER 13

EPILOGUE

When I was a postgraduate student at Guy's Hospital Medical School of the University of London, I had the opportunity of reading the first case of murder by an anti-diabetic drug, insulin, published in the British Medical Journal in 1958.

On the morning of 4th May 1957, just after 2 a.m., Dr. David Price, a forensic pathologist, was called to the home of Elizabeth and Kenneth Barlow in a residential suburb of Bradford, Yorkshire. Kenneth Barlow, a 38-year-old unemployed state registered nurse, had discovered his wife unconscious in the bath at about 11.20 p.m. the previous night and called his own doctor, who diagnosed her as dead. Kenneth had married Elizabeth eleven months earlier and was to all outward appearances, living happily with her and his 10-year-old son by his first wife.

Elizabeth was eight weeks pregnant. At a second post-mortem examination on Elizabeth's body, two hypodermic injection sites were identified in each buttock. Dr. Price removed these, with their surrounding tissues, and their analysis showed 84 units of insulin!

Kenneth Barlow vehemently denied the charge of murder by injecting insulin but at his trial at Leeds Assizes he could not explain the insulin found in Elizabeth's body apart from suggesting that she had administered it herself. The jury found him guilty and Mr. Justice Diplock sentenced him to life imprisonment on 13th December 1957. He was released from prison twenty six years later, in 1984, still maintaining his innocence.

The fascinating article by Professor Vincent Marks on "Murder by Insulin" published in the Medico-Legal Journal in 1999 gives a review of cases where murders were committed by injecting insulin.

Dr. P.A.P. Joseph, as far as I know, is the only witness who wrote about the case. Titled, "The scientific killer in cassock", he wrote an authoritative article to 'The Observer' on 21st May 1992.

In 1999, I published an article titled "Homicidal poisoning with glibenclamide" in the British journal 'Medicine Science and the Law', based on Rev. Mathew Peiris case.

The case of insulinoma mentioned in the judgement was reported in the Jaffna Medical Journal by Dr. S. Yoganathan, Consutant Physician, and Dr. M. Vetpillai, Consultant Surgeon, in 1982. A 67-year-old lady who had hypoglycaemic attacks were operated for an insulinoma at Point Pedro Base Hospital. Unfortunately she died two days after surgery from haemetemesis (vomiting blood) due to small ulcers in the stomach. This must be the first reported case of insulinoma in Sri Lanka.

In 2002, the 'Legal Medicine' journal (published in Japan) documented a case of a 5-year-old girl, who was given 25 mg of glibenclamide (ten tablets of Euglucon) with some other drugs, by her 37-year-old pharmacist father, who then injected her with 70 units of insulin. She died several hours after the injection of insulin. The post-mortem carried out 12 hours after the death showed very high glibenclamide and insulin levels in blood, which caused her death.

In the 'Ceylon Medical Journal', a case of a 79-year-old man, who had one centimeter diameter firm, vascular, blood red, encapsulated insulinoma at the superior pole of the pancreas has been reported in 2004. It was removed successfully at surgery.

In this unique murder trial in Sri Lanka, where two victims were murdered by glibenclamide (Euglucon), the first reported trial in the world, many medical personnel were involved in the management of victims in two wards in the General Hospital, Colombo, and in the post-mortem examination of Mrs. Peiris. Now I wish to mention briefly about some of those eminent doctors.

Dr. A.H. Sheriffdeen, the Consultant Surgeon, was appointed to the Chair in Surgery in the Faculty of Medicine, University of Colombo. He performed the first kidney transplantation in Sri Lanka. I had the privilege of closely associating with him as the Medico-Legal Advisor in the transplantation team. Dr. Dayasiri Fernando was appointed to the Chair in Surgery of the University of Sri Jayewardenepura and later became its Vice Chancellor. Dr. Anula Wijesundera, Dr. Sujatha Ruwanpathirana and Dr. Bandula Wijesiriwardena are Consultant Physicians, and Dr. Upali Banagala is a Consultant Orthopaedic Surgeon. The last two were my school mates.

Dr. Terrence de Silva became a Specialist in Community Medicine and later went on to Head the General Hospital. He saw its transformation into the National Hospital of Sri Lanka and rose to be the Deputy Director-General of Medical Services at the Department of Health Services.

Dr. Kanthi Pinto (now Dr. Kanthi Jayawardena), is a Consultant Community Paediatrician in the North East London Foundation Trust. She served as a Senior Lecturer in Paediatrics, Faculty of Medicine, University of Kelaniya, before migrating to England. She recalls that the doctors were very suspicious and excited when they heard that the same priest had admitted another patient a few months before with a suspected insulinoma and he had died. "We thought that two cases of insulinoma, as it was a rare condition, was too good to be true. Both patients were brought by the same priest. We told our Consultant Physician Dr. Nanayakkara that we suspected poisoning. He scolded us for been melodramatic! He said the priest was the hospital chaplain. Although both Terrence and I were Christians, as Dr. Nanayakkara was a Buddhist he was worried that people will criticize him for blaming the hospital chaplain for poisoning and asked us to keep quiet. When Dr. Nanayakkara went on leave, an acting Resident Physician came to cover the ward. We told him the story and made him to inform the hospital police post that poisoning cannot be excluded in Mrs. Peiris. Then only the police investigation commenced," she says.

Dr. S. Subramaniam, with whom I had the privilege of working when he was the JMO Colombo, migrated a few years after the trial and worked as a University Lecturer in Malaysia. He passed away on 1st November 2006 in London. He did the post-mortem of Mrs. Eunice Peiris with his former teacher Professor H.V.J. Fernando of the University of Colombo, who passed away on 2nd May 1998.

I met Dr. J.G.C. Peiris, the family doctor of the Rev. Mathew Peiris, at a function in London soon after he returned to England after giving evidence in the trial. He very enthusiastically discussed the evidence he gave.

Dr. S.C. Abeysuriya, the only medical witness for the defence, was honoured by the Neurosurgeons Association of Sri Lanka by electing him the Founder President in 2006.

Having spent fifteen years in jail, Rev. Mathew Peiris, now 79 years old, was released under a general amnesty on 28th October 1997, his birthday, for good conduct. His death sentence was commuted to life imprisonment in 1994. Rev. Peiris was confined to a nine feet by ten feet prison cell with a 15 feet high roof. It had only a single high window and iron barred door. The cell was kept locked from 5 p.m. to 5 a.m. every day.

Rev. Peiris said that his future was in God's hand and he was looking forward to a family reunion. Still in his robes, he denied media reports that he had plans to get married again.

"The release came as a surprise to me. A couple who visited me in jail with a birthday cake drove me back to my sister's home in Moratuwa," he said in an interview on first November 1997.

The relatives hurriedly prepared a party on the second where he was expecting scores of family members.

A Commissioner of Prisons has said that he was most helpful in prison, knowing three languages and helping with reports and administrative work. Rev. Peiris was to be under the supervision of Prison welfare officials until January 1999.

Rev. Peiris was interviewed by Roshan Peiris for 'Sunday Times' at his sister Cissy's suburban home in Moratuwa, one month after his release.

Says Roshan Peiris, "Clad still in robes, he wore a stainless steel chain made while in prison by his co-prisoners, from which hung a cross with a statue of Christ embossed on it. The cross was given to him, he said, by a doting mother and is believed to be of Italian origin. His white flowing beard like that of a Biblical prophet has not been cut or trimmed for the last fifty years. He has also not cut his now thinning grey brown hair for about the same time. He made this decision, he says while he lived in an *ashram* in India."

"Prison memories still fresh, Rev. Peiris reminisced of the days behind bars. In prison he was given the diabetic diet of a bun and *pol sambol* (scraped coconut mixed with chillies) for breakfast, two vegetables, leeks and carrot or cabbage for lunch with fish or soya or lentil, and for dinner, bread with the same two vegetables he had for lunch, with two eggs and a slice of papaw. He lived on a daily intake of sixteen ounces of white bread."

Rev. Peiris said, "I must explain that I controlled my diabetic condition with this Spartan diet. But this did not prevent me being cricket captain of the prison team. Thanks to the prison officials I had a bed to sleep on, though I used the common toilets."

"I am the sort of person who routinely goes to sleep around midnight and, so I was allowed to keep my light burning to enable me to read. I always woke up at four in the morning, did yoga exercises, physical jerks and indulged in yoga methods of breathing and breath control."

"I want the world to know that throughout my traumatic experiences my family was with me, and gave me a glorious party last Sunday with my brothers and sisters present."

"As a matter of Courtesy, I attended the mass followed by the Anglican service the next hour, every Sunday. The Bishop then had given me permission to administer the Chalice i.e. give wine and I also read from the Gospels and sang hymns. Yes I do play the piano. There was an old world piano at home."

Rev. Peiris said, "No never, never did I lose faith in God."

Rev. Peiris was known to manifest the stigmata, marks resembling the wounds of the crucified Christ. Roshan Peiris asked him whether he experienced this phenomenon in prison. He replied, "Of course I did on special days. Here is the mark you can see at the centre of my right palm. On Good Friday and the like I also bled from the site. It is a special spiritual experience given to me by God."

A celebrated exorcist, Rev. Peiris explained, "Exorcism means that in a given instance any individual is pressured by an external entity in an evil manner. In theological language, it is described as a discernate spirit haunting a person. Therefore, by claiming clearly the authority that Jesus Christ gave his Apostles, authorizing them to deal with such afflicted individuals, an ordained priest accepts that he has the continuity of that authority. In some instances, dwelling places and lonely spots are affected by such spiritual entities. An exorcist or priest will cleanse such situations. In parlour language it is called poltergeist appearance. It is a ritual authorized by Pope Leo the 13th."

In prison Rev. Peiris spent time studying comparative religions, Christianity, Buddhism, Hinduism and Islam.

"I now have a manuscript to be published as a book called Gautama Buddha and the Creator God. It deals with all four religions. Who knows what tomorrow will hold? I have many enemies and a few friends, I hope they are still my friends," said Rev. Peiris.

Still claiming he was not guilty of the murders, he said his life had changed and a new dimension would begin after a reunion with his family.

"The day after I was released I visited my family Church - the Holy Emmanuel Church in Moratuwa. A young priest, who was surprised to see me, spoke about me from the pulpit. I was deeply touched with the act of goodwill by the congregation that greeted me," he said.

Mr. S.W.R.D. Bandaranaike, the fourth Prime Minister of independent Ceylon, was assassinated by a Buddhist priest, Rev. Talduwe Somarama in 1959. At his murder trial, in spite of a resourceful defence, the jury unanimously found Rev. Somarama guilty and sentenced to death. Although Mr. Bandaranaike had suspended capital punishment, after his death the new government had it restored. On 22nd June 1961, Rev. Somarama, then in Welikada prison, made an application to the prison authorities that he be granted permission to discuss matters pertaining to the Christian faith with Rev Mathew Peiris. On 5th July, Rev. Somarama was duly baptized as a member of the Anglican Church by Rev. Peiris and given the name 'Peter'. Two days later he was hanged. What a strange irony it was that Rev. Peiris escaped the executioner at Welikada because of the Presidential pardon!

A few days after I read in the newspapers that Rev. Peiris was released from prison on a pardon, my secretary told me that there was a call from Rev. Peiris. He wanted me to contact him. The telephone number given was from Moratuwa area. Unfortunately, I could not contact him due to pressure of work. A few days later I heard that Rev. Peiris has passed away. That was on 12th May 1998, at his home in Moratuwa.

I still regret that I could not find time to call Rev. Peiris. I do not know why he wanted to meet me. He must have read about my interest in poisoning (toxicology) and wanted to discus about the two deaths. What was he going to tell me? Was he thinking of getting a medico-legal opinion favourable to him from me?

AUTHOR'S OTHER BOOKS

- "Bibliography of Publications in Legal Medicine and Forensic Sciences Relating to Sri Lanka 1811-1984"

- "Management of Pesticide Poisoning"

- "First-Aid and Treatment for Poisoning"

- "Management of Poisoning"

- "Pesticide Poisoning in Sri Lanka - Review of Eighties and the Outlook for nineties" (with Professor Dulitha Fernando)

- "Principles of Medical Negligence" (with Dr. L.C. de Silva)

- "Impunity in Sri Lanka", (with Ms D.S.W. Munasinghe).

- "Medico-Legal Aspects of Torture"

- "Inquest" (in Sinhala)

- "First-aid and Prevention of Poisoning" (with Dr. Shantha de Silva) (in Sinhala).

- "Medical aspects of torture as seen in Sri Lanka"

- "A Murder in Ceylon – The Sathasivam Case"

- "Banned Chemicals in Sri Lanka" (with Dr. Shantha de Siva)

- "Sri Lanka, LTTE and the British Parliament"

- "20 Years of Life Saving Information: National Poisons Information Centre"

- "Trends of Firearm Injuries in Sri Lanka"

- "Poisoning – A Modern Epidemic in Sri Lanka" the Olcott Memorial Oration 2008.

- "Sathasivam of Ceylon – the batting genius"